THINKING GREEN

THINKING GREEN

AN ANTHOLOGY OF
ESSENTIAL ECOLOGICAL WRITING

EDITED BY
MICHAEL ALLABY

BARRIE & JENKINS
LONDON

First published in Great Britain in 1989 by
Barrie & Jenkins Ltd
289 Westbourne Grove, London W11 2QA

British Library Cataloguing in Publication Data
Thinking green: an anthology of essential
ecological writing
1. Environment
I. Allaby, Michael, *1933-*
333.7

ISBN 0-7126-3489-4

Typeset by SX Composing Limited
Printed and bound in Portugal by
Printer Portuguesa

CONTENTS

FOREWORD

BY MICHAEL ALLABY

The modern environmental movement probably began in 1963, the year which saw the publication of Rachel Carson's *Silent Spring*, a book that seems to have triggered the movement's birth.

It was the decade journalists nicknamed 'the swinging 60s', a brief period during which young people felt liberated from the constraints under which their parents had toiled. Yet beneath the well publicized frivolity and apparent superficiality ran a serious undercurrent of concern and a demand for change. Despite having 'never had it so good', all was not well with the world, and many young people knew it.

There were protest movements. In Britain there were marches and mass rallies demanding an end to the nuclear arms race, an end to South African apartheid, an end to the war in Vietnam. In the United States the civil rights movement was followed by the anti-war movement. In France, in 1968, the protests came close to revolution.

It was to these people, this concern, that Rachel Carson spoke, and her audience was ready to listen. Hers was, as they say, 'an idea whose time had come'.

What was the idea, and what was the basis of its appeal? The idea was simple. She argued, and produced a vast catalogue of mainly anecdotal evidence in support of her argument, that the use of modern pesticides was leading inexorably to an ecological catastrophe – the 'silent spring' of her title in which no birds sang because the insects on which they fed had been killed. The message was alarming. Nuclear war would be appalling, but it was an event that might or might not occur. Carson was presenting us with a threat no less serious in its destructive power, but insidious, happening already, well advanced.

It seems to me, though, that there was more. Especially in the United States, the protesters comprised the most highly educated and wealthiest generation the world had ever seen. The dreams of economic security and guarantees of sufficient food, born in the years of depression, had been realized. People had money, yet it was not enough, for they began to suspect they had paid too high a price for their lifestyle. They began to reject their affluence, to dress shabbily, to identify themselves with the poor and oppressed, and eventually with the planet itself. In *The Night of the Iguana*, Tennessee Williams describes our treatment of the world as 'man's inhumanity to God'. It was a phrase that described accurately the way many people felt. With twenty years' hindsight it is easy to dismiss those attitudes as the self-indulgence of youngsters playing at poverty with the assured backing of rich parents. Hindsight is always cruel, and always misleading. From the viewpoint of the much tougher, much harsher, 1980s the protesters may appear both innocent and ignorant, but I believe they were sincere.

The established conservation organizations were slow to respond. Their interests centred on the protection of wildlife, landscapes, buildings, but they took little account of the effect environmental damage might have on people themselves. The only exceptions were the much smaller, less influential, marginal groups that for some twenty years had been promoting organic farming and gardening – at that time led in Britain by The Soil Association and in America by the Rodale Organization. Their interest in the long-term effects of modern farming, including pesticide use, and the consequences for human health placed them in a unique position. For a time they led the emerging movement.

The growth was fast, and governments could not ignore it. Britain claimed to be the first country to create, in 1970, a Department of the Environment, headed by a Secretary of State (Anthony Crosland was the first), but other countries soon followed and within a few years most governments included an environmental ministry. The United Nations became involved and in 1972 held the first of its 'megaconferences', the UN Conference on the Human Environment, in Stockholm.

By the mid 1970s the professionals were taking over. Environmental problems were passed to government scientists for critical examination and for a time the popular movement seemed to wane, a victim, perhaps, of its own phenomenal success.

Now, as we approach the end of another decade, it has re-emerged. Worries about 'acid rain' and for the future of the ozone layer are not new – they were being discussed as long ago as the early 70s. The 'greenhouse effect' is a new concern only to environmentalists – it has been on the scientific agenda since the turn of the century. Other problems are new. The international trade in urban and industrial wastes is a new phenomenon, for example, and while the clearance of tropical forests has been going on a long time it is only recently that we have begun to appreciate its extent and to realize its possible consequences.

This revival of interest makes it appropriate to look again at some of the great volume of environmentalist literature produced over the years. Of course, the movement of the 60s and 70s did not spring, fully formed, from nowhere. Scientists had been expressing concern for many years, and even they were not the first to complain of the way humans treat the natural world. Some of the passages in this book date from the eighteenth and nineteenth centuries. You will find Malthus here, and Thomas Hobbes, Charles Dickens, and William Morris.

I have tried to arrange the extracts around the themes with which they deal, rather than presenting them in a chronological order of their dates of publication, although the difference is more apparent than real since the themes tended to emerge one after the other. The book begins with agriculture, because that is where the modern movement began. It proceeds from there to more general considerations of the background to our relationship with the natural environment. This leads to the second major concern of environmentalists: population growth. It is here you will find Thomas Malthus and Paul Ehrlich. The main fear, of course, is that a limit may exist to the number of people the world can feed, so the extracts that follow deal with the world food problem. The third strand of the environmentalist argument addresses pollution and, the strands now drawn together, we are led directly into the broad analyses and manifestos, which began with 'A Blueprint for Survival', but were preceded, eighty years earlier, by William Morris's *News from Nowhere* and, more than a century earlier, by J.S. Mill's proposal for a 'stationary state'. With Mill we enter economics. Fears about nuclear power entered the debate in the late 1970s and originally they centred not on public health and safety but on what some writers believed to be the political and social consequences of large-scale industrial centralization.

Finally, the book contains passages from some of the major reports that have appeared since 1980 and introduces some new ideas. Here you will find James Lovelock's 'Gaia', and his new science of 'geophysiology', both described in his own words.

History is recorded in our language and the environmental movement has made its mark. Ruth Harrison, for example, is believed to have coined the phrase 'factory farming', although not in the extract I have chosen here. Elsewhere in the book, however, you will find what may well have been the first uses in their modern sense of what are now common expressions − 'there's no such thing as a free lunch', 'soft energy paths', 'the cowboy economy', and 'the tragedy of the commons'.

Each extract is preceded by a short introduction to set the piece in its context. In only one or two instances have I qualified the extracts to bring figures or concepts up to date. Otherwise I have not seen my task as that of the critic. I believe the pieces represent views that are, or were, widely held and that they are expounded here either by those who first presented them to the public, or by those who expressed them most forcefully. Whether the views are reasonable, or supported by the arguments presented, it is for you to judge.

Michael Allaby
Cornwall, 1989

A FABLE
FOR TOMORROW
BY RACHEL CARSON

The book begins where the movement began, with Rachel Carson. She first suggested writing about the abuses of pesticides in 1945, but it was not until 1958 that she began serious work on *Silent Spring*. As she wrote it she was already ill. She died in 1964, having written a foreword to Ruth Harrison's *Animal Machines* but too soon to see the growth of the vast, world-wide, popular movement she had inspired. Would she have approved of what followed? We can never know.

There was once a town in the heart of America where all life seemed to live in harmony with its surroundings. The town lay in the midst of a checkerboard of prosperous farms, with fields of grain and hillsides of orchards where, in spring, white clouds of bloom drifted above the green fields. In autumn, oak and maple and birch set up a blaze of colour that flamed and flickered across a backdrop of pines. Then foxes barked in the hills and deer silently crossed the fields, half hidden in the mists of the autumn mornings.

Along the roads, laurel, viburnum and alder, great ferns and wildflowers delighted the traveller's eye through much of the year. Even in winter the roadsides were places of beauty, where countless birds came to feed on the berries and on the seed heads of the dried weeds rising above the snow. The countryside was, in fact, famous for the abundance and variety of its bird life, and when the flood of migrants was pouring through in spring and autumn people travelled from great distances to observe them. Others came to fish the streams, which flowed clear and cold out of the hills and contained shady pools where trout lay. So it had been from the days many years ago when the first settlers raised their houses, sank their wells, and built their barns.

Then a strange blight crept over the area and everything began to change. Some evil spell had settled on the community: mysterious maladies swept the flocks of chickens; the cattle and sheep sickened and died. Everywhere was a shadow of death. The farmers spoke of much illness among their families. In the town the doctors had become more and more puzzled by new kinds of sickness appearing among their patients. There had been several sudden and unexplained deaths, not only among adults but even among children, who would be stricken suddenly while at play and die within a few hours.

There was a strange stillness. The birds, for example – where had they gone? Many people spoke of them, puzzled and disturbed. The feeding stations in the backyards were deserted. The few birds seen anywhere were moribund; they trembled violently and could not fly. It was a spring without voices. On the morning that had once throbbed with the dawn chorus of robins, catbirds, doves, jays, wrens, and scores of other bird voices there was now no sound; only silence lay over the fields and woods and marsh.

On the farms the hens brooded, but no chicks hatched. The farmers complained that they were unable to raise any pigs – the litters were small and the young survived only a few days. The apple trees were coming into bloom but no bees droned among the blossoms, so there was no pollination and there would be no fruit.

The roadsides, once so attractive, were now lined with browned and withered vegetation as though swept by fire. These, too, were silent, deserted by all living things. Even the streams were now lifeless. Anglers no longer visited them, for all the fish had died.

In the gutters under the eaves and between the shingles of the roofs, a white granular powder still showed a few patches; some weeks before it had fallen like snow upon the roofs and the lawns, the fields and streams.

No witchcraft, no enemy action had silenced the rebirth of new life in this stricken world. The people had done it themselves.

This town does not actually exist, but it might easily have a thousand counterparts in America or elsewhere in the world. I know of no community that has experienced all the misfortunes I describe. Yet every one of these disasters has actually happened somewhere, and many real communities have already suffered a substantial number of them. A grim spectre has crept upon us almost unnoticed, and this imagined tragedy may easily become a stark reality we all shall know.

ELIXIRS OF DEATH

BY RACHEL CARSON

For the first time in the history of the world, every human being is now subjected to contact with dangerous chemicals, from the moment of conception until death. In the less than two decades of their use, the synthetic pesticides have been so thoroughly distributed throughout the animate and inanimate world that they occur virtually everywhere. They have been recovered from most of the major river systems and even from streams of ground-water flowing unseen through the earth. Residues of these chemicals linger in soil to which they may have been applied a dozen years before. They have entered and lodged in the bodies of fish, birds, reptiles, and domestic and wild animals so universally that scientists carrying on animal experiments find it almost impossible to locate subjects free from such contamination. They have been found in fish in remote mountain lakes, in earthworms burrowing in soil, in the eggs of birds – and in man himself. For these chemicals are now stored in the bodies of the vast majority of human beings, regardless of age. They occur in the mother's milk, and probably in the tissues of the unborn child.

All this has come about because of the sudden rise and prodigious growth of an industry for the production of man-made or synthetic chemicals with insecticidal properties. This industry is a child of the Second World War. In the course of developing agents of chemical warfare, some of the chemicals created in the laboratory were found to be lethal to insects. The discovery did not come by chance: insects were widely used to test chemicals as agents of death for man.–

DDT (short for dichloro-diphenyl-trichloro-ethane) was first synthesized by a German chemist in 1874, but its properties as an insecticide were not discovered until 1939. Almost immediately DDT was hailed as a means of stamping out insect-borne disease and winning the farmers' war against crop destroyers overnight. The discoverer, Paul Müller of Switzerland, won the Nobel Prize.

DDT is now so universally used that in most minds the product takes on the harmless aspect of the familiar. Perhaps the myth of the harmlessness of DDT rests on the fact that one of its first uses was the wartime dusting of many thousands of soldiers, refugees, and prisoners, to combat lice. It is widely believed that since so many people came into extremely intimate contact with DDT and suffered no immediate ill effects the chemical must certainly be innocent of harm. This understandable misconception arises from the fact that – unlike other chlorinated hydrocarbons – DDT *in powder form* is not readily absorbed through the skin. Dissolved in oil, as it usually is, DDT is definitely toxic. If swallowed, it is absorbed slowly through the digestive tract; it may also be absorbed through the lungs. Once it has entered the body it is stored largely in organs rich in fatty substances (because DDT itself is fat-soluble) such as the adrenals, testes, or thyroid. Relatively large amounts are deposited in the liver, kidneys, and the fat of the large, protective mesenteries that enfold the intestines.

This storage of DDT begins with the smallest conceivable intake of the chemical (which is present as residues on most foodstuffs) and continues until quite high levels are reached. The fatty storage depots act as biological magnifiers, so that an intake of as little as one-tenth of one part per million in the diet results in the storage of about 10 to 15 parts per million, an increase of one hundredfold or more. These terms of reference, so commonplace to the chemist or the pharmacologist, are unfamiliar to most of us. One part in a million sounds like a very small amount – and so it is. But such substances are so potent that a minute quantity can bring about vast changes in the body. In animal experiments, three parts per million has been found to inhibit an essential enzyme in heart muscle; only five parts per million has brought about necrosis or disintegration of liver cells; only 2.5 parts per million of the closely related chemicals dieldrin and chlordane did the same.–

The poison may also be passed on from mother to offspring. Insecticide residues have been recovered from human milk in samples tested by Food and Drug Administration scientists. This means that the breast-fed human infant is receiving small but regular additions to the load of toxic chemicals building up in his body. It is by no means his first exposure, however: there is good reason to believe this begins while he is still in the womb. In experimental animals the chlorinated hydrocarbon insecticides freely cross the barrier of the placenta, the traditional protective shield between the embryo and harmful substances in the mother's body. While the quantities so received by human infants would normally be small, they are not unimportant because children are more susceptible to poisoning than adults. This situation also means that today the average individual almost certainly starts life with the first deposit of the growing load of chemicals his body will be required to carry henceforth.

DISTURBANCE
AND DILEMMA
BY ROBERT L. RUDD

One of the first scientists to draw attention to the possible consequences to wildlife of the use of modern pesticides was Robert L. Rudd, of the University of Wisconsin, in a technical handbook he published as early as 1956. *Pesticides and the Living Landscape*, from which the following extract is taken, was intended for the general reader and was first published in 1964.

Man's accomplishments in preventing disease, in providing himself with food and shelter, and in increasing the efficiency of his labours to permit himself more leisure time are impressive. Many are so impressed with his abilities to change the living landscape in a fashion best suited to his immediate interests that they believe man can become exempt from the biological laws which govern his life and the lives of perhaps two million species of plants and animals. Man has been termed an *ecological dominant* – a creature capable of moulding his environment to his will, yet independent of it. Biblical allegory reinforces this belief that he was apart from, not a part of, the naturalistic world.

But his dominance is not so firmly based. The living fabric of the earth's surface is of delicate and complicated weave. Nature is quite as capable of preventing fulfilment of our aspirations if mistreated as of rewarding us if understandingly managed. Sustained dominance can come only through genuine understanding of the natural forces we have set about to guide and of which we are an integral part. Concomitance – living with natural forces – rather than dominance is the only route to enduring self-interest.

The illusion of ecological dominance can be illustrated with a multitude of examples of environmental abuse – the barren lands induced by overgrazing of livestock; the soils worn away by inappropriate plantings; the once-forested watersheds that no longer store and restrain water; the streams, formerly clean and productive, that became the sewers of urban and industrial man; the threat to living beings from uncontrolled fall-out from nuclear explosions. But none of these examples illustrates any more clearly than the subject of this book – chemical pest control – the need for ecological concomitance.

The tools of pest control are now largely synthetic chemicals. These chemicals – pesticides – are designed to kill or in some way inhibit the plant and animal competitors that interfere with our health, comfort, or production of foods and fibres. Some 200 basic chemicals are commonly used in agriculture and these are commercially presented in thousands of different formulations under many trade names. These chemicals are broadly categorized, according to their intended targets, as insecticides, rodenticides, fungicides, and herbicides. Most can be considered 'biocides' – they kill living things. The same or similar chemicals are used away from agriculture in public health, forestry, fish and game management, rights-of-way maintenance, property protection, and recreation.

Generally speaking, the purposes of pesticidal use are clear and widely accepted. We realize, for example, that successes in pest control have, along with other technological applications, greatly changed the yields in American forest, grazing, and crop environments. Indirectly, we may be assured that crop production, toward which empirical pest control has contributed, has risen greatly in the last five decades. The area now under agriculture, for example, is about the same as it was in 1910; but only one person in five now lives and works on a farm in contrast to the three out of five in 1910. We may also take as a measure of the success of agricultural technology – in which pest control prominently figures – the ratio between numbers of farm workers and consumers. In 1920, one farm worker produced food and fibre for eight, whereas in 1957 the ratio was one to twenty-three. Finally we can accept as common observation that agricultural products of high quality and great diversity are readily available to us all. In the basic crops at least, we can also note that surpluses necessitating federal support and storage schemes cost a great deal of money – and political contention.

But if chemical pest control is indeed so valuable, why should anyone argue against it? Here are a few reasons:

(1) Most pesticides are nonselective; they kill forms of life other than their pest targets.

(2) Their manner of use, though often increasing selectivity, is in most cases not precise, the pesticide being restricted neither to the pest species nor to the area where applied.

(3) Insufficient attention has been given to alternative means of crop protection. Most alternative methods of pest control are culturally or biologically based and result in greater diversity and stability in the biota. Pesticides reduce faunal diversity – a natural control – and ensure instability.

(4) Many kinds of chemicals (notably the chlorinated hydrocarbon group to which DDT belongs) are chemically stable; their survival in soil, water, and living tissue is assured.

(5) Insidious pathways of biological transfer of toxic chemicals are now well known. These channels of potential harm, long suspected by biologists, include delayed toxicity; secondary poisoning; transfer, storage, and concentration along plant and animal food chains; and, at least potentially, mutagenic and carcinogenic effects. Yet many chemically oriented persons continue to disregard the importance of these biological consequences of pesticide use.

(6) Their use is entirely too single-minded in relation to the manifold effects they produce. It is not enough to restrict our concern to their value in crop and personal protection.

(7) The technically supported viewpoints of the conservationist, the resource analyst, the biologist, and the sociologist are too frequently overlooked in pest control recommendations and in governmental programming.

(8) Equally lacking is any overt concern for the aesthetic and moral values that must be considered in any application of technology to the satisfaction of humans needs and desires.

There are other reasons for complaint and those listed are not to be weighed equally. None denies the clear value of pesticides in safeguarding ourselves and our food supply. All have been debated in the limited circles in which technologists, regulatory officials, agriculturalists, industrial representatives, and governmental policy-makers move. However, the era of closed debate has ended. *Silent Spring* made the debate public property.

The fields, forests, ranges, and waters are living systems capable of change. With wise and cautious manipulation these producing environments will continue to supply our needs and pleasures. Prudently directed ecological disturbances for the special satisfactions of man require no justification. When pesticides are skilfully intercalated into living systems with comprehensive knowledge of their target purposes, the effects they produce, and the values they influence, they too require no justification. Unfortunately, most pesticide practices do not measure up to these standards. We have little enough understanding of the dynamics of biological environments. Yet now we are altering them at a rate that precludes our understanding. Moreover, the appearance of new kinds of pesticides and of new and profound effects from those long in use has outpaced the rate at which their effects can be investigated. The dilemma is a choice of directions. Shall we take the path to achieve what Aldo Leopold (1949) called '. . . a state of harmony between men and land' – a recognition of the concomitant place of man in living systems? Or shall the path be toward the seeming dominance that chemically maintained, ecological simplification promises?

THE CHLORINATED HYDROCARBONS

BY KENNETH MELLANBY

A distinguished entomologist and for many years Director of the Monk's Wood Experimental Station of what was then the Nature Conservancy, Kenneth Mellanby followed the development of pesticides with a close professional interest. In 1967, in Collins prestigious 'New Naturalist' series, he published *Pesticides and Pollution*, which described the British experience, explaining the development and effects of each major group of pesticides. The following extract refers particularly to DDT.

DDT was first synthesized in the laboratory in 1874, but at that time no one thought it had any economic value. Its insecticidal properties were not discovered until 1939, and it was only during the 1939-45 war that it was used to kill insects. I well remember when I first heard what was then a closely-guarded secret about this new 'wonder chemical'. During the 1914-18 war insect-carried diseases were a menace to all troops of all nations concerned. Lice, particularly during trench warfare on the Western front, and under conditions where hygiene was impossible in Eastern Europe, were found on almost every soldier, and the diseases (typhus, trench fever, relapsing fever) which they carried caused millions of deaths. In Southern Europe and Africa malaria was a greater danger than any human enemy, and deaths from disease far outnumbered battle casualties. It was not until the war had gone on for several years that serious attempts were made to control insects of medical importance. In 1939, however, we in Britain were more alert to the dangers of insect-borne diseases, particularly under crowded conditions, such as might be expected in civilian air-raid shelters as well as in trenches, and in Africa and the Far East. We even had a high-powered committee of leading scientists called the

'Insecticide Panel' which sponsored research on these problems, and entomologists were organised even before the war began. However, we had few efficient pesticides at our disposal. Pyrethrum was the best substance available, but only in limited amounts and production could not be rapidly increased. Derris preparations were also valuable, but again only limited quantities could be produced. Every attempt was made to get the best results from these limited stocks. . . . Then DDT appeared. It seemed miraculous, for it killed insects at dilutions which, at that time, seemed greater than could be easily explained, yet it seemed practically harmless to man. Volunteers went for days in underclothes which had been impregnated with DDT; lice on their persons died at once, and, more important still, it proved impossible to reinfest them for weeks, though no more DDT was used. In many experiments of this kind no single volunteer showed any symptoms of poisoning. DDT was used in many ways, with similar results. Swamps were freed from mosquitoes by applying as little as one pound of DDT to the acre; men drank the water which had been so treated and were unharmed. Experiments showed that it *was* possible to poison warm-blooded animals and birds with DDT, and that it was most dangerous if given in solution in oil, but in general the impression was that we had at last discovered the perfect insecticide, one which was quite safe to use if reasonable precautions were observed. Under war-time conditions, it really was very nearly perfect.

It may be significant to note that the acute toxicity of DDT is almost exactly the same as that of the drug aspirin. This does *not* mean that it is non-poisonous, for aspirin, taken 100 tablets at a time, is a common suicide drug. The same quantity (about an ounce) of DDT would be lethal to most men. There is, however, one very important difference. Many people can take smaller doses of ten or twenty grains of aspirin a day for a long period without any serious result. This drug is not retained in the body. But a substantial part of the DDT is stored in the tissues, particularly the fat, so a cumulative effect, not obtained with aspirin, can be obtained. Fortunately much of the DDT retained in the body is changed into the much-less-poisonous DDE. A substantial fraction is also excreted, and the larger the dose the higher this fraction. Nevertheless the effects of chronic exposure can be serious.

It is almost impossible to over-estimate the war-time importance of DDT. In the west, where DDT was available, louse-borne typhus was controlled, a thing that never happened under similar conditions in World War I. In areas occupied by the Germans, who did not use DDT for louse control, the disease was serious. Mosquito control was equally efficient. Results with malaria were not as dramatic for prophylactic atabrin had already reduced its incidence from about three attacks per man per year in New Guinea to an almost negligible figure, but other mosquito-borne diseases, as well as nuisances from house flies and other insects, were effectively contained. Most important of all, the knowledge that DDT was available allowed military operations to be planned in areas in the tropics where previously insect-borne disease would have made such operations unacceptably hazardous. DDT certainly helped the western powers to win the war.

After the war, entomologists continued in this optimistic frame of mind. We thought that we now had the answer to insect-borne disease, and in fact campaigns to eradicate malaria using DDT as the main weapon were launched, with every hope of success, in many countries. This substance undoubtedly saved many millions of civilian lives. At first DDT was not available in sufficient amounts for widespread use in agriculture, but production increased, and it was used with success on many crops. Increased food production in areas where famine is endemic once again alleviated what would otherwise have been great suffering. Control seemed so easy that some professional entomologists feared unemployment! When one reads the attacks which are being made today on the use of persistent organo-chlorine insecticides, it is difficult to recall the optimism of the late nineteen-forties, and the tremendous benefits these substances have conferred and are still conferring.

In fact, up to about 1954, few complaints were heard against the organo-chlorine insecticides, though some medical authorities were worried by residues, particularly when these were secreted in the milk of cows fed on foodstuffs which had been treated with insecticides. Fish poisoning in streams treated in anti-malaria campaigns was accepted as unavoidable. As long as DDT was mainly used to control human disease, little notice was taken even when such incidents occurred. In fact in Britain there is little evidence that even to-day DDT has caused any great amount of damage to wild-life, and it appears to have been almost entirely harmless to man. This is not because we have always been wiser than others, but it is because we have not had comparable problems of insect damage to deal with. It is also possible that our authorities have not had sufficient money to carry out the extensive campaigns which have been a feature of insecticide use in the United States. Nevertheless, . . . although we may have avoided gross poisoning, our environment has been contaminated with amounts of DDT which cannot be accepted without question, and we may have escaped serious danger more by luck than good management. And *some* organo-chlorine insecticides have in fact done considerable damage in Britain.

DDT, used with care, and at minimum doses, has successfully controlled insects in many countries, and has usually done so without any recognisable harmful side effects. Used in ways which we now consider unwise it has done a great deal of damage to wild life.

FACTORY FARMING

BY RUTH HARRISON

Fears about pesticide use were soon followed by concern over other aspects of modern farming. In particular, the new intensive, indoor livestock units were felt to be cruel as well as unhealthy. Attention was drawn to them by Ruth Harrison, whose *Animal Machines*, from which this extract is taken, and ceaseless campaigning led to an official enquiry and the recommendations on the welfare of farm animals that exist today.

Let me tell you about a visit to one of the more extreme units where veal calves were reared. We came out of the bright sunlight into the dark, windowless shed. The farmer switched on the light and there was instant pandemonium within a row of narrow, enclosed crates at one end of the shed. When the noise subsided he carefully let down the shutter in front of one of the crates and revealed a calf standing in a space barely large enough to hold it, its eyes wide and staring, its face a picture of misery. Twice a day it saw electric light when it was fed. Otherwise it dragged out its existence in the dark, cramped and motionless, barely living before it was slaughtered.

As I looked at that calf I wondered how many people knew anything of these new farming methods, I wondered how necesssary they were and what possible justification there could be for them. I wondered whether there could be any goodness in the flesh as an end product. I wondered most of all that this unbelievable thing could be happening in the middle of the twentieth century when man was discovering space and so many exciting and wonderful new worlds were opening up to him. It seemed incongruously primitive for a people who prided themselves on being civilised and, moreover, on being a 'nation of animal lovers'.

Most people, especially in towns, tend to be ignorant of the processes by which food reaches their table, or if not ignorant they find it more comfortable to forget. Farm produce is still associated with mental pictures of animals browsing in fields and hedgerows, of cows waiting patiently in picturesque farmyards for the milking, of hens having a last forage before going to roost or sheep being rounded up by zealous dogs, and all the family atmosphere embracing the traditional farmyard. This association of ideas is cleverly kept alive by the giants of the advertising world who realise that the public still associates quality with healthy surroundings. A picture of the close-tethered veal calf standing uncomfortably on slats in its gloomy crate, the battery hen cramped in its cage, the closely packed, inert mass of pigs on the floor of the sweat-box piggery, or the sea of broilers in their dim shed, would not, they rightly surmise, help to sell their products.

The sad thing is that the further people get absorbed into large commercial combines and turn their minds purely to efficiency and material progress, the more they must sink their consciences or salve them with woolly thinking. You will be able to see how this is happening in the field of factory farming. Life is cheap to the factory farmer. He is dealing with so many animals that 'culls' are an everyday occurrence. To cull is to take out an animal which is not making a profit and to kill it. The principle of exterminating less hardy animals starts right from the beginning. Thus a hatchery is advised to cull all chicks which hatch somewhat later than the others, not because they are deformed in any way, but because they are stragglers and therefore assumed to be weaklings. Chickens can be turned out in their millions and are therefore considered a more expendable commodity than larger and more expensive forms of livestock. But the principle is the same, the cheapness of life itself, the lowering of standards. A danger of accepting any form of life as cheap is that each successive generation might accept slightly lower standards.

How far have we the right to take our domination of the animal world? Have we the right to rob them of all pleasure in life simply to make more money more quickly out of their carcasses? Have we the right to treat living creatures solely as food converting machines? At what point do we acknowledge cruelty?

To some extent, as the Minister of Agriculture is so fond of telling us, farm animals have always been exploited by man in that he rears them specifically for food. But until recently they were individuals, allowed their birthright of green fields, sunlight and fresh air; they were allowed to forage, to exercise, to watch the world go by, in fact to live. Even at its worst, with insufficient protection against inclement weather or poor supplementation of natural food, the animal had some enjoyment in life before it died. Today the exploitation has been taken to a degree which involves not only the elimination of all enjoyment, the frustration of almost all natural instincts, but its replacement with acute discomfort, boredom and the actual denial of health. It has been taken to a degree where the animal is not allowed to live before it dies.

For the factory farmer and the agri-industrial world behind him, cruelty is acknowledged only where profitability ceases. If an animal continues to grow and put on flesh, even when this depends on the heavy use of drugs, he deems that this treatment of it cannot be said to be cruel, though it be crated up in the dark all its life. The law relating to animals is loose and ill-defined and, moreover, hopelessly out of date. So we fall back on public conscience, easily roused and as easily lulled. Whether it be ignorance of these methods or just lack of thought on the part of the public, factory farming has paid off as far as the industry is concerned and each year sees the introduction of new niceties and the exploitation of ever more animals.–

I was originally drawn to the subject because I felt the modern methods by which farm animals are increasingly being reared are, quite frankly, cruel. But the more I studied the subject the deeper became my conviction that other issues are involved. The degradation of the animal in the appalling ways it is now made to eke out its existence must have an impact on human self-respect, and ultimately on man's treatment of man – 'Inasmuch as ye have done it unto the least of these my brethren ye have done it unto Me'. Some find it easy to lull their consciences when only animals are concerned, but the issues under discussion extend beyond conscience and impinge in the most practical manner on the physical well-being of the human race in so far as the food produced by these means is not only inferior but dangerous.

AN AGRICULTURAL REVOLUTION

BY MARION SHOARD

In 1980, Marion Shoard broadened the criticism of modern agriculture by arguing from a new standpoint, that of ownership. She maintained that the aesthetic quality of the countryside is the property of society at large. Therefore whoever reduces that quality without first obtaining general public consent is guilty of theft. This thought provided the title for her very successful and influential book, *The Theft of the Countryside*. In this passage she outlines her view of the changes wrought by modern farming.

Writing just after World War II, George Orwell was still able to describe the kind of English rural scene that had enthralled English writers for hundreds of years before his day: 'the railway cuttings smothered in flowers, the deep meadows where the great shining horses browse and meditate, the slow-moving streams bordered by willows, the green bosoms of the elms, all sleeping the deep, deep sleep of England'. When Orwell was writing, the peace of the English countryside had survived a history of energetic economic exploitation and periods of intense and far-reaching change. The Industrial Revolution had devastated certain areas and twentieth century development sprawl had pushed its fingers all through England. But the countryside had proved it could live with all these intrusions, just as it has since shown it can live with the other intrusions of advanced industrial society – from pylons to motorways, quarries to hypermarkets. Today the pace of this kind of development has slowed and the threat it poses has been contained. Now, as for most of our history, agriculture remains in control of the landscape – over 70 per cent of the land surface of England is farmed. It is farming more than any other single force which created the glories of the

English countryside. But in the years since Orwell wrote, the nature of our great rural industry has changed. Today, far from enriching and conserving the landscape, farming has started to destroy it. The 'deep, deep sleep of England', which survived the factory, the car, the bungalow and the electricity power-line, is at last being shattered – by, of all things, farming. An Agricultural Revolution, which is now in full swing, will destroy the character of our landscape completely if allowed to proceed unhindered.

England's landscape has been evolving through what has been described as the 'centuries-long conversation between man and nature' since Neolithic Man first made clearings in the great forest that once clothed virtually all of England in order to grow crops and graze livestock. The landscape we see today – land tilled and land left uncultivated, paths and roads, hamlets and villages – is for the most part the product of gradual social and economic change over a period of six thousand years. At three points in this long history there have however been periods in which a change in agricultural methods has produced dramatic effects on our landscape over large areas. The changes which occurred in the first two such 'Agricultural Revolutions' enriched our countryside immeasurably. They established many of the features which have given our traditional landscape its distinction. We are now living through the third major transformation. But unlike its two predecessors, this present Agricultural Revolution is devastating rather than enriching the environments in which it is occurring.

The first Agricultural Revolution was the discovery in Neolithic times, probably about 3,800 BC, that the same piece of land could grow crops more than once if it was left fallow between periods of cultivation. This breakthrough, combined with the availability of strains of grass suitable for cultivation as crops and animals that could be domesticated, enabled nomadic tribes to settle in one spot. The first Neolithic and Bronze Age villages sprang up as the centres of settled agricultural communities, laying the foundations of the medieval manorial system with its open fields and rotational farming.–

The second Agricultural Revolution, which occurred mainly between 1750 and 1850, partially dismantled this system. The population of England was increasing sharply, and rising demand made new methods of producing more food highly lucrative. Developments in stock rearing held out new hope of enhanced profit. But these could not be exploited as long as landowners' animals were able to mate freely in common pastures shared with peasants' animals, in accordance with traditional practice. So the landowners decided to enclose fields hitherto farmed in common by villagers. They imposed a network of hedges, stone walls and roads on the countryside to divide up the land into units suitable for scientific stock-rearing and other new forms of arable farming that were more productive than those they replaced.

The roots of the third (and current) Agricultural Revolution lie in World War II. The war stimulated demand for home-produced food, just as population increase had done in the eighteenth century. For most of the hundred years leading up to 1939, agriculture had been in decline. Britain had relied on cheap food from abroad to feed her population.–

It was the U-boat campaign in the Western Approaches in the 1940s which revived interest in domestic agriculture by demonstrating the risks of reliance on imported food. After the war, the belief that a healthy agriculture was a strategic necessity led to a wide-ranging programme of government support for farmers. Since 1945 demand for home-grown food has been artificially stimulated through tariffs on imports and direct subsidies of many different kinds to British farmers from the taxpayer and consumer. Against the background of a guaranteed income, farmers have become businessmen anxious to make the most of new opportunities for financial gain. And, as it has happened, this change in attitude has coincided with a breakthrough in technology on a par with those of the two earlier agricultural revolutions. New techniques have made it possible to turn food production into a large-scale industry run quite differently from pre-war agriculture. And the combination of technological change and highly favourable financial conditions has made farming far more profitable than anyone would have imagined possible in 1945. As a result, big business is turning the countryside into a huge production line. Of course, everyone has forgotten that the original reason for boosting home production – fear of a blockade of imports – is no longer very real. And it makes no difference that much of what is produced in Britain joins the EEC's mountains of surplus food.

The traditional English landscape is an inconvenient obstruction to the activities of the agri-businessmen. They could adapt the new methods to fit the environment they have inherited. But instead they are dismantling it. Profit dictates this course, and there are no real counter-pressures. Few of the people involved are unthinking vandals. Many of them are attached to the countryside and some are active in certain forms of conservation. But they have been taken over by a new professional orthodoxy which is propped up not only by the agricultural establishment but by the Government too, which is speeding the transformation with financial incentives and technical advice. In practising what is now understood to be their trade to the limits of their ability, farmers, mesmerized by the combination of technological change and excessive subsidies, have become the often unwitting agents of destruction.–

The central process in the current agricultural revolution is the replacement of men and animals with machines. Machines enable farmers to reduce their labour costs, and to cram more crops into a rotation: harrowing, harvesting and so on can be done much more quickly by tractors than by horses. Machines also enable farmers to produce a better crop, as mechanical operations can be timed more accurately than those dependent on human activity.–

There are two main reasons why the acquisition of machinery leads farmers to remove hedgerows, woods, clumps of trees and any other landscape feature on uncultivated land. First, the machines need large sweeps in which to turn: a lot of the equipment in which farmers have been investing heavily in recent years has a width of 20 or 30 feet, and it is clearly easier to operate if hedges and copses – 'obstructions' in the agricultural machinery trade's vocabulary – are removed, so that the spaces in which the machines work are larger and more regular. The other reason is that since the point of mechanization is to enable farmers to shed workers and cut labour costs, they want the operation of their new machines to consume as few man-hours as possible. So they want to see their machines driven as quickly as possible around unencumbered fields.–

To clear the path for these new machines, other machines, mainly bulldozers and hydraulic lifters, have been developed. These make operations ranging from the clearance of a wood to the creation of a moorland road much easier than they used to be. By attaching special blades and a lifter to his tractor, a farmer can rid himself of a mile-long hedge in an afternoon; thirty years ago the task would have taken him several days. Another range of machines has been developed to make possible the 'reclamation' of rough uncultivated land on steep slopes.–

It is easy, then, to see how mechanization leads directly to the destruction of landscape features on farmland. But it has also had indirect effects on features not directly involved in rationalization plans. As a result of the mechanization process, agricultural workers too have been leaving the land. – So the new machines have not only stripped many parts of rural England of landscape features; they have also provoked change in the countryside's social structure.–

The decline of rural communities has a further impact on the landscape. Since fewer people are available to work on farms, the maintenance of landscape features on marginal land has become more difficult to arrange. – Where hedges are kept, they are nowadays often cut as quickly as possible by a man driving a flail cutter alongside them and chopping them off almost to the stumps – a method which destroys most of their landscape value.–

Until the present agricultural revolution, farming operations were closely conditioned by the natural biological processes of the earth. The idea was still: 'We plough the fields and scatter The good seed on the land But it is fed and watered By God's Almighty Hand'. Now, however, farming is a capital- and energy-intensive process in which industrial products are turned into other industrial products that happen to be edible.–

Chemical fertilizers and pesticides have undoubtedly increased yields dramatically. And they enable farmers to abandon crop rotations. The soil is no longer allowed to rest under a root crop or fallow field every three or four years in order to recover naturally the fertility it lost under intensive cultivation: fertility is maintained at as high a level as possible almost indefinitely through the application of huge quantities of fertilizer and pesticide. – The abandonment of rotation has provided farmers with another reason for hedge removal. When crops are rotated, land is left fallow some of the time and animals graze it. So each field needs to be stock-proof. But when crop rotation has been abandoned, farmers can specialize completely in arable farming and get rid of all their animals. When they have done this, hedges are no longer needed and they can be bulldozed away. But this is far from being the only ill effect of the chemical takeover of farming.

Arable land occupies nearly 30 per cent of the land surface of Great Britain. And the most obvious direct impact of chemical pesticides and fertilizers here has been the elimination of wildlife. Thirty years ago wildlife in our countryside was not, as it is today, effectively confined to uncultivated, marginal land – hedgerows, woods, marshes and so on. Even productive arable land growing barley, wheat, cabbages, peas and potatoes also supported abundant wildlife, though it was less rich than that of uncultivated land. English cornfields were splashed with red poppies. Cornflowers grew among the ears of wheat, and here and there the delicate, rose-coloured blossoms of the bind-weed on their green, string-like stems twined themselves in and out of the wheat stalks. A walk after harvest revealed little plants which had been hidden by the tall crop, like the tiny heartsease or wild pansy with its single creamy flower, dabbed with a spot of deepest yellow streaked with purple at its centre. Hares and partridges were thick on the ground. Now, however, farmers have the means to grow 'clean crops', so all 'weeds' are banished by pesticides. Animals are affected in turn by the elimination of weeds. The survival of the partridge, for instance, depends on an adequate supply of insects to feed its newly-hatched chicks. The Game Conservancy estimates that the partridge chick survival rate is now running one-third lower than the level of the 1930s, and it attributes this to starvation of chicks through the elimination of insect 'pests' by pesticides. Stubble-burning, which accompanies chemical control, accentuates the impact on wildlife. When wheat or barley is harvested, farmers burn the stubble to destroy it as quickly as possible so they can sow another crop at the first possible moment after the last one was harvested. Stubble-burning burns or chars not only the remains of the crop, however, but also the microfauna and flora of the soil surface. In one study, stubble-burning reduced the number of insects living above ground by 85 per cent, the number of insects emerging in the following year by 71 per cent and the number of species present by 61 per cent. One of the more visible effects of this process is the absence of flocks of birds feeding on the stubble.–

Like mechanization, the switch to chemical fertilizers and pesticides was a product of the era of cheap oil. – And the efficiency of our agriculture in terms of output per man, which is undoubtedly high, exacts a high price in energy use. – Now that the real cost of energy has increased, the benefits to the nation of such energy-intensive agriculture are even less obvious than they were.

WHERE DOES RESPONSIBILITY LIE?

BY FRANK FRASER DARLING

In 1969, the distinguished biologist and conservationist Sir Frank Fraser Darling was invited by the BBC to deliver the annual series of six broadcast Reith Lectures, to which he gave the title 'Wilderness and Plenty'. This is his final lecture, in which he expands the area under discussion to embrace the whole of the relationship between people and their natural environment.

The euphoria of landing on the moon has been less hallucinatory than that of the flight of the first man in space. Ten years of this extraordinary way of getting around have almost got rid of the notion that if we wear out, eat up and generally defile our very unusual planet we shall be able to blast off to some other virgin globe. The Earth is our home; it was made ready for the rapid evolution of exploiting man by many millions of years of organic activity. Man had no place in an earlier world.

There may be other planets we can live on, reached in travel time longer than our normal life span, but the chances of our reaching a new world precisely at a time when man could make good use of it are remote. If advanced or even primitive cultures were present, should we employ forthwith the weapon of war to make room for ourselves, or should we exercise our usual unctuous hypocrisy of washing our hands in imaginary soap and water?

We can set aside this kind of day-dreaming and make up our minds that our concern is here on Earth in so far as persistence, nutrition and social wellbeing are our aims. Some economists and organic chemists have forecast the possibilities of extreme densities of human beings on our Earth which is over two-thirds covered by ocean, and assume that a social adjustment in our mentality will evolve as rapidly as our numbers increase. This seems to me unlikely and as an ecologist living on a known Earth now well surveyed from the air, and even minutely by satellites, I am bound to continue thinking in terms of solar energy and photosynthesis by chlorophyll. And I see these not only in terms of possible food production, but in the power of the forest wildernesses to be storage banks and regulators of our vital atmosphere, and our rising to continual awareness of the nobility of wilderness. Mere food plants would not act as such a store, because our bodies would recirculate the products so quickly. Energy flow and recycling is of the essence of organic existence, but there are different rates of flow.

In plain terms, we cannot give up our world to the production of human beings, yet as I have said more than once in these lectures, the biggest problems facing the world today are the continuing rise in human population, the continuing rise and diversity of pollution, and finally, the increasing difficulty of preserving examples of the world's natural ecosystems with their species of plants and animals. In so far as the world of man is prepared to concede this last to be a problem at all, its gestures are patronising and conciliatory rather than actions of prudence in conserving as wilderness those portions of our planet which the ecologists of all men are now making articulate. 'Speak to the earth and it shall teach thee', is the task and reward of the ecologist, but as he learns these truths of the wilderness silently contributing to man's own existence, his knowledge also becomes his sorrow and burden as he sees the wilderness recede.

Increasing population for years ahead is an inevitability; pollution need not increase, and were we ready to accept the idea that technology should use its own inventiveness resolutely to clean up after itself, we could have a healthier and more beautiful world within a reasonable time. There is an ethic of responsibility for the environment which is a growing body of philosophy, but it is not generally understood and it is followed only expediently. Did I not admit to using petrol containing lead, and that I fly fifty thousand miles a year? Yet I am supposed to be in the spearhead of thought and action attempting to contain the pollution, and wondering how we can contain the population. I repeat that I live in my era; I could do no good by following the ultimate misapplication of logic by walking out naked to live by my beliefs, for I should be naked also of many of the skills of the average savage in collecting his food and trying to live from a depleted wilderness. Nevertheless, it still does behove me to continue in the field of discovery and probe intellectually into an emergent ethic.

I believe that thought on the problem of population has been too pragmatic, though understandably so. Any intellectual change of attitude might take a long time to filter through society, but such change must carry a conviction from within and *a priori*, quite distinct from hope of benefits to be derived.

For many years I have been interested in the patterns of sexual convention in human beings and the phenomenon of reproduction. Though sexual intercourse is still necessary for reproduction, reproduction is not necessarily the desired end of love-making. Religion has often wished to imply that whether desired or not, reproduction should be accepted as a consequence not to be hindered. Even among the many who do not feel that way, and with the great advances in the techniques of contraception, there is insufficient acceptance of the idea that sexuality is something existing in its own right, not to be confused with and clouded by unwanted reproduction. The necessity in our present world problem is to accept sexuality in this way, untrammelled by doubt. The extreme right wing of religion would imply that man should be able to rise above the animal function of sexuality except in the service of reproduction. The extreme left of behaviourism on the other hand would say, of course sexuality is animal and so are we, and therefore we should be free to exercise it as animals.

The animal quality is the common factor in these two views, but I think they are both mistaken. Why not look upon human sexuality as something that is potentially uniquely human? Presumably, the feathers of a bird first developed as a form of insulation against heat and cold. Feathers as a means of flight were an entirely different development, but they still continued to serve the function of insulation. A third entirely different function has developed in the patterns and colourings of feathers which have become means of recognition and of conveying signals as in display and in the almost unison of action in a flying flock. The other functions remain, nevertheless. There is nothing teleological about this, of course, just natural selection upon existing natural equipment. I think human sexuality should be looked upon in this way, that as an adjunct to reproduction was its first function, it is not necessarily its final one.

The phenomenon of human love has been observed for a long time in our history, certainly ever since we had means of conveying our thoughts through the instruments of speech and then writing. The great love stories of the world have a warm place in our hearts, even in periods and cultures where love by equal choice has been uncommon. We do not doubt the existence of love. At its highest, human love is exclusive and absolute, as expressed by Lancelot in his love for Guinevere. He could not go through the act of love with

25

any other woman, even when such an act would have liberated him from captivity to continue his mission to rescue Guinevere, who was about to be burnt. And you will remember the story of the paternity of Galahad, when Elaine had no power over Lancelot until magic was employed to deceive him into thinking Elaine was Guinevere.

Nowadays we profess to believe in falling in love as the basis of marriage. Love as part of the expression of sexuality is the added human function which the act holds above and beyond the reproductive function which should be exercised so rarely. Within the ideal, by which I mean the relationship of love between two people which leads to that exclusive state, sexuality should not be restrained but let free for its influence on spiritual development between the sexes. Modern contraceptive technique and the emancipation of women in our age make possible this emancipation for man and woman together, of reproduction set in its right perspective. I consider the fears sometimes expressed of the dangers of such freedom becoming available to the adolescent as being quite prurient. Leave them alone, with the example of parents in love.

If our culture learned the potential quality of human sexuality as part of its very being, it would be more helpful in the world at large where population control is even more urgent than it is here. It is time that church and behaviourism dropped the 'animal' connotation and thought more of the uniquely human potential of developed sexuality not bound up with reproduction. The sexual act between lovers is of the very essence of unselfishness. The rare intention to conceive would then be approached as a sacrament of joy, rather than the possibility of conception being feared as the cloud of so many lives.

I have heard it said that the constant sexual desire of humanity is one of the crosses we bear. I would rather consider it the other way round as one of our greatest potential gifts. Over thirty years ago the anthropologist J.D. Unwin wrote of the drive of peoples in which there was apparent greater restriction of sexual freedom. The Epicurean and the Stoic would agree with that, and so would I, if restriction comes from within and is not imposed from without, because the spiritual force of human sexuality is within love and compassion and the naturally exclusive ideal. Within these restrictions there can be no over-indulgence because the individual appetite takes care of that. The human being ennobled by the sexual selflessness of love is ready to be the servant of the world. Promiscuity is dissipation of creative force.

An ethic of sexuality joined with an ethic of the wholeness of life, giving us a reverence for lowlier animal forms, and reacting on population growth or limitation, should influence the attitudes of the

West towards our exploitation of land and animal life. We are degrading animals in our day by the methods of reproduction and rearing we are now employing. De-beaked hens, cooped-up calves fed on antibiotics, and our growing denial of the personal association to our domesticated animals, which is their right if we domesticate them, constitutes degradation not only of the animals but of ourselves. On these systems individual keepers of animals are not thinking in terms of starving millions but of profits easiest gotten; our acceptance from our positions of remoteness encourages these practices and so does governmental acquiescence, because governments really are fearful about what starving millions might do. When I read in a scientific journal of a bull in its brutish decency ultimately declining to serve the canvas cow and the rubber tube, and having to be chased round a paddock with a stick to make it do so, I say that civilisation is failing. Artificial insemination of cattle can be a force for good, but bulls should not be brought to a state of revulsion, to give us our 'pintaday' and all that. All governments should boldly face their responsibility to work out population and nutritional policies, not play the opposite game of subsidising irresponsibly reproductive families. Is vote-catching to be the incurable weakness of democracy?

There is the third ethic of the land, our responsibility for the environment of the human species now and in the future. Such qualified pessimism as I have voiced in these lectures allows no relaxation in our care for the face of the planet in a problematic future. Care of the wilderness is part of that environmental conservation in which we now include the human being. The exclusion of man from the hierarchy of nature, so common in the past and even in our own time, is to put him in the position of a bourgeois *rentier*, living off an economy but having no responsibility for it. To make him an integrated functional member of the plant and animal world about us is no denigration of his high estate, no assumption of a mealy-mouthed egalitarian folksiness. Rather does man accept his position in nature as the species granted the privilege of fulfilling the aristocratic ideal of *noblesse oblige*, of being the servant of his people.

This is our responsibility towards the Earth and its denizens. We shall doubtless make honest mistakes in our exercise of service, but that is where research itself is no luxury, only one part of the fulfilment of our obligation. I have expressed my doubts whether we shall have a long posterity if we continue as we are doing, living off the capital of the world's ecosystems that evolved long before we were consciously men, throwing our poisonous refuse into air and water arrogantly as well as in ignorance. In the fulfilment of our humanity we should act as if posterity stretched into infinitude, and by thus acting we shall make this more possible. We know that the evolution of our species probably rests now in the psychological and, as I believe, in the spiritual sphere, and we have so far to go. When the apocryphal Middle-West farmer contributing by his practices to the eventual dust-bowl said, 'Posterity never did nothin' fer me,' he was indeed turning his back on the evolutionary potential of his species, selling his birthright for a mess of pottage. We have seen in recent years a deep questioning of the attitude that natural riches are there for the exploitation of man. A less anthropocentric philosophy of restraint, of identification with, rather than exclusion from, nature is developing its own ethic of love.

If we accept the philosophy of respect for life with its view that organisms exist in their own right as fellow members with us in the world community of living things, we must be guided constantly by the discipline of ecological observation, otherwise we are in danger of being rather silly. Man as an omnivore becoming philosophically a hyper-vegetarian does not reach his own ideals when he swallows lowly and invisible organisms on his lettuce, and the Jain bent double peering at the ground before each step lest he should kill anything, would need eyes of an order not granted to us to see the still smaller creatures in his way. There is no room in our philosophy of responsibility for preciousness. We tread and eat and live as man, prepared to kill if the necessity or inevitability is there, but not for fun.

The American ecologist Aldo Leopold was in my opinion the clearest exponent of an emergent ethic of the land. He said, 'That land is a community is the basic concept of ecology, but that land is to be loved and respected is an extension of ethics – We abuse land because we regard it as a commodity belonging to us. When we see land as a community to which we belong, we may begin to use it with love and respect.'

The form and style of the land is part of our environment as surely as the community of living things. Landscape is near and touching to some of us, a constant and urgent concern as of someone we love. To others it does not seem to have this quality. You remember the Yorkshireman's comment on seeing the Lake District in an earlier day – 'There's nowt 'ere but scenery.' Yet even if not of conscious concern to enough people, landscape is of importance. The reciprocation of conscious concern is of the very nature of love, which is essential to all human relationship.

Perpetuation of a derelict landscape as a background to children's lives is like rearing them to some extent in lovelessness, even if a rusting motorcar does provide a lot of fun. Sometimes when I see examples of presumed art made up from the scrap-iron dump and hear music not unlike the sound of a tin can being kicked down some sunless alley, I feel that perhaps this is what must happen to the sensitive child reared in the industrial miasma. They have to express themselves and this is how they feel the upwelling of art, having no sense of season, flower, or flow; there are only staccato skylines and cacophony and an outraged Earth.

By definition landscape architecture carries the connotation of artefact. If man enters into landscape at all he is influencing and reshaping it. If he merely exploits a landscape he is almost certainly degrading it and making it less beautiful. If he lives with it as a husbandman calling it home, he will almost unconsciously produce many of the rural landscapes and small towns of Europe which we find pleasing and which we know to be biologically productive. Sometimes landscapes have been engineered, but rarely of more than a few hundred acres in extent. Most of these we find pleasant, but they were made for the favoured few. We have now reached a point in time when we can deduce the history of land, and in so far as the land use has been deleterious we have sufficient ecological knowledge to architect the landscape on a regional plan for biological productivity and the content of man. Human tastes vary, but all in all the most general consensus of beautiful landscape would be found to be that which is in ecological repose or near to it.

Ian McHarg, a Scotsman who found freedom to work and develop his thought in America, has become an outstanding voice in this field, a highly individual one trying always to justify his ecological planning of landscape by return to basic principles of interrelationships and interdependencies within the site. The placement of buildings and their design, in following ecological principles, can so often be justified aesthetically. Whether we are conscious of it or not as subsequent observers, most of us find this kind of landscape architecture to be satisfying. The odd and idiosyncratic rarely give content, and the bull-at-a-gatepost method of carving a landscape usually ends up in real trouble. McHarg's new book, *Design with Nature*, is at once a testament of belief backed by well-chosen case histories, and a thing of beauty in itself.

I have said little of the wilderness as a place where such men as can should spend their forty days alone or with a companion. This is a time for re-creation of the spirit for which too few men find opportunity. Whether it is forest, mountain or desert is immaterial as long as the wilderness is not a man-degraded one of recent time. I do not wish to dwell on this aspect because the fulfilment of it is the privilege of the few and I have an uneasy feeling deep down that we should not burden the wilderness with this egocentric human purpose. The wilderness does not exist *for* our re-creation or delectation. This is something we gain from its great function of being, with the oceans part of the guardianship of the world in which we have come so recently to be a denizen.

The true natural wilderness from which we have carved our precarious plenty cannot be re-created in our time, possibly never. But that which we have taken from the wilderness we can treat with gratitude and responsibility. The full awareness of what man has done in creating dereliction and squalor has only come in our time. There has also come the knowledge of how to cope with it. The great earth-moving machines of our technological era can make some return by fashioning pleasances from these depressing landscapes.

Some of the pit heaps in the North of England, of Durham and Northumberland, are becoming wooded hills. They will not be true wilderness but places that the folk of the villages can reach in an afternoon or evening. The dark landscapes of industrial Wales, Glamorgan and the Rhondda, may disappear if a recommendation of local bodies is implemented. The designers have planned 'a radically changed physical environment, with extensive forests clothing the mountains, and substantial areas of new development and rehabilitation'. The designers have consulted with the Forestry Commission, the Agricultural Land Service, the Derelict Land Unit, the National Coal Board, and the Nature Conservancy. Once again, in a country in which land is getting scarcer, there is a realisation of the need for multiple use. It would seem that the land ethic has taken root in this place of so much suffering in the past. Those who create dereliction in our day in the brickfields and iron ore deposits of the Midlands should see what poorer folk are doing or trying to do, till eventually we could expect plain shame to be enough to efface previous dereliction and prevent new areas. The birds and wild flowers are the natural opportunists ready to people and enrich the new acceptable environments. Such, I repeat, is the therapy of the green leaf.

The British are but one nation concerned among so many. As part of a world movement of conservation and rehabilitation, linked with a positive population policy, we could have a changed industrial scene within a generation – and we have not more than that in which to do it. There can be no greater moral obligation in the environmental field than to ease out the living space and replace dereliction by beauty. Most people will never know true wilderness although its existence will not be a matter of indifference to them. The near landscape is valuable and lovable because of its nearness, not something to be disregarded and shrugged off; it is where children are reared and what they take away in their minds to their long future. What ground could be more hallowed?

THE HISTORICAL ROOTS OF OUR ECOLOGICAL CRISIS

BY LYNN WHITE, JR.

As the issues troubling environmentalists became more widely known, some authors sought to probe the historical and ethical roots of the modern relationship between people and their natural surroundings. In 1967, Lynn White, Jr., Professor of History at the University of California at Los Angeles, wrote an article in *Science* in which he traced the origin of the contemporary human dilemma to ideas that became current some 1,700 years ago. Because it introduced a new dimension to the debate, the article, from which the following extract is taken, appeared in many publications and was widely read.

One thing is so certain that it seems stupid to verbalize it: both modern technology and modern science are distinctively *occidental*. Our technology has absorbed elements from all over the world, notably from China; yet everywhere today – successful technology is western. Our science is the heir to all the sciences of the past, especially perhaps to the work of the great Islamic scientists of the Middle Ages, who so often outdid the ancient Greeks in skill and perspicacity –.

A second pair of facts is less well recognized because they result from quite recent historical scholarship. The leadership of the West, both in technology and in science, is far older than the so-called scientific revolution of the seventeenth century or the so-called industrial revolution of the eighteenth century. These terms are in fact outmoded and obscure the true nature of what they try to describe – significant stages in two long and separate developments. By AD 1000 at the latest – and perhaps, feebly, as much as 200 years earlier – the West began to apply water power to industrial processes other than milling grain. This was followed in the late twelfth century by the harnessing of wind power. From simple beginnings, but with remarkable consistency of style, the West rapidly expanded its skills in the development of power machinery, labour-saving devices, and automation. Those who doubt should contemplate that most monumental achievement in the history of automation: the weight-driven mechanical clock, which appeared in two forms in the early fourteenth century. Not in craftsmanship but in basic technological capacity, the Latin West of the later Middle Ages far outstripped its elaborate, sophisticated, and aesthetically magnificent sister cultures, Byzantium and Islam. In 1444 a great Greek ecclesiastic, Bessarion, who had gone to Italy, wrote a letter to a prince in Greece. He is amazed by the superiority of Western ships, arms, textiles, glass. But above all he is astonished by the spectacle of waterwheels sawing timber and pumping the bellows of blast furnaces. Clearly, he had seen nothing of the sort in the Near East.

By the end of the fifteenth century the technological superiority of Europe was such that its small, mutually hostile nations could spill out over all the rest of the world, conquering, looting, and colonizing. The symbol of this technological superiority is the fact that Portugal, one of the weakest states of the Occident, was able to become, and to remain for a century, mistress of the East Indies. And we must remember that the technology of Vasco da Gama and Albuquerque was built by pure empiricism, drawing remarkably little support or inspiration from science.

In the present-day vernacular understanding, modern science is supposed to have begun in 1543, when both Copernicus and Vesalius published their great works. It is no derogation of their accomplishments, however, to point out that such structures as the *Fabrica* and the *De revolutionibus* do not appear overnight. The distinctive Western tradition of science, in fact, began in the late eleventh century with a massive movement of translation of Arabic and Greek scientific works into Latin. A few notable books – Theophrastus, for example – escaped the West's avid new appetite for science, but within less than 200 years effectively the entire corpus of Greek and Muslim science was available in Latin, and was being eagerly read and criticized in the new European universities. Out of criticism arose new observation, speculation, and increasing distrust of ancient authorities. By the late thirteenth century Europe had seized global scientific leadership from the faltering hands of Islam. It would be as absurd to deny the profound originality of Newton, Galileo, or Copernicus as to deny that of the fourteenth century scholastic scientists like Buridan or Oresme on whose work they built. Before the eleventh century, science scarcely existed in the

Latin West, even in Roman times. From the eleventh century onward, the scientific sector of occidental culture has increased in a steady crescendo.

Since both our technological and our scientific movements got their start, acquired their character, and achieved world dominance in the Middle Ages, it would seem that we cannot understand their nature or their present impact upon ecology without examining fundamental medieval assumptions and developments.

Until recently, agriculture has been the chief occupation even in 'advanced' societies; hence, any change in methods of tillage has much importance. Early ploughs, drawn by two oxen, did not normally turn the sod but merely scratched it. Thus, cross-ploughing was needed and fields tended to be squarish. In the fairly light soils and semi-arid climates of the Near East and Mediterranean, this worked well. But such a plough was inappropriate to the wet climate and often sticky soils of northern Europe. By the latter part of the seventh century after Christ, however, following obscure beginnings, certain northern peasants were using an entirely new kind of plough, equipped with a vertical knife to cut the line of the furrow, a horizontal share to slice under the sod, and a mouldboard to turn it over. The friction of this plough with the soil was so great that it normally required not two but eight oxen. It attacked the land with such violence that cross-ploughing was not needed, and fields tended to be shaped in long strips.

In the days of the scratch-plough, fields were distributed generally in units capable of supporting a single family. Subsistence farming was the presupposition. But no peasant owned eight oxen: to use the new and more efficient plough, peasants pooled their oxen to form large plough-teams, originally receiving (it would appear) ploughed strips in proportion to their contribution. Thus, distribution of land was based no longer on the needs of a family but, rather, on the capacity of a power machine to till the earth. Man's relationship to the soil was profoundly changed. Formerly man had been part of nature; now he was the exploiter of nature. Nowhere else in the world did farmers develop any analogous agricultural implement. Is it coincidence that modern technology, with its ruthlessness toward nature, has so largely been produced by descendants of those peasants of northern Europe?

The same exploitive attitude appears slightly before AD 830 in Western illustrated calendars. In older calendars the months were shown as passive personifications. The new Frankish calendars, which set the style for the Middle Ages, are very different: they show men coercing the world around them – ploughing, harvesting, chopping trees, butchering pigs. Man and nature are two things, and man is master.

These novelties seem to be in harmony with larger intellectual patterns. What people do about their ecology depends on what they think about themselves in relation to things around them. Human ecology is deeply conditioned by beliefs about our nature and destiny – that is, by religion. To Western eyes this is very evident in, say, India or Ceylon. It is equally true of ourselves and of our medieval ancestors.

The victory of Christianity over paganism was the greatest psychic revolution in the history of our culture. It has become fashionable today to say that, for better or worse, we live in 'the post-Christian age'. Certainly the forms of our thinking and language have largely ceased to be Christian, but to my eye the substance often remains amazingly akin to that of the past. Our daily habits of action, for example, are dominated by an implicit faith in perpetual progress which was unknown either to Greco-Roman antiquity or to the Orient. It is rooted in, and is indefensible apart from, Judaeo-Christian teleology. The fact that Communists share it merely helps to show what can be demonstrated on many others grounds: that Marxism, like Islam, is a Judaeo-Christian heresy. We continue to live today, as we have lived for about 1,700 years, very largely in a context of Christian axioms.

What did Christianity tell people about their relations with the environment?

While many of the world's mythologies provide stories of creation, Greco-Roman mythology was singularly incoherent in this respect. Like Aristotle, the intellectuals of the ancient West denied that the visible world had had a beginning. Indeed, the idea of a beginning was impossible in the framework of their cyclical notion of time. In sharp contrast, Christianity inherited from Judaism not only a concept of time as non-repetitive and linear but also a striking story of creation. By gradual stages a loving and all-powerful God had created light and darkness, the heavenly bodies, the earth and all its plants, animals, birds, and fishes. Finally, God had created Adam and, as an afterthought, Eve, to keep man from being lonely. Man named all the animals, thus establishing his dominance over them. God planned all of this explicitly for man's benefit and rule: no item in the physical creation had any purpose save to serve man's purposes. And, although man's body is made of clay, he is not simply part of nature: he is made in God's image.

Especially in its Western form, Christianity is the most anthropocentric religion the world has seen. As early as the second

35

century both Tertullian and Saint Irenaeus of Lyons were insisting that when God shaped Adam he was foreshadowing the image of the Incarnate Christ, the Second Adam. Man shares, in great measure, God's transcendence of nature. Christianity, in absolute contrast to ancient paganism and Asia's religions (except, perhaps, Zoroastrianism), not only established a dualism of man and nature but also insisted that it is God's will that man exploit nature for his proper ends.

At the level of the common people this worked out in an interesting way. In antiquity every tree, every spring, every stream, every hill had its own *genius loci*, its guardian spirit. These spirits were accessible to men, but were very unlike men; centaurs, fauns, and mermaids show their ambivalence. Before one cut a tree, mined a mountain, or dammed a brook, it was important to placate the spirit in charge of that particular situation, and to keep it placated. By destroying pagan animism, Christianity made it possible to exploit nature in a mood of indifference to the feelings of natural objects.

It is often said that for animism the Church substituted the cult of saints. True; but the cult of saints is functionally quite different from animism. The saint is not *in* natural objects; he may have special shrines, but his citizenship is in heaven. Moreover, a saint is entirely a man; he can be approached in human terms. In addition to saints, Christianity of course also had angels and demons inherited from Judaism and perhaps, at one remove, from Zoroastrianism. But these were all as mobile as the saints themselves. The spirits *in* natural objects, which formerly had protected nature from man, evaporated. Man's effective monopoly on spirit in this world was confirmed, and the old inhibitions to the exploitation of nature crumbled.

When one speaks in such sweeping terms, a note of caution is in order. Christianity is a complex faith, and its consequences differ in differing contexts. What I have said may well apply to the medieval West, where in fact technology made spectacular advances. But the Greek East, a highly civilized realm of equal Christian devotion, seems to have produced no marked technological innovation after the late seventh century, when Greek fire was invented. The key to the contrast may perhaps be found in a difference in the tonality of piety and thought which students of comparative theology find between the Greek and Latin churches. The Greeks believed that sin was intellectual blindness, and that salvation was to be found in illumination, orthodoxy – that is, clear thinking. The Latins, on the other hand, felt that sin was moral evil, and that salvation was to be found in right conduct. Eastern theology has been intellectualist. Western theology has been voluntarist. The Greek saint contemplates; the Western saint acts. The implications of Christianity for the conquest of nature would emerge more easily in the Western atmosphere.

The Christian dogma of creation, which is found in the first clause of all the Creeds, has another meaning for our comprehension of today's ecologic crisis. By revelation, God had given man the Bible, the Book of Scripture. But since God had made nature, nature also must reveal the divine mentality. The religious study of nature for the better understanding of God was known as natural theology. In the early Church, and always in the Greek East, nature was conceived primarily as a symbolic system through which God speaks to men: the ant is a sermon to sluggards; rising flames are the symbol of the soul's aspiration. This view of nature was essentially artistic rather than scientific. While Byzantium preserved and copied great numbers of ancient Greek scientific texts, science as we conceive it could scarcely flourish in such an ambience.

However, in the Latin West by the early thirteenth century natural theology was following a very different bent. It was ceasing to be the decoding of the physical symbols of God's communication with man and was becoming the effort to understand God's mind by discovering how his creation operates. The rainbow was no longer simply a symbol of hope first sent to Noah after the Deluge; Robert Grosseteste, Friar Roger Bacon, and Theodoric of Freiberg produced startlingly sophisticated works on the optics of the rainbow, but they did it as a venture in religious understanding. From the thirteenth century onward, up to and including Leibniz and Newton, every major scientist, in effect, explained his motivations in religious terms. Indeed, if Galileo had not been so expert an amateur theologian he would have got into far less trouble: the professionals resented his intrusion. And Newton seems to have regarded himself more as a theologian than as a scientist. It was not until the late eighteenth century that the hypothesis of God became unnecessary to many scientists.

It is often hard for the historian to judge, when men explain why they are doing what they want to do, whether they are offering real reasons or merely culturally acceptable reasons. The consistency with which scientists during the long formative centuries of Western science said that the task and the reward of the scientist was 'to think God's thoughts after him' leads one to believe that this was their real motivation. If so, then modern Western science was cast in a matrix of Christian theology. The dynamism of religious devotion, shaped by the Judaeo-Christian dogma of creation, gave it impetus.

We would seem to be headed toward conclusions unpalatable to many Christians. Since both *science* and *technology* are blessed words in our contemporary vocabulary, some may be happy at the notions, first, that, viewed historically, modern science is an extrapolation of natural theology and, second, that modern technology is at least partly to be explained as an occidental, voluntarist realization of the Christian dogma of man's transcendence of, and rightful mastery over, nature. But, as we now recognize, somewhat over a century ago science and technology – hitherto quite separate activities – joined to give mankind powers which, to judge by many of the ecologic effects, are out of control. If so, Christianity bears a huge burden of guilt.

I personally doubt that disastrous ecologic backlash can be avoided simply by applying to our problems more science and more technology. Our science and technology have grown out of Christian attitudes toward man's relation to nature which are almost universally held not only by Christians and neo-Christians but also by those who fondly regard themselves as post-Christians. Despite Copernicus, all the cosmos rotates around our little globe. Despite Darwin, we are *not*, in our hearts, part of the natural process. We are superior to nature, contemptuous of it, willing to use it for our slightest whim. The newly elected governor of California, like myself a churchman, but less troubled than I, spoke for the Christian tradition when he said (as is alleged), 'when you've seen one redwood tree, you've seen them all'. To a Christian a tree can be no more than a physical fact. The whole concept of the sacred grove is alien to Christianity and to the ethos of the West. For nearly two millenia Christian missionaries have been chopping down sacred groves, which are idolatrous because they assume spirit in nature.

What we do about ecology depends on our ideas of the man-nature relationship. More science and more technology are not going to get us out of the present ecologic crisis until we find a new religion, or rethink our old one.–

Possibly we should ponder the greatest radical in Christian history since Christ: Saint Francis of Assisi. The prime miracle of Saint Francis is the fact that he did not end at the stake, as many of his left-wing followers did. He was so clearly heretical that a general of the Franciscan Order, Saint Bonaventura, a great and perceptive Christian, tried to suppress early accounts of Franciscanism. The key to an understanding of Francis is his belief in the virtue of humility – not merely for the individual but for man as a species. Francis tried to depose man from his monarchy over creation and set up a democracy of all God's creatures. With him the ant is no longer simply a homily for the lazy, flames a sign of the thrust of the soul toward union with God; now they are Brother Ant and Sister Fire, praising the Creator in their own ways as Brother Man does in his. Later commentators have said that Francis preached to the birds as a rebuke to men who would not listen. The records do not read so: he urged the little birds to praise God, and in spiritual ecstasy they flapped their wings and chirped rejoicing. Legends of saints, especially the Irish saints, had long told of their dealings with animals but always, I believe, to show their human dominance over creatures. With Francis it is different. The land around Gubbio in the Apennines was being ravaged by a fierce wolf. Saint Francis, says the legend, talked to the wolf and persuaded him of the error of his ways. The wolf repented, died in the odour of sanctity, and was buried in consecrated ground.

What Sir Steven Runciman calls 'the Franciscan doctrine of the animal soul' was quickly stamped out. Quite possibly it was in part inspired, consciously or unconsciously, by the belief in reincarnation held by the Cathar heretics who at that time teemed in Italy and southern France, and who presumably had got it originally from India. It is significant that at just the same moment, about 1200, traces of metempsychosis are found also in western Judaism, in the Provençal *Cabbala*. But Francis held neither to transmigration of souls nor to pantheism. His view of nature and of man rested on a unique sort of pan-psychism of all things animate and inanimate, designed for the glorification of their transcendent Creator, who, in the ultimate gesture of cosmic humility, assumed flesh, lay helpless in a manger, and hung dying on a scaffold.

I am not suggesting that many modern Americans who are concerned about our ecologic crisis will be either able or willing to counsel with wolves or exhort birds. However, the present increasing disruption of the global environment is the product of a dynamic technology and science which were originating in the Western medieval world against which Saint Francis was rebelling in so original a way. Their growth cannot be understood historically apart from distinctive attitudes toward nature which are deeply grounded in Christian dogma. The fact that most people do not think of these attitudes as Christian is irrelevant. No new set of basic values has been accepted in our society to displace those of Christianity. Hence we shall continue to have a worsening ecologic crisis until we reject the Christian axiom that nature has no reason for existence save to serve man.

The greatest spiritual revolutionary in Western history, Saint Francis, proposed what he thought was an alternative Christian view of nature and man's relation to it: he tried to substitute the idea of the equality of all creatures, including man, for the idea of man's limitless rule of creation. He failed. Both our present science and our present technology are so tinctured with orthodox Christian arrogance toward nature that no solution for our ecologic crisis can be expected from them alone. Since the roots of our trouble are so largely religious, the remedy must also be essentially religious, whether we call it that or not. We must rethink and refeel our nature and destiny. The profoundly religious, but heretical, sense of the primitive Franciscans for the spiritual autonomy of all parts of nature may point a direction. I propose Saint Francis as a patron saint for ecologists.

PROSPECT

BY LEWIS MUMFORD

In the summer of 1955, long before the attention of most people had been drawn to environmental problems, the Wenner-Gren Foundation for Anthropological Research held a symposium in Princeton, New Jersey, on the subject of 'Man's Role in Changing the Face of the Earth'. Lewis Mumford was one of the three chairmen and the following extract is taken from his summing up of part of the symposium. Professor Mumford has explored more deeply than most scholars into architecture, town planning, and the history of human societies, and thus into the effects people have on the world around them.

I n passing from the past to the future, we pass from memory and reflection to observation and current practice and thence to anticipation and prediction. As usually conceived, this is a movement from the known to the unknown, from the probable to the possible, from the domain of necessity to the open realm of choice. But in fact these aspects of time and experience cannot be so neatly separated. Some part of the past is always becoming present in the future; and some part of the future is already present in the past. Instead of thinking of these three segments of time in serial order, we would do well to take the view of a mathematician like A.N. Whitehead and narrow the time band to a tenth of a second before and the tenth of a second after any present event. When one does this, one understands that the past, the present, and the future are in that living moment almost one; and, if our minds were only capable of holding these three elements together in consciousness over a wider span of time, we should deal with our problems in a more organic fashion, doing justice not merely to the succession of events but to their virtual coexistence through anticipation and memory.

Now part of the future we face has already been determined, and we have no control over it. To begin at the physical level, we are limited by the forces of inertia; at the biological level, by the facts of organic inheritance. At the social level we must reckon with institutional persistences which, if not so ingrained as biological structures, cannot be suddenly altered; even at the highest level of the human personality, memory and habit tend to keep our actions in a groove. We do well to reckon with these constant factors and their sluggish ways; if they fetter our creativity, they also tend to limit the possibility of chaos. For good or bad, a part of our future is given; and, like a Christmas gift, we must accept it gracefully, before we try to exchange it for something that fits us better.

We might, for example, in view of the special role that sexuality and love were to play in man's life, have wished that nature – sometime about the point when the structure of the frog was under consideration – had put the reproductive organs and the organs of excretion in different parts of the body. But we cannot hope that this fatal topographical mistake will be corrected. We have many similar commitments that carry over from the past. Some of us now wish, it seems, to feed the growing population of the earth with a synthetic concentrate; but if they succeed with the concentrate – I for one do not wish them well! – they will still have to furnish people with some bulk-producing jelly, as we do a sick person who has been on a liquid diet, in order to keep their bowels functioning; and they may even find it necessary, despite man's inordinate adaptability, to create some illusion of gustatory pleasure, lest the appetite for life itself should wane.

So again the fact that man has been an active, roaming, searching, prying animal, never at ease when he feels imprisoned or involuntarily hemmed in, should make us think twice, it seems to me, before we make any estimate of possible or desirable populations for the planet. Before we convert our rocks and rills and templed hills into one spreading mass of low-grade urban tissue, under the delusion that, because we accomplish this degradation with the aid of bulldozers and atomic piles and electronic computers, we are advancing civilization, we might ask what all this implies in terms of the historic nature of man.

Already there are metropolitan bathing beaches and 'wild' recreation areas, where, on a Sunday afternoon in summer, the sign 'Standing Room Only' describes the facilities available. Perhaps some of the perversity and criminal mischief exhibited in our cities, particularly by the more muscular types, may be due to this very constriction of space. Are we prepared to breed legless men, satisfied in their urban pens, as we now breed almost wingless fowl? If not, should we wonder that a race that flourished for some five hundred thousand years or more with a population density of perhaps ten per square mile may not find life altogether satisfactory at a constant density of four hundred per acre?

In calling attention to these constants, I am trying to emphasize what the French philosopher Raymond Ruyer, in his book *Neofinalisme*, characterizes as the fibrous structure of history. Just because of the nature of time, memory, and inheritance, we cannot make sensible plans for the future without doing justice to the threads and fibres that run through every past stage of man's development and will follow through the future as well. In dealing with man's history, it is convenient to cut it off into stages and periods; so we speak as though the Stone Age were represented in our society only by museum showcases of axes and arrowheads. But the fact is that about four-fifths of the planet's population are still living under conditions that approximate those of a Neolithic village, certainly far closer than they touch those of a twentieth-century metropolis. And when the other day some of our friends here said, almost a little contemptuously, 'Don't let us go back to Palaeolithic society,' I was tempted to ask them how far they thought they could express that idea without using one of the tools of Palaeolithic society, namely, language.

To sum up this point: the future is not a blank page; and neither is it an open book. The current notion that one has only to measure existing trends and to project, on a grander scale, the forces and institutions that dominate our present-day society in order to give a true picture of the future is based on another kind of illusion – the statistical illusion. This method overweights those elements in the present which are observable and measurable and seemingly powerful, and it overlooks many other elements that are hidden, unmeasured, irrational. In the third century AD an objective observer might well have predicted, on the basis of the imperial public works programme, an increase in the number of baths, gladiatorial arenas, garrison towns, and aqueducts. But he would have had no anticipation of the real future, which was the product of a deep subjective rejection of the whole classic way of life and so moved not merely away from it but in the opposite direction. Within three centuries the frontier garrisons were withdrawn, the Roman baths were closed, and some of the great Roman buildings were either being used as Christian churches or treated as quarries for building new structures. Can anyone who remembers this historic transformation believe that the rate of scientific and technical change must accelerate indefinitely or that this technological civilization will inevitably remain dominant and will absorb all the energies of life for its own narrow purposes – profit and power?

Often the most significant factors in determining the future are the irrationals. By 'irrational' I do not mean subjective or neurotic, because from the standpoint of science any small quantity or unique occasion may be considered as an irrational, since it does not lend itself to statistical treatment and repeated observation. Under this head, we must allow, when we consider the future, for the possibility of miracles – not something outside the order of nature but something occurring so infrequently and bringing about such a radical change that one cannot include it in any statistical prediction.–

This brings me to another doctrine that qualifies and completes that which does justice to the fibrous structure of history. I refer to the doctrine of emergence. By emergence there is signified the change that comes about when a structure or organism alters, not in this or that part, but as a whole; when the new emergent possibilities that did not exist at a lower level of existence become visible and operative.–

Now it seems to me that complex social transformations, capable of affecting every part of society, are often true emergents and are as undiscoverable in advance, on the basis of past observations, as was radium. No matter how fully we know the facts, we cannot predict the new dynamic pattern into which they will fall when they reach the moment of emergence. So the best observer of Neolithic society could not have predicted the new type of large-scale, wide-reaching urban organization that grew out of it in Egypt, Babylon, and China. Nor yet can the most exact student of national organizations and mechanical collectives predict the nature of the world community that may emerge in our time and, by the very act of emergence, alter our current values and habits. Yet many of the most difficult problems we face today, like that of overpopulation, which remain insoluble so long as men face each other in competing political and religious units, may be simplified, or become non-existent, once a world culture comes into existence.

All in all, there is no simple formula for dealing with either probabilities or possibilities in human society. Even if we had full knowledge of all the constants and variables – and, of course, we are far from that – we would still be in need of something more important in order to make wise decisions; and that is a theory of human development. – We tend to make false goals out of the processes that we control; so the increase of quantity, or the promotion of change for the sake of change, like the actions of a bored child turning from one toy to another, constitutes our only directive. As a result of our failure, there are anthropologists and psychologists who look upon the whole experiment of civilization as a mistake or who, even if they do not go so far, treat each culture as a confined, self-subsistent entity, with no other goal than that of continuing in its ancient 'way of life'. But surely we cannot make good use of the earth unless we have some notion as to what is 'good' and what is 'useful', what is aimless change and what is goal-directed transformation. And how can we arrive at these concepts unless we have some definite understanding of man's nature, his development, and his goals?–

We get along much more rapidly if we reduce all factors to their simplest terms, paying attention to the quantitative and repeatable elements and eliminating, as Galileo and Kepler agreed, the secondary and subjective qualities like colour, form, and pattern. But, when all events are subjected to this process of reduction and isolation, the most obvious characteristics of organic life disappear from view, namely, the fact that the organism is an autonomous, self-perpetuating, self-transforming being, in dynamic equilibrium, but with a definite cycle of growth; and, the higher the scale of life, the more plainly does growth record itself in superorganic forms and creative activities, detached from mere survival. – It is not enough for man to live in the purely physiological sense; he must live the good life, that is, he must expand the realm of significance, value, and form. On any sound reading of biological evolution or human history, it seems to me, development is often at odds with immediate security or ultimate survival. All higher life is precarious, as the highest states of life are themselves fleeting and evanescent.

As man has gone on with his own development, he has become more conscious both of the general process of organic transformation and of the important role he himself has come to play. Instead of bowing himself out of the picture, as he did when he followed the canons of seventeenth-century science, he now takes a central position on the stage, knowing that the performance itself, in the theatre of consciousness at least, cannot go on without him. He begins as an actor, singling himself out from his animal colleagues, already something of a prima donna, but uncertain of what part he shall learn. In time he becomes scene-painter, modifying the natural background and finding himself modified by it, too; and he is driven to be a stagehand likewise, shifting the properties to make his entrances and his exits more manageable. It is only after much practice in all these roles, as actor, scene-painter, stagehand, costumer, that he discovers that his main function is to write the drama, using many of the old plots left by nature, but giving them a new turn of the imagination and working the events up to a climax that nature without his aid might not have blundered upon in another hundred million years.

Just because man has now become the dominant species on the planet, he needs both the knowledge of the external world, independent of his wishing, that science provides him and a knowledge of his own inner life, detached from the operation of extraneous forces and institutions, directed toward goals he himself projects. What will happen to this earth depends very largely upon man's capacities as a dramatist and a creative artist, and that in turn depends in no slight measure upon the estimate he forms of himself. What he proposes to do with the earth, utilizing its soils, its mineral resources, its water, its flow of energies, depends largely upon his knowledge of his own historic nature and his plans for his own further self-transformations. As the dominant biological species, man now has a special responsibility to his fellow creatures as well as to himself. Will he turn the cosmic energies at his disposal to higher ends, or will he, wilfully or carelessly, exterminate life and bring his own existence to a premature end? If he thinks of himself as an insignificant bag of chemicals, he may wantonly reduce all forms and structures to mere dust and rubble.

If you force me to talk about probabilities, not about possibilities, still less hopes, I would say that man's future seems black – The difficulty is that our machine technology and our scientific methodology have reached a high pitch of perfection at a moment when other important parts of our culture, particularly those that shape the human personality – religion, ethics, education, the arts – have become inoperative or, rather, share in the general disintegration and help to widen it. Objective order has gone hand in hand with subjective disorder and formlessness. We seem to be forgetting the art of creating whole human beings, immunized to pathological temptations. The widening wave of neuroticism and criminality, so visible in every advanced society, indicates, it would seem, some lack in the human nutrients needed to create full human beings – a lack that no increased production of snakeroot, for use in psychotherapy, will make up for. If we are to achieve some degree of ecological balance, we must aim at human balance too.–

In most of our prognoses about man's relation with the earth we have tended, I am afraid, simply to carry forward processes now observable, with such acceleration as may be expected from the cumulative nature of scientific and technical changes, provided that these remain constant and undisturbed. Thus, we have taken technological civilization as a base line and have assumed that its spread to more primitive technological cultures will continue, with results similar to those now visible in highly industrialized countries. In these predictions we overlook the effects of human consciousness, of human reactions, of human purposes that would possibly project a different destination; some of us, if we do not regard human nature as fixed, treat it as a dependent variable, entirely governed by the machine. Surely, only by regarding man's own self-transformation as negligible would anyone think it worthwhile to speculate – on the transformations of energy that might make the earth capable of sustaining as many as thirty billion people. That increase of population could not in fact be accomplished without a wholesale regimentation of humanity, so limiting its field of action, so curtailing its choices, so adapting it to merely physiological criteria of survival – with no thought of development – that the result would no longer be recognizable as man but as an inferior creature with an inferior planet to work and play in.

Now the facts are, I submit, quite different from those assumed to operate under this too simple assumption. – To assume that there is only one possibility left, that represented by our now-dominant technological civilization, is an act of religious faith, committed by those who believe in this civilization, and in no sense an objective scientific judgement. All our present statistical curves may be deflected and altered in the real future by human choice and human contrivance; and in making these choices our normative ideas and ideals – indeed, our unconscious resistances and drives – will play no less a part than our knowledge.–

If the production of posthistoric man were to become the dominant purpose of our culture, not a few of the problems – would be automatically disposed of. If the goal is uniformity, why should we seek to preserve any of the richness of environmental and cultural individuality that still exists on the earth and, in turn, widens the range of human choice? Why should we not, on these terms, create by mechanical processes one single climate, uniform from the pole to the equator? Why should we not grind down the mountains, whether to obtain granite and uranium and soil, or just for the pleasure of bulldozing and grinding, until the whole round earth becomes planed down to one level platform. Then let us, if we need trees at all, reduce them to a few marketable varieties, as we have already reduced the six hundred varieties of pear that were commonly cultivated in the United States only a century ago. Let us remove, as a constant temptation for man to sin against his god, the machine, any memory

47

of things that are wild and untameable, pied and dappled, unique and precious: mountains one might be tempted to climb, deserts where one might seek solitude and inner peace, jungles whose living creatures would remind us of nature's original prodigality in creating a grand diversity of habitats and habits of life out of the primeval protoplasm with which it began.

If the goal is a uniform type of man, reproducing at a uniform rate, in a uniform environment, kept at a constant temperature, pressure, and humidity, living a uniform life, without internal change or choice, from incubator to incinerator, most of our historic problems concerning man's relation to the earth will disappear. Only one problem will remain: Why should anyone, even a machine, bother to keep this kind of creature alive?

If this is not to be mankind's fate, how are we to save ourselves from it? The simple answer reduces itself to a platitude: We must throw overboard this childishly inadequate picture of man's nature and destiny and resume the functions of men. The greatest of these functions, capable of dominating all others, is that of conscious self-fabrication. We shall be ill prepared to meet the real challenges of the future if we imagine that our present institutions, because of the extraordinary successes of the machine economy in production, have congealed into a final mould from which man can never hope to escape. – For the first time man may, as a conscious, interrelated comprehensive group, take possession of the whole planet. For the last century, not merely have we been able to think of the world as a whole, in time and space, but we have been able through our manifold inventions to act in the same fashion. Yet both our thinking and our acting have been crude, not to say primitive, because we have not yet created the sort of self, freed from nationalistic and ideological obsessions, capable of acting within this global theatre.

THE SOCIAL USE
AND MISUSE
OF TECHNOLOGY

BY BARRY COMMONER

Director of the Center for the Biology of Natural Resources at Washington University, St Louis, Professor Barry Commoner became one of the most respected environmental writers and speakers. Over the winter of 1970-71 the Institute of Contemporary Arts, in London, devoted its series of evening lectures to the theme 'Ecology, The Shaping Enquiry'. Professor Commoner delivered the final lecture in the series. What follows is taken from the text of that lecture.

I should like to share some of the ideas that my group in St Louis has developed in the last six to twelve months, regarding the origins of the environmental crisis. I do not need to produce any more horror stories about birds covered with oil, DDT in people's bodies and so on. It is known that there are environmental problems. It seems to me that the issue now has become what to do about it. I take the view, which is perhaps old-fashioned, that the historical approach is a valuable way to decide what has got to be done, that is, asking how we got into this mess, in the hope that understanding the past will point to some way out. And so I shall discuss some tentative ideas about the origin of the environmental problems that we face.–

First, I shall outline the features that characterize the environment, and then ask the question: what has happened to this system that has made it go so bad?

The basic characteristic of the environmental system is that it comprises a thin skin on the globe of the planet. It is a few miles of air, the surface waters and relatively few inches of soil. This is the ecosphere. One might ask 'Well, why choose the skin?' That happens to be the place where living things are found on the globe. In other words it is the habitat of living things. This may seem like a biologist's parochial view of the world. After all, the environment also contains physical and chemical systems and they might be independent of life. As it turns out, they are not; rather, one of the important things about the environmental system and its chemical and physical attributes is that they are largely the products of living things.

For example, before green plants appeared on the surface of the earth there was no oxygen in the atmosphere. The development of photosynthesis changed the chemistry of the air, and, with the development of oxygen, ozone was produced. Ozone in the higher levels of the atmosphere shields the surface of the earth from ultraviolet light. So the physical ambience of the earth's surface – the fact that it is not now subjected to a high level of this light – is a consequence of a *biological* development. In other words, the environment is something which physically and chemically is largely determined by the activity of living things. Then, with the marvellous reciprocity characteristic of living things, they became adapted to the particular environment they had created. So, for example, when oxygen was produced by green plants, it became possible in the course of evolution for organisms that used oxygen to evolve and survive. Moreover, when oxygen, hence ozone, appeared, and the level of ultraviolet radiation on the surface of the earth was cut down, living animals could come out from under their shelter of water, which was all that kept them from being burnt by the ultraviolet light, and could emerge on to the surface of the earth.

In other words, there is an interdigitation of the evolution of life and the physical and chemical attributes of the earth's surface, generating a very complex system.

A major feature of the dynamics of this system is that it is characterized by circular activity. I think it is very important to become sensitive to the significance of the ecological cycle. Let me run through a couple of ecological cycles in order to develop some feeling for them.

Let us take a typical aquatic cycle. Start with a fish swimming in the water. The fish has a lot of water in it and some solid material; much of that solid material is organic – that is, complex molecules containing networks of carbon atoms; and as the fish does its business of metabolizing, it produces waste, which is largely organic matter. The waste in turn turns out to be food for other organisms – bacteria, fungi, and so on – which live on organic wastes, converting them to inorganic material. Urea, for example, excreted by the fish, is converted by bacteria into nitrate and carbon dioxide. You can think of these inorganic products – phosphates, nitrates, carbon dioxide – as the waste products of the bacteria that eat the waste produced by the fish. In turn, these inorganic materials are the food of algae, green plants, which synthesize from them organic matter. Then the organic matter in the form of algae provides food for the fish, which brings us right back to the point of departure.

Now the fact that this is a circular progression has some very important consequences. In the first place, the stability of the cycle is self-determined. Let us take a simple analogy. Consider how a ship is kept on course, the way in which her course is stabilized. A cybernetic feed-back cycle is involved. The helmsman watches the compass; the compass-needle moves; the helmsman moves the rudder; and there is a relationship between the rudder and the ship, such that when the rudder moves, the ship's direction changes, and that in turn changes the relative orientation of the compass, which signals the helmsman that he should stop making adjustments. The result is a cycle of events involving the compass, the helmsman, the rudder, the ship and the compass. This is what keeps the ship on course. When any external agitation – the wind, or the helmsman sneezing – changes these interrelationships, the cyclical relationship brings the ship back on course.

The ecological cycle operates similarly. In our fishpond, suppose, for example, by some quirk, the temperature changes so that algae grow rapidly, reducing the level of algal nutrients. With more algae than there were before, the fish will eat more algae, which will cut down the algae while increasing the number of fish. Now, with more fish, more organic waste is produced – which the bacteria convert to inorganic material. Things come back into balance.

That is one characteristic then of a system of this sort. Now a very interesting question is, 'How does it break down?' Any member of an ecological cycle, functioning in its ordinary way, is incapable of causing trouble. For example, if human beings were part of an ecological cycle – say the soil cycle – and we ate animals that ate the grass and deposited our organic waste on the soil which the cycle converts back into the grass, then it would be impossible for us to stress the system. There would be no way that we could degrade such an environment. We should simply be part of the system.

But once outside of the system, we can degrade it. For example, man is taken off the soil and put into a city, food crops must now be transported to the city, eaten, and converted into sewage, which goes into the aquatic system instead of back to the soil. Now there is more organic matter coming into the aquatic cycle than the cycle itself produces. It is rapidly decayed by bacteria, which in the process, may use up all the oxygen. With no oxygen left, the bacteria die off and the cycle stops. This external stress breaks the cycle.

There are some very simple principles of ecology that I suppose one could call 'cocktail party' principles – the very simple ideas that allow one to talk about it in layman's language. One is that in a cycle *every separate entity is connected to all the rest*. A second principle is that *everything has to go somewhere*. If you get into an ecological conversation, you can do quite well by simply repeating one question: 'Where does it go?' Someone raises the question about mercury. He says, 'There's mercury in the hearing-aid battery'. And you say, 'Well, that's interesting. Where does it go?' 'Oh, I never thought of that.' 'Well, what happens when the hearing-aid battery wears out?' 'Well, I throw it away.' And you just say, 'Well, where does it go?' 'Into the rubbish.' 'Well, that's interesting. Where does *that* go?' And then finally you discover that it goes to an incinerator which heats up the mercury in the hearing-aid battery and drives it into the air. And then you ask, 'Where does that go?' – and the answer is that it comes down in rain and gets into water where bacteria convert it to methyl mercury, which poisons fish. And so you accomplish quite an ecological *tour de force*.

The third simple law is one that can be borrowed from economics. There is a well-known fable about the Middle East kingdom that discovered oil. The sheikh was suddenly very rich and needed to know what to do with the money. So he ordered his advisers to retire for a year and come back with a set of volumes that embodied all the wisdom of economics – otherwise their heads would be removed. The next year he said, 'No, I can't read ten volumes, I want it all in one volume.' Finally he said, 'You've got to come back with one sentence which contains the total wisdom of economics or you lose your heads.' And they came back with one sentence: '*There is no such thing as a free lunch*'. Now I think that applies quite well to ecological systems. In a cycle you can't get away with anything. There is a limit to the speed with which it can be exploited, the rate at which it runs; *you can't get something for nothing from it*.

Which brings me to the fourth law of ecology: *nature knows best*. I talked to a group of chemists recently and, as I expected, really horrified some of them. Because, you see, a number of chemists think that Dupont knows best. After all, nature never made Nylon or Terylene; nature never made Wisk or Tide. They are all made by man. Of course we are very proud of what man can do, so the whole notion that man does not know best about these things is rather upsetting.

Let me use an analogy. I have a watch. Suppose I were to open the back, shut my eyes and poke a pencil into the works. It is very likely the watch would be spoiled. The question I want to raise is this: isn't it at all *possible* that the watch might be improved? The watch might have been out of adjustment exactly at the point I happened to hit it, and I might, after all, have just done what was needed to bring it back into adjustment. I think you have to admit there is a finite possibility that the watch might be improved by this random hit. But the next question that comes up is: why is this possibility so very small? The reason is that the watchmakers know best. Watchmakers have tried most of the random arrangements of bits and pieces and have discarded many of them because they are not compatible with the system as a whole. In short this watch is a very complex integrated system, with a lot of research and development behind it. And all of the mistakes – most of them – have been tried out, so that the chance of any new random change being an improvement is extremely small.

How does this relate to the present problem? There are perhaps two or three billion years of research and development behind biological systems: the entire course of biological evolution. A chief feature of this evolutionary process is that living things produced a number of complex molecules, such as proteins. Proteins are long chains of amino acid units, with perhaps two hundred units in a chain. There are twenty different amino acids that can participate in the chain, and the chemistry is such that any one can be put at any position. A series of different proteins can be made simply by arranging and re-arranging the order of amino acids in the molecules. So we have a 200-place molecule and twenty choices to make for each place. Elsasser has calculated the weight that would be represented by only one molecule of each of the possible proteins that can be compared in this way: it is larger than the weight of the known universe. Clearly biological organisms do not make all the proteins that they *could*; there are very severe restrictions.

This means that when an organic compound is not found in a living system, it is probably not compatible with the rest of that system. I have a sort of fantasy that I think about – that two billion years ago in some corner of the globe some cell took it upon itself to synthesize DDT and has never been heard of since. In other words, DDT simply was incompatible with the rest of the system. Incidentally there are data to support this notion. Random inherited changes can be brought about in the chemistry of cells by X-rays. The overwhelming proportion of X-ray-induced mutations are damaging. In other words, most of the new features that are generated in living cells by such means are worse than the original ones; nature knows best.

I have taken a long time to present my own approach to ecology. The problem now is this: the ecosphere was created before man appeared on the earth. Man occupies a very peculiar position. He is both part of an ecological cycle – as a terrestrial animal – and at the same time an organism which wields huge power outside of the ecological cycle. He can get away from the soil, live in the cities, fly in the air, and so on. The question which arises is this: what activities of human beings have led to environmental pollution? Because clearly we are not suffering from any natural catastrophe. Something has gone wrong in what *people do*.

Let us look at the situation in the United States, beginning at the end of the Second World War. If we trace back the data on levels of pollutants, we find that many of them made their frist appearance in the mid-1940s. That is, when detergents, photochemical smog, synthetic insecticides and radiation came on the scene. At the same time older pollutants – such as phosphate and nitrate in surface waters and various air pollutants – became much more concentrated than before. The Second World War is a kind of watershed between the scientific revolution that preceded it and the technological revolution which followed it. This explains why we have been looking at changes in the factors that might influence ecological systems in the United States since 1946.

Now what are the factors? First, if human beings are outside of the ecosystem they belong to, wherein they eat food produced in the soil and contribute their waste to the soil, they can constitute an environmental impact or stress. – Clearly, the more people are in that situation, the more stress is placed on the environment. So we have to be concerned with the size of the population.

Other important factors represent non-biological activities: for example, the production of power and goods. The amount of production *per capita* – affluence if you like – is another factor that might be influential in the environment; both population and affluence are frequently invoked by ecological speakers. Some say the more people there are, the worse the pollution; that people are polluters. Others speak of an 'effluent society', meaning that effluents arise from our affluence.–

There is a third environmental factor: the amount of pollution produced per unit production. A simple formula connects the three factors: the amount of pollution emitted is the product of the population times the production per unit population (the 'affluence' factor) multiplied by the amount of pollutant emitted per unit production. What this formula does is to divide the amount of pollutant up into three interacting factors: population, affluence and the nature of production technology (which determines the amount of pollution emitted per unit production).

In the United States, most of the pollutants have increased in level by an order of magnitude that is, generally, between 200 per cent and 2,000 per cent since 1946. So we are looking for some change in the three relevant factors that give rise to somewhere between twofold and twentyfold changes in pollution intensity. – The size of the US population – has gone up about 42 per cent in that period of time. This change is not enough to generate a tenfold increase in pollution level. Is it rather affluence which is to blame? Affluence might be measured by GNP – which has gone up perhaps 50 to 60 per cent. So that too is not big enough to be the cause we seek.

Let us look instead at individual productive activities, that is, particular technologies, and examine them to see how population, affluence and technology may have influenced the emission of pollutants.–

What has happened in the United States is as follows. Most of the production of basic necessities *per capita* is being maintained at about the same level, but the techniques used for providing for those necessities has shifted (for example, from natural products to unnatural ones) and it turns out that every shift has intensified the impact on the environment.

And here is another interesting fact: those productive activities at the top of the growth curve are also the most profitable. No one makes much money these days investing in railroads; many in the United States are in receivership. We do not make much on growing cotton fibre, or on raising work animals, or making soap. We do make a good deal selling nitrogen fertilizer and detergents and so on. In other words we have shifted the way in which we produce goods in the direction of greater economic return, but, tragically, this has caused a more intensified pollution of the environment.

Am I against technology? The answer is no. Take the present situation as regards sewage. At present a crop is removed from the soil, taken to the city where people are concentrated, converted to sewage which is introduced with surface waters, with or without treatment. This imposes a strain on the aquatic system and a drain on the soil system; introducing fertilizers only makes things worse. But we can get back to zero environmental impact by introducing new technology. The new technology would be a pipeline to conduct sewage from the city back to the land. Man would then be back in the soil cycle. The organic waste would be conducted back to the soil to be converted into humus, taking the strain off the system. The point I am making is that it is not technology *per se* which is harmful but technology which violates the principles of ecology. A technology which replaces a fibre obtained naturally, which you get gratis, without air pollution, with a fibre obtained only by consuming a non-renewable resource and polluting the air, makes no ecological sense. In the same way it makes no sense to use trucks instead of railroads, thereby polluting the air more for the same economic good. The basic cause of environmental pollution, at least in the United States since 1946, appears to be largely the transformation of our productive system in such a way as to intensify the stress on the environment.

We are not going to be able to deal with environmental problems unless we recognize that we are going to have to undo the huge change in our productive system that has taken place since 1946. This means rebuilding our industry. It means building railroads rather than roads. It means using soap made from fats produced by an ecologically sound method rather than detergents. And it is immediately obvious that none of these things are going to happen without first confronting very serious economic, and inevitably political, problems.

So, for example, there is no way that I can see of going back to natural products without confronting the problem of our relations with the Third World, where most of such materials originate. The manufacture of synthetic rubber pollutes the environment, whereas natural rubber is made calmly and cooly by rubber plants. The reason why the United States has synthetic rubber plants is partly because the military insist that this is a vital military supply and must be independent of any foreign country. Since this way of thinking leads to an intolerable stress on the environment, then one step towards solving environmental problems is to make sure that military considerations do not control our productive system. It becomes essential that, rather than think of other countries as potential enemies, we consider the world as an ecological whole.

The main message that I want to leave is that the environmental crisis originates in the social misuse of technology, in purposes more closely related to profit than to human welfare. A transformation of our productivity during the Second World War led to general use of environmentally unsuitable technologies. The solution to the problems these unsuitable technologies have caused is a new transformation – this time to technologies that are compatible with the environment.

THE TRAGEDY OF
THE COMMONS

BY GARRETT HARDIN

In 1968, Garrett Hardin, Professor of Biology at the University of California, Santa Barbara, published 'The Tragedy of the Commons' as an article in *Science*. His exposition of Malthusianism was hardly original, and he pointed out that the central idea is taken from a little known pamphlet published in 1833 by William Forster Lloyd (1794-1852), an amateur mathematician. Nevertheless, Hardin's essay, from which the following extract is taken, quickly became part of the 'required reading' for the new environmentalists and was reprinted widely.

The tragedy of the commons develops in this way. Picture a pasture open to all. It is to be expected that each herdsman will try to keep as many cattle as possible on the commons. Such an arrangement may work reasonably satisfactorily for centuries because tribal wars, poaching, and disease keep the numbers of both man and beast well below the carrying capacity of the land. Finally, however, comes the day of reckoning, that is, the day when the long-desired goal of social stability becomes a reality. At this point, the inherent logic of the commons remorselessly generates tragedy.

As a rational being, each herdsman seeks to maximize his gain. Explicitly or implicitly, more or less consciously, he asks, 'What is the utility *to me* of adding one more animal to my herd?' This utility has one negative and one positive component.

1. The positive component is a function of the increment of one animal. Since the herdsman receives all the proceeds from the sale of the additional animal, the positive utility is nearly +1.

2. The negative utility is a function of the additional overgrazing

created by one more animal. Since, however, the effects of overgrazing are shared by all the herdsmen, the negative utility for any particular decision-making herdsman is only a fraction of −1.

Adding together the component partial utilities, the rational herdsman concludes that the only sensible course for him to pursue is to add another animal to his herd. And another; and another. . . . But this is the conclusion reached by each and every rational herdsman sharing a commons. Therein is the tragedy. Each man is locked into a system that compels him to increase his herd without limit − in a world that is limited. Ruin is the destination toward which all men rush, each pursuing his own best interest in a society that believes in the freedom of the commons. Freedom in a commons brings ruin to all.

Some would say that this is a platitude. Would that it were! In a sense, it was learned thousands of years ago, but natural selection favours the forces of psychological denial. The individual benefits as an individual from his ability to deny the truth even though society as a whole, of which he is a part, suffers. Education can counteract the natural tendency to do the wrong thing, but the inexorable succession of generations requires that the basis for this knowledge be constantly refreshed. −

In a reverse way, the tragedy of the commons reappears in problems of pollution. Here it is not a question of taking something out of the commons, but of putting something in − sewage, or chemical, radioactive, and heat wastes into water; noxious and dangerous fumes into the air; and distracting and unpleasant advertising signs into the line of sight. The calculations of utility are much the same as before. The rational man finds that his share of the cost of the wastes he discharges into the commons is less than the cost of purifying his wastes before releasing them. Since this is true for everyone, we are locked into a system of 'fouling our own nest', so long as we behave only as independent, rational, free-enterprisers. −

The pollution problem is a consequence of population. It did not much matter how a lonely American frontiersman disposed of his waste. 'Flowing water purifies itself every ten miles,' my grandfather used to say, and the myth was near enough to the truth when he was a boy, for there were not too many people. But as population became denser, the natural chemical and biological recycling processes became overloaded, calling for a redefinition of property rights.

Analysis of the pollution problem as a function of population density uncovers a not generally recognized principle of morality, namely: *the morality of an act is a function of the state of the system at the time it is performed*. Using the commons as a cesspool does not harm the general public under frontier conditions because there is no public; the same behaviour in a metropolis is unbearable. A hundred and fifty years ago a plainsman could kill an American bison, cut out only the tongue for his dinner, and discard the rest of the animal. He was not in any important sense being wasteful. Today, with only a few thousand bison left, we would be appalled at such behaviour. –

Perhaps the simplest summary of this analysis of man's population problems is this: the commons, if justifiable at all, is justifiable only under conditions of low-population density. As the human population has increased, the commons has had to be abandoned in one aspect after another.

First we abandoned the commons in food gathering, enclosing farm land and restricting pastures and hunting and fishing areas. These restrictions are still not complete throughout the world.

Somewhat later we saw that the commons as a place for waste disposal would also have to be abandoned. Restrictions on the disposal of domestic sewage are widely accepted in the Western world; we are still struggling to close the commons to pollution by automobiles, factories, insecticide sprayers, fertilizing operations, and atomic energy installations.

In a still more embryonic state is our recognition of the evils of the commons in matters of pleasure. There is almost no restriction on the propagation of sound waves in the public medium. The shopping public is assaulted with mindless music, without its consent. Our government is paying out billions of dollars to create supersonic transport which will disturb 50,000 people for every one person who is whisked from coast to coast three hours faster. Advertisers muddy the airwaves of radio and television and pollute the view of travellers. We are a long way from outlawing the commons in matters of pleasure. Is this because our Puritan inheritance makes us view pleasure as something of a sin, and pain (that is, the pollution of advertising) as the sign of virtue?

Every new enclosure of the commons involves the infringement of somebody's personal liberty. Infringements made in the distant past are accepted because no contemporary complains of a loss. It is the newly proposed infringements that we vigorously oppose; cries of 'rights' and 'freedom' fill the air. But what does 'freedom' mean? When men mutually agreed to pass laws against robbing, mankind became more free, not less so. Individuals locked into the logic of the commons are free only to bring on universal ruin; once they see the necessity of mutual coercion, they become free to pursue other goals. I believe Hegel said, 'Freedom is the recognition of necessity'.

The most important aspect of necessity that we must now recognize, is the necessity of abandoning the commons in breeding. No technical solution can rescue us from the misery of overpopulation. Freedom to breed will bring ruin to all. At the moment, to avoid hard decisions many of us are tempted to propagandize for conscience and responsible parenthood. The temptation must be resisted, because an appeal to independently acting consciences selects for the disappearance of all conscience in the long run, and an increase in anxiety in the short.

The only way we can preserve and nurture other and more precious freedoms is by relinquishing the freedom to breed, and that very soon. 'Freedom is the recognition of necessity' – and it is the role of education to reveal to all the necessity of abandoning the freedom to breed. Only so, can we put an end to this aspect of the tragedy of the commons.

DESTRUCTIVENESS OF MAN

BY GEORGE PERKINS MARSH

The pioneering ethic that inspired the human colonization of North America encouraged a view that the land and its resources were limitless, an issue Garrett Hardin addressed. The view was understandable. The colonists, or their immediate ancestors, had escaped the poverty of overcrowded Europe to find a continent that was vast and almost empty. As early as the middle of the nineteenth century, however, such profligacy was being challenged, and by no one more strongly than George Perkins Marsh (1801-82). Lawyer, politician, diplomat, and master of twenty languages, from 1862 until his death Marsh was US ambassador to Italy, and it was in Italy that he wrote *Man and Nature* from which this extract is taken. Published in 1864, the book received wide attention and led to the establishment of federal forest reserves in the United States and various forest conservation measures in other countries. More important, perhaps, was Marsh's challenge to the accepted view of the relationship between humans and their environment.

Man has too long forgotten that the earth was given to him for usufruct alone, not for consumption, still less for profligate waste. Nature has provided against the absolute destruction of any of her elementary matter, the raw material of her works; the thunderbolt and the tornado, the most convulsive throes of even the volcano and the earthquake, being only phenomena of decomposition and recomposition. But she has left it within the power of man irreparably to derange the combinations of inorganic matter and of organic life, which through the night of aeons she had been proportioning and balancing, to prepare the earth for his habitation, when, in the fullness of time, his Creator should call him forth to enter into its possession.

Apart from the hostile influence of man, the organic and the inorganic world are, as I have remarked, bound together by such mutual relations and adaptations as secure, if not the absolute permanence and equilibrium of both, a long continuance of the established conditions of each at any given time and place, or at least, a very slow and gradual succession of changes in those conditions. But man is everywhere a disturbing agent. Wherever he plants his foot, the harmonies of nature are turned to discords. The proportions and accommodations which insured the stability of existing arrangements are overthrown. Indigenous vegetable and animal species are extirpated, and supplanted by others of foreign origin, spontaneous production is forbidden or restricted, and the face of the earth is either laid bare or covered with a new and reluctant growth of vegetable forms, and with alien tribes of animal life. These intentional changes and substitutions constitute, indeed, great revolutions; but vast as is their magnitude and importance, they are, as we shall see, insignificant in comparison with the contingent and unsought results which have flowed from them.

The fact that, of all organic beings, man alone is to be regarded as essentially a destructive power, and that he wields energies to resist nature which, nature – that nature whom all material life and all inorganic substance obey – is wholly impotent, tends to prove that, although living in physical nature, he is not of her, that he is of more exalted parentage, and belongs to a higher order of existences than those born of her womb and submissive to her dictates.

There are, indeed, brute destroyers, beasts and birds and insects of prey – all animal life feeds upon, and, of course, destroys other life, – but this destruction is balanced by compensations. It is, in fact, the very means by which the existence of one tribe of animals or of vegetables is secured against being smothered by the encroachments of another; and the reproductive powers of species, which serve as the food of others, are always proportioned to the demand they are destined to supply. Man pursues his victims with reckless destructiveness; and, while the sacrifice of life by the lower animals is limited by the cravings of appetite, he unsparingly persecutes, even to extirpation, thousands of organic forms which he cannot consume.

The earth was not, in its natural condition, completely adapted to the use of man, but only to the sustenance of wild animals and wild vegetation. These live, multiply their kind in just proportion, and attain their perfect measure of strength and beauty, without producing or requiring any change in the natural arrangements of surface, or in each other's spontaneous tendencies, except such mutual repression of excessive increase as may prevent the extirpation of one species by the encroachments of another. In short, without man, lower animal and spontaneous vegetable life would have been constant in type, distribution, and proportion, and the physical geography of the earth would have remained undisturbed for indefinite periods, and been subject to revolution only from possible, unknown cosmical causes, or from geological action.

But man, the domestic animals that serve him, the field and garden plants the products of which supply him with food and clothing, cannot subsist and rise to the full development of their higher properties, unless brute and unconscious nature be effectually combated, and, in a great degree, vanquished by human art. Hence, a certain measure of transformation of terrestrial surface, of suppression of natural, and stimulation of artificially modified productivity becomes necessary. This measure man has unfortunately exceeded. He has felled the forests whose network of fibrous roots bound the mould to the rocky skeleton of the earth; but had he allowed here and there a belt of woodland to reproduce itself by spontaneous propagation, most of the mischiefs which his reckless destruction of the natural protection of the soil has occasioned would have been averted. He has broken up the mountain reservoirs, the percolation of whose waters through unseen channels supplied the fountains that refreshed his cattle and fertilized his fields; but he has neglected to maintain the cisterns and the canals of irrigation which a wise antiquity had constructed to neutralize the consequences of its own imprudence. While he has torn the thin glebe which confined the light earth of extensive plains, and has destroyed the fringe of semi-aquatic plants which skirted the coast and checked the drifting of the sea sand, he has failed to prevent the spreading of the dunes by clothing them with artificially propagated vegetation. He has ruthlessly warred on all the tribes of animated nature whose spoil he could convert to his own uses, and he has not protected the birds which prey on the insects most destructive to his own harvests.

Purely untutored humanity, it is true, interferes comparatively little with the arrangements of nature, and the destructive agency of man becomes more and more energetic and unsparing as he advances in civilization, until the impoverishment, with which his exhaustion of the natural resources of the soil is threatening him, at last awakens him to the necessity of preserving what is left, if not of restoring what has been wantonly wasted. The wandering savage grows no cultivated vegetable, fells no forest, and extirpates no useful plant, no noxious weed. If his skill in the chase enables him to entrap numbers of the animals on which he feeds, he compensates this loss by destroying also the lion, the tiger, the wolf, the otter, the seal, and the eagle, thus indirectly protecting the feebler quadrupeds and fish and fowls, which would otherwise become the booty of beasts and birds of prey. But with stationary life, or rather with the pastoral state, man at once commences an almost indiscriminate warfare upon all the forms of animal and vegetable existence around him, and as he advances in civilization, he gradually eradicates or transforms every spontaneous product of the soil he occupies.

It has been maintained by authorities as high as any known to modern science, that the action of man upon nature, though greater in *degree*, does not differ in *kind*, from that of wild animals. It appears to me to differ in essential character, because, though it is often followed by unforeseen and undesired results, yet it is nevertheless guided by a self-conscious and intelligent will aiming as often at secondary and remote as at immediate objects. The wild animal, on the other hand, acts instinctively, and, so far as we are able to perceive, always with a view to single and direct purposes. The backwoodsman and the beaver alike fell trees; the man that he may convert the forest into an olive grove that will mature its fruit only for a succeeding generation, the beaver that he may feed upon their bark or use them in the construction of his habitation. Human differs from brute action, too, in its influence upon the material world, because it is not controlled by natural compensations and balances. Natural arrangements, once disturbed by man, are not restored until he retires from the field, and leaves free scope to spontaneous recuperative energies; the wounds he inflicts upon the material creation are not healed until he withdraws the arm that gave the blow. On the other hand, I am not aware of any evidence that wild animals have ever destroyed the smallest forest, extirpated any organic species, or modified its natural character, occasioned any permanent change of terrestrial surface, or produced any disturbance of physical conditions which nature has not, of herself, repaired without the expulsion of the animal that had caused it.

The form of geographical surface, and very probably the climate of a given country, depend much on the character of the vegetable life belonging to it. Man has, by domestication, greatly changed the habits and properties of the plants he rears; he has, by voluntary selection, immensely modified the forms and qualities of the animated creatures that serve him; and he has, at the same time, completely rooted out many forms of both vegetable and animal being. What is there, in the influence of brute life, that corresponds to this? We have no reason to believe that in that portion of the American continent which, though peopled by many tribes of quadruped and fowl, remained uninhabited by man, or only thinly occupied by purely savage tribes, any sensible geographical change had occurred within twenty centuries before the epoch of discovery and colonization while, during the same period, man had changed millions of square miles, in the fairest and most fertile regions of the Old World, into the barrenest deserts.

The ravages committed by man subvert the relations and destroy the balance which nature had established between her organized and her inorganic creations; and she avenges herself upon the intruder, by letting loose upon her defaced provinces destructive energies hitherto kept in check by organic forces destined to be his best auxiliaries, but which he has unwisely dispersed and driven from the field of action. When the forest is gone, the great reservoir of moisture stored up in its vegetable mould is evaporated, and returns only in deluges of rain to wash away the parched dust into which that mould has been converted. The well-wooded and humid hills are turned into ridges of dry rock, which encumbers the low grounds and chokes the watercourses with its debris, and – except in countries favoured with an equable distribution of rain through the seasons – the whole earth, unless rescued by human art from the physical degradation to which it tends, becomes an assemblage of bald mountains, of barren, turfless hills, and of swampy and malarious plains. There are parts of Asia Minor, of Northern Africa, of Greece, and even of Alpine Europe, where the operation of causes set in action by man has brought the face of the earth to a desolation almost as complete as that of the moon; and though, within that brief space of time which we call 'the historical period', they are known to have been covered with luxuriant woods, verdant pastures, and fertile meadows, they are now too far deteriorated to be reclaimable by man, nor can they become again fitted for human use, except through great geological changes, or other mysterious influences or agencies of which we have no present knowledge, and over which we have no prospective control. The earth is fast becoming an unfit home for its noblest inhabitant, and another era of equal human crime and human improvidence, and of like duration with that through which traces of that crime and that improvidence extend, would reduce it to such a condition of impoverished productiveness, of shattered surface, of climatic excess, as to threaten the depravation, barbarism, and perhaps even extinction of the species.

True, there is a partial reverse to this picture. On narrow theatres, new forests have been planted; inundations of flowing streams restrained by heavy walls of masonry and other constructions; torrents compelled to aid, by depositing the slime with which they are charged, in filling up lowlands, and raising the level of morasses which their own overflows had created; ground submerged by the encroachments of the ocean, or exposed to be covered by the tides, has been rescued from its dominion by diking, swamps and even lakes have been drained, and their beds brought within the domain of agricultural industry; drifting coast dunes have been checked and made productive by plantation; seas and inland waters have been repeopled with fish, and even the sands of the Sahara have been fertilized by artesian fountains. These achievements are more glorious than the proudest triumphs of war, but, thus far, they give but faint hope that we shall yet make full atonement for our spendthrift waste of the bounties of nature.

It is, on the one hand, rash and unphilosophical to attempt to set limits to the ultimate power of man over inorganic nature, and it is unprofitable, on the other, to speculate on what may be accomplished by the discovery of now unknown and unimagined natural forces, or even by the invention of new arts and new processes. But since we have seen aerostation, the motive power of elastic vapours, the wonders of modern telegraphy, the destructive explosiveness of gunpowder, and even of a substance so harmless, unresisting, and inert as cotton, nothing in the way of mechanical achievement seems impossible, and it is hard to restrain the imagination from wandering forward a couple of generations to an epoch when our descendants shall have advanced as far beyond us in physical conquest, as we have marched beyond the trophies erected by our grandfathers.

I must therefore be understood to mean only, that no agencies now known to man and directed by him seem adequate to the reducing of great Alpine precipices to such slopes as would enable them to support a vegetable clothing, or to the covering of large extents of denuded rock with earth, and planting upon them a forest growth.–

Comparatively short as is the period through which the colonization of foreign lands by European emigrants extends, great, and it is to be feared, sometimes irreparable, injury has been already done in the various processes by which man seeks to subjugate the virgin earth; and many provinces, first trodden by the *homo sapiens Europae* within the last two centuries, begin to show signs of that melancholy dilapidation which is now driving so many of the peasantry of Europe from their native hearths. It is evidently a matter of great moment, not only to the population of the states where these symptoms are manifesting themselves, but to the general interests of humanity, that this decay should be arrested, and that the future operations of rural husbandry and of forest industry, in districts yet remaining substantially in their native condition, should be so conducted as to prevent the widespread mischiefs which have been elsewhere produced by thoughtless or wanton destruction of the natural safeguards of the soil. This can be done only by the diffusion of knowledge on this subject among the classes that, in earlier days, subdued and tilled ground in which they had no vested rights, but who, in our time, own their woods, their pastures, and their ploughlands as a perpetual possession for them and theirs, and have, therefore, a strong interest in the protection of their domain against deterioration.–

I have remarked that the effects of human action on the forms of the earth's surface could not always be distinguished from those resulting from geological causes, and there is also much uncertainty in respect to the precise influence of the clearing and cultivating of the ground, and of other rural occupations, upon climate. It is disputed whether either the mean of the extremes of temperature, the periods of the seasons, or the amount or distribution of precipitation and evaporation, in any country whose annals are known, have undergone any change during the historical period. It is, indeed, impossible to doubt that many of the operations of the pioneer settler tend to produce great modifications in atmospheric humidity, temperature, and electricity; but we are at present unable to determine how far one set of effects is neutralized by another, or compensated by unknown agencies. This question scientific research is inadequate to solve, for want of the necessary data; but well conducted observation, in regions now first brought under the occupation of man, combined with such historical evidence as still exists, may be expected at no distant period to throw much light on this subject.–

In order to arrive at safe conclusions, we must first obtain a more exact knowledge of the topography, and of the present superficial and climatic condition of countries where the natural surface is as yet more or less unbroken. This can only be accomplished by accurate surveys, and by a great multiplication of the points of meteorological registry, already so numerous; and as, moreover, considerable changes in the proportion of forest and of cultivated land, or of dry and wholly or partially submerged surface, will often take place within brief periods, it is highly desirable that the attention of observers, in whose neighbourhood the clearing of the soil, or the drainage of lakes and swamps, or other great works of rural improvement, are going on or meditated, should be especially drawn not only to revolutions in atmospheric temperature and precipitation, but to the more easily ascertained and perhaps more important local changes produced by these operations in the temperature and the hygrometric state of the superficial strata of the earth, and in its spontaneous vegetable and animal products.

The rapid extension of railroads, which now everywhere keeps pace with, and sometimes even precedes, the occupation of new soil for agricultural purposes, furnishes great facilities for enlarging our knowledge of the topography of the territory they traverse, because their cuttings reveal the composition and general structure of the surface, and the inclination and elevation of their lines constitute known hypsometrical sections, which give numerous points of departure for the measurement of higher and lower stations, and of course for determining the relief and depression of surface, the slope of the beds of watercourses, and many other not less important questions.–

But we are, even now, breaking up the floor and wainscoting and doors and window frames of our dwelling, for fuel to warm our bodies and seethe our pottage, and the world cannot afford to wait till the slow and sure progress of exact science has taught it a better economy. Many practical lessons have been learned by the common observation of unschooled men; and the teachings of simple experience, on topics where natural philosophy has scarcely yet spoken, are not to be despised.

TOO MANY PEOPLE

BY PAUL R. EHRLICH

The impending 'environmental crisis' was felt to be so awesome, so overwhelming and so multifaceted that many of those involved in the environmental movement concluded that its implications must be stated in the most dramatic of terms if popular attention was to be drawn to it and sufficient political will generated for action to be taken. Paul Ehrlich, a professor at Stanford University, California, was perhaps the most renowned of such 'dramatizers'. Published in 1968, his book *The Population Bomb* became a best-seller and for years afterwards Ehrlich was in constant demand as a writer and speaker. One spring evening in 1972 I remember him filling Caxton Hall in London literally to overflowing. The following extract demonstrates the passion with which he popularized demography, until then hardly the most gripping of academic disciplines. (To update Ehrlich's figures for the 21 years that have elapsed since he prepared them, world population is now (early 1989) estimated to be a little over five billion, and is expected to reach six billion by 1998; the 1981 population of Calcutta was about 3.3 million.)

Americans are beginning to realize that the undeveloped countries of the world face an inevitable population-food crisis. Each year food production in undeveloped countries falls a bit further behind burgeoning population growth, and people go to bed a little bit hungrier. While there are temporary or local reversals of this trend, it now seems inevitable that it will continue to its logical conclusion: mass starvation. The rich are going to get richer, but the more numerous poor are going to get poorer. Of these poor, a minimum of three and one-half million will starve to death this year, mostly children. But this is a mere handful compared to the numbers that will be starving in a decade or so. And it is now too late to take action to save many of those people.

In a book about population there is a temptation to stun the reader with an avalanche of statistics. I'll spare you most, but not all, of that. After all, no matter how you slice it, population is a numbers game. Perhaps the best way to impress you with numbers is to tell you about the 'doubling time' – the time necessary for the population to double in size.

It has been estimated that the human population of 6000 BC was about five million people, taking perhaps one million years to get there from two and a half million. The population did not reach 500 million until almost 8,000 years later – about 1650 AD. This means it doubled roughly once every thousand years or so. It reached a billion people around 1850, doubling in some 200 years. It took only 80 years or so for the next doubling, as the population reached two billion around 1930. We have not completed the next doubling to four billion yet, but we now have well over three billion people. The doubling time at present seems to be about 37 years. Quite a reduction in doubling times: 1,000,000 years, 1,000 years, 200 years, 80 years, 37 years. Perhaps the meaning of a doubling time of around 37 years is best brought home by a theoretical exercise. Let's examine what might happen on the absurd assumption that the population continued to double every 37 years into the indefinite future.

If growth continued at that rate for about 900 years, there would be some 60,000,000,000,000,000 people on the face of the earth. Sixty million billion people. This is about 100 persons for each square yard of the Earth's surface, land and sea. A British physicist, J.H. Fremlin, guessed that such a multitude might be housed in a continuous 2,000-storey building covering our entire planet. The upper 1,000 storeys would contain only the apparatus for running this gigantic warren. Ducts, pipes, wires, elevator shafts, etc., would occupy about half of the space in the bottom 1,000 storeys. This would leave three or four yards of floor space for each person. I will leave to your imagination the physical details of existence on this ant heap, except to point out that all would not be black. Probably each person would be limited in his travel. Perhaps he could take elevators through all 1,000 residential storeys but he could travel only within a circle of a few hundred yards' radius on any floor. This would permit, however, each person to choose his friends from among ten million people! And, as Fremlin points out, entertainment on the worldwide TV should be excellent, for at any time one could expect some ten million Shakespeares and rather more Beatles to be alive.

Could the growth of the human population of the Earth continue beyond that point? Not according to Fremlin. We would have reached a 'heat limit'. People themselves, as well as their activities, convert other forms of energy into heat which must be dissipated. In order to permit this excess heat to radiate directly from the top of the 'world building' directly into space, the atmosphere would have been pumped into flasks under the sea well before the limiting population size was reached. The precise limit would depend on the technology of the day. At a population size of one billion billion people, the temperature of the 'world roof' would be kept around the melting point of iron to radiate away the human heat generated.

But, you say, surely Science (with a capital 'S') will find a way for us to occupy the other planets of our solar system and eventually of other stars before we get all that crowded. Skip for a moment the virtual certainty that those planets are uninhabitable. Forget also the insurmountable logistic problems of moving billions of people off the Earth. Fremlin has made some interesting calculations on how much time we could buy by occupying the planets of the solar system. For instance, at any given time it would take only about 50 years to populate Venus, Mercury, Mars, the moon, and the moons of Jupiter and Saturn to the same population density as Earth.

What if the fantastic problems of reaching and colonizing the other planets of the solar system, such as Jupiter and Uranus, can be solved? It would take only about 200 years to fill them 'Earth-full'. So we could perhaps gain 250 years of time for population growth in the solar system after we had reached an absolute limit on Earth. What then? We can't ship our surplus to the stars. Professor Garrett Hardin of the University of California at Santa Barbara has dealt effectively with this fantasy. Using extremely optimistic assumptions, he has calculated that Americans, by cutting their standard of living down to 18% of its present level, could in *one year* set aside enough capital to finance the exportation to the stars of *one day's* increase in the population of the world.

Interstellar transport for surplus people presents an amusing prospect. Since the ships would take generations to reach most stars, the only people who could be transported would be those willing to exercise strict birth control. Population explosions on space ships would be disastrous. Thus we would have to export our responsible people, leaving the irresponsible at home on Earth to breed.

Enough of fantasy. Hopefully, you are convinced that the population will have to stop growing sooner or later and that the extremely remote possibility of expanding into outer space offers no escape from the laws of population growth. If you still want to hope for the stars, just remember that, at the current growth rate, in a few thousand years everything in the visible universe would be converted into people, and the ball of people would be expanding with the speed of light! Unfortunately, even 900 years is much too far in the future for those of us concerned with the population explosion. As you shall see, the next *nine* years will probably tell the story.

Of course, population growth is not occurring uniformly over the face of the Earth. Indeed, countries are divided rather neatly into two groups: those with rapid growth rates, and those with relatively slow growth rates. The first group, making up about two-thirds of the world population, coincides closely with what are known as the 'undeveloped countries' (UDCs). The UDCs are not industrialized, tend to have inefficient agriculture, very small gross national products, high illiteracy rates and related problems. That's what UDCs are technically, but a short definition of undeveloped is 'starving'. Most Latin American, African, and Asian countries fall into this category. The second group consists, in essence, of the 'developed countries' (DCs). DCs are modern, industrial nations, such as the United States, Canada, most European countries, Israel, Russia, Japan, and Australia. Most people in these countries are adequately nourished.

Doubling times in the UDCs range around 20 to 35 years. – Think of what it means for the population of a country to double in 25 years. In order just to keep living standards at the present inadequate level, the food available for the people must be doubled. Every structure and road must be duplicated. The amount of power must be doubled. The capacity of the transport system must be doubled. The number of trained doctors, nurses, teachers, and administrators must be doubled. This would be a fantastically difficult job in the United States – a rich country with a fine agricultural system, immense industries, and rich natural resources. Think what it means to a country with none of these.

Remember also that in virtually all UDCs, people have gotten the word about the better life it is possible to have. They have seen coloured pictures in magazines of the miracles of Western technology. They have seen automobiles and airplanes. They have seen American and European movies. Many have seen refrigerators, tractors, and even TV sets. Almost all have heard transistor radios. They *know* that a better life is possible. They have what we like to call 'rising expectations'. If twice as many people are to be happy, the miracle of doubling what they now have will not be enough. It will only maintain today's standard of living. There will have to be a tripling or better. Needless to say, they are not going to be happy.

Doubling times for the DCs tend to be in the 50-to-200-year range. – These are industrialized countries that have undergone the so-called demographic transition – a transition from high to low growth rate. As industrialization progressed, children became less important to parents as extra hands to work on the farm and as support in old age. At the same time they became a financial drag – expensive to raise and educate. Presumably these are the reasons for a slowing of population growth after industrialization. They boil down to a simple fact – people just want to have fewer children.

This is not to say, however, that population is not a problem for the DCs. First of all, most of them are overpopulated. They are overpopulated by the simple criterion that they are not able to produce enough food to feed their populations. It is true that they have the money to buy food, but when food is no longer available for sale they will find the money rather indigestible. Then, too, they share with the UDCs a serious problem of population distribution. Their urban centres are getting more and more crowded relative to the countryside. This problem is not as severe as it is in the UDCs (if current trends should continue, which they cannot, Calcutta could have 66 million inhabitants in the year 2000). As you are well aware, however, urban concentrations are creating serious problems even in America. In the United States, one of the more rapidly growing DCs, we hear constantly of the headaches caused by growing population: not just garbage in our environment, but overcrowded highways, burgeoning slums, deteriorating school systems, rising crime rates, riots, and other related problems.

From the point of view of a demographer, the whole problem is quite simple. A population will continue to grow as long as the birth rate exceeds the death rate – if immigration and emigration are not occurring. It is, of course, the balance between birth rate and death rate that is critical. The birth rate is the number of births per thousand people per year in the population. The death rate is the number of deaths per thousand people per year. Subtracting the death rate from the birth rate, and ignoring migration, gives the rate of increase. If the birth rate is 30 per thousand per year, and the death rate is 10 per thousand per year, then the rate of increase is 20 per thousand per year (30-10=20). Expressed as a percent (rate per hundred people), the rate of 20 per thousand becomes 2%. If the rate of increase is 2%, then the doubling time will be 35 years. Note that if you simply added 20 people per thousand per year to the population, it would take 50 years to add a second thousand people (20x50=1,000). But the doubling time is actually much less because populations grow at compound interest rates. Just as interest dollars themselves earn interest, so people added to populations produce more people. It's growing at compound interest that makes populations double so much more rapidly than seems possible. Look at the relationship between the annual percent increase (interest rate) and the doubling time of the population (time for your money to double):

Annual percent increase	Doubling time
1.0	70
2.0	35
3.0	24
4.0	17

Those are all the calculations – I promise.–

There are some professional optimists around who like to greet every sign of dropping birth rates with wild pronouncements about the end of the population explosion. They are a little like a person who, after a low temperature of five below zero on December 21, interprets a low of only three below zero on December 22 as a cheery sign of approaching spring. First of all, birth rates, along with all demographic statistics, show short-term fluctuations caused by many factors. For instance, the birth rate depends rather heavily on the number of women at reproductive age. In the United States the current low birth rates will be replaced by higher rates as more post World War II 'baby boom' children move into their reproductive years. In Japan, 1966, the Year of the Fire Horse, was a year of very low birth rates. There is a widespread belief that girls born in the Year of the Fire Horse make poor wives, and Japanese couples try to avoid giving birth in that year because they are afraid of having daughters.

But, I repeat, it is the relationship between birth rate and death rate that is most critical. –

One of the most ominous facts of the current situation is that roughly 40% of the population of the undeveloped world is made up of people *under 15 years old*. As that mass of young people moves into its reproductive years during the next decade, we're going to see the greatest baby boom of all time. Those youngsters are the reason for all the ominous predictions for the year 2000. They are the gunpowder for the population explosion.

How did we get into this bind? It all happened a long time ago, and the story involves the process of natural selection, the development of culture, and man's swollen head. The essence of success in evolution is reproduction. Indeed, natural selection is simply defined as differential reproduction of genetic types. That is, if people with blue eyes have more children on the average than those with brown eyes, natural selection is occurring. More genes for blue eyes will be passed on to the next generation than will genes for brown eyes. Should this continue, the population will have progressively larger and larger proportions of blue-eyed people. This differential reproduction of genetic types is the driving force of evolution; it has been driving evolution for billions of years. Whatever types produced more offspring became the common types. Virtually all populations contain very many different genetic types (for reasons that need not concern us), and some are always out-reproducing others. As I said, reproduction is the key to winning the evolutionary game. Any structure, physiological process, or pattern of behaviour that leads to greater reproductive success will tend to be perpetuated. The entire process by which man developed involves thousands of millenia of our ancestors being more successful breeders than their relatives. Facet number one of our bind – the urge to reproduce has been fixed in us by billions of years of evolution.

Of course through all those years of evolution, our ancestors were fighting a continual battle to keep the birth rate ahead of the death rate. That they were successful is attested to by our very existence, for, if the death rate had overtaken the birth rate for any substantial period of time, the evolutionary line leading to man would have been extinct. Among our ape-like ancestors, a few million years ago, it was still very difficult for a mother to rear her children successfully. Most of the offspring died before they reached reproductive age. The death rate was near the birth rate. Then another factor entered the picture – cultural evolution was added to biological evolution.

Culture can be loosely defined as the body of non-genetic information which people pass from generation to generation. It is the accumulated knowledge that, in the old days, was passed on entirely by word of mouth, painting, and demonstration. Several thousand years ago the written word was added to the means of cultural transmission. Today culture is passed on in these ways, and also through television, computer tapes, motion pictures, records, blueprints, and other media. Culture is all the information man possesses except for that which is stored in the chemical language of his genes.

The large size of the human brain evolved in response to the development of cultural information. A big brain is an advantage when dealing with such information. Big-brained individuals were able to deal more successfully with the culture of their group. They were thus more successful reproductively than their smaller-brained relatives. They passed on their genes for big brains to their numerous offspring. They also added to the accumulating store of cultural information, increasing slightly the premium placed on brain size in the next generation. A self-reinforcing selective trend developed – a trend toward increased brain size.

But there was, quite literally, a rub. Babies had bigger and bigger heads. There were limits to how large a woman's pelvis could conveniently become. To make a long story short, the strategy of evolution was not to make a woman bell-shaped and relatively immobile, but to accept the problem of having babies who were helpless for a long period while their brains grew after birth. How could the mother defend and care for her infant during its unusually long period of helplessness? She couldn't, unless Papa hung around. The girls are still working on that problem, but an essential step was to get rid of the short, well-defined breeding season characteristic of most mammals. The year-round sexuality of the human female, the long period of infant dependence on the female, the evolution of the family group, all are at the roots of our present problem. They are essential ingredients in the vast social phenomenon that we call sex. Sex is not simply an act leading to the production of offspring. It is a varied and complex cultural phenomenon penetrating into all aspects of our lives – one involving our self-esteem, our choice of friends, cars, and leaders. It is tightly interwoven with our mythologies and history. Sex in man is necessary for the production of young, but it also evolved to ensure their successful rearing. Facet number two of our bind – our urge to reproduce is hopelessly entwined with most of our other urges.

Of course, in the early days the whole system did not prevent a very high mortality among the young, as well as among the older members of the group. Hunting and food-gathering is a risky business. Cavemen had to throw very impressive cave bears out of their caves before the men could move in. Witch doctors and shamans had a less than perfect record at treating wounds and curing disease. Life was short, if not sweet. Man's total population size doubtless increased slowly but steadily as human populations expanded out of the African cradle of our species.

Then about 8,000 years ago a major change occurred – the agricultural revolution. People began to give up hunting food and settled down to grow it. Suddenly some of the risk was removed from life. The chances of dying of starvation diminished greatly in some human groups. Other threats associated with the nomadic life were also reduced, perhaps balanced by new threats of disease and large-scale warfare associated with the development of cities. But the overall result was a more secure existence than before, and the human population grew more rapidly. Around 1800, when the standard of living in what are today the DCs was dramatically increasing due to industrialization, population growth really began to accelerate. The development of medical science was the straw that broke the camel's back. While lowering death rates in the DCs was due in part to other factors, there is no question that 'instant death control', exported by the DCs, has been responsible for the drastic lowering of death rates in the UDCs. Medical science, with its efficient public health programmes, has been able to depress the death rate with astonishing rapidity and at the same time drastically increase the birth rate; healthier people have more babies. –

It is, of course, socially very acceptable to reduce the death rate. Billions of years of evolution have given us all a powerful will to live. Intervening in the birth rate goes against our evolutionary values. During all those centuries of our evolutionary past, the individuals who had the most children passed on their genetic endowment in greater quantities than those who reproduced less. Their genes dominate our heredity today. All our biological urges are for more reproduction, and they are all too often reinforced by our culture. In brief, death control goes with the grain, birth control against it.

In summary, the world's population will continue to grow as long as the birth rate exceeds the death rate; it's as simple as that. When it stops growing or starts to shrink, it will mean that either the birth rate has gone down or the death rate has gone up or a combination of the two. Basically, then, there are only two kinds of solutions to the population problem. One is a 'birth rate solution', in which we find ways to lower the birth rate. The other is a 'death rate solution', in which ways to raise the death rate – war, famine, pestilence – *find us*. The problem could have been avoided by *population control*, in which mankind consciously adjusted the birth rate so that a 'death rate solution' did not have to occur.

THE THEORY
OF POPULATION
BY THOMAS MALTHUS

The Reverend Thomas Robert Malthus (1766-1834) is credited with having discovered the principle that limits the size of populations. Like most theories, that of Malthus had antecedents, but it was the anonymous publication of his *Essay on the Principle of Population* in 1798 that advanced the argument and that received wide publicity. It was written to refute the belief of those such as William Godwin, Godwin's son-in-law the poet Shelley, Condorcet, and Malthus's own father, that it was possible to construct an egalitarian society and abolish poverty and injustice. The *Essay* was expanded and amended in later editions, particularly by the introduction of 'moral restraint' as a limiting factor, an omission pointed out to Malthus by Godwin. Malthus's principle was seized on by those opposing reform of the Poor Law. Eventually Malthus himself maintained it was pointless to provide relief for the poor since it merely perpetuated their misery, and in the end he held that the poor had no right to relief. Malthus's argument influenced Charles Darwin in the development of his theory of evolution by natural selection, but politically it has usually been used to argue against help for the poor. This extract is the whole of the second chapter of the first edition.

I said that population, when unchecked, increased in a geometrical ratio, and subsistence for man in an arithmetical ratio. Let us examine whether this position be just.

I think it will be allowed, that no state has hitherto existed (at least that we have any account of) where the manners were so pure and simple, and the means of subsistence so abundant, that no check whatever has existed to early marriages, among the lower classes, from a fear of not providing well for their families, or among the higher classes, from a fear of lowering their condition in life. Consequently in no state that we have yet known has the power of population been left to exert itself with perfect freedom.

Whether the law of marriage be instituted or not, the dictate of nature and virtue seems to be an early attachment to one woman. Supposing a liberty of changing in the case of an unfortunate choice, this liberty would not affect the population till it arose to a height greatly vicious; and we are now supposing the existence of a society where vice is scarcely known.

In a state therefore of great equality and virtue, where pure and simple manners prevailed, and where the means of subsistence were so abundant that no part of the society could have any fears about providing amply for a family, the power of population being left to exert itself unchecked, the increase of the human species would evidently be much greater than any increase that has been hitherto known.

In the United States of America, where the means of subsistence have been more ample, the manners of the people more pure, and consequently the checks to early marriages fewer, than in any of the modern states of Europe, the population has been found to double itself in twenty-five years.

This ratio of increase, though short of the utmost power of population, yet as the result of actual experience, we will take as our rule, and say, that population, when unchecked, goes on doubling itself every twenty-five years or increases in a geometrical ratio.

Let us now take any spot of earth, this Island for instance, and see in what ratio the subsistence it affords can be supposed to increase. We will begin with it under its present state of cultivation.

If I allow that by the best possible policy, by breaking up more land and by great encouragements to agriculture, the produce of this Island may be doubled in the first twenty-five years, I think it will be allowing as much as any person can well demand.

In the next twenty-five years, it is impossible to suppose that the produce could be quadrupled. It would be contrary to all our knowledge of the qualities of land. The very utmost that we can conceive, is, that the increase in the second twenty-five years might equal the present produce.

Let us then take this for our rule, though certainly far beyond the truth, and allow that, by great exertion, the whole produce of the Island might be increased every twenty-five years, by a quantity of subsistence equal to what it at present produces. The most enthusiastic speculator cannot suppose a greater increase than this.

In a few centuries it would make every acre of land in the Island like a garden. Yet this ratio of increase is evidently arithmetical.

It may be fairly said, therefore, that the means of subsistence increase in an arithmetical ratio. Let us now bring the effects of these two ratios together.

The population of the Island is computed to be about seven millions, and we will suppose the present produce equal to the support of such a number. In the first twenty-five years the population would be fourteen millions, and the food being also doubled, the means of subsistence would be equal to this increase. In the next twenty-five years the population would be twenty-eight millions, and the means of subsistence only equal to the support of twenty-one millions. In the next period, the population would be fifty-six millions, and the means of subsistence just sufficient for half that number. And at the conclusion of the first century the population would be one hundred and twelve millions and the means of subsistence only equal to the support of thirty-five millions, which would leave a population of seventy-seven millions totally unprovided for.

A great emigration necessarily implies unhappiness of some kind or other in the country that is deserted. For few persons will leave their families, connections, friends, and native land, to seek a settlement in untried foreign climes, without some strong subsisting causes of uneasiness where they are, or the hope of some great advantages in the place to which they are going.

But to make the argument more general and less interrupted by the partial views of emigration, let us take the whole earth, instead of one spot, and suppose that the restraints to population were universally removed. If the subsistence for man that the earth affords was to be increased every twenty-five years by a quantity equal to what the whole world at present produces, this would allow the power of production in the earth to be absolutely unlimited, and its ratio of increase much greater than we can conceive that any possible exertions of mankind could make it.

Taking the population of the world at any number, a thousand millions, for instance, the human species would increase in the ratio of – 1, 2, 4, 8, 16, 32, 64, 128, 256, 512, etc. and subsistence as – 1, 2, 3, 4, 5, 6, 7, 8, 9, 10, etc. In two centuries and a quarter, the population would be to the means of subsistence as 512 to 10: in three centuries as 4096 to 13, and in two thousand years the difference would be almost incalculable, though the produce in that time would have increased to an immense extent.

No limits whatever are placed to the productions of the earth; they may increase for ever and be greater than any assignable quantity;

yet still the power of population being a power of a superior order, the increase of the human species can only be kept commensurate to the increase of the means of subsistence by the constant operation of the strong law of necessity acting as a check upon the greater power.

The effects of this check remain now to be considered.

Among plants and animals the view of the subject is simple. They are all impelled by a powerful instinct to the increase of their species, and this instinct is interrupted by no reasoning or doubts about providing for their offspring. Wherever therefore there is liberty, the power of increase is exerted, and the superabundant effects are repressed afterwards by want of room and nourishment, which is common to animals and plants, and among animals by becoming the prey of others.

The effects of this check on man are more complicated. Impelled to the increase of his species by an equally powerful instinct, reason interrupts his career and asks him whether he may not bring beings into the world for whom he cannot provide the means of subsistence. In a state of equality, this would be the simple question. In the present state of society, other considerations occur. Will he not lower his rank in life? Will he not subject himself to greater difficulties than he at present feels? Will he not be obliged to labour harder? and if he has a large family, will his utmost exertions enable him to support them? May he not see his offspring in rags and misery, and clamouring for bread that he cannot give them? And may he not be reduced to the grating necessity of forfeiting his independence, and of being obliged to the sparing hand of charity for support?

These considerations are calculated to prevent, and certainly do prevent, a very great number in all civilized nations from pursuing the dictate of nature in an early attachment to one woman. And this restraint almost necessarily, though not absolutely so, produces vice. Yet in all societies, even those that are most vicious, the tendency to a virtuous attachment is so strong that there is a constant effort towards an increase of population. This constant effort as constantly tends to subject the lower classes of the society to distress and to prevent any great permanent amelioration of their condition.

The way in which these effects are produced seems to be this. We will suppose the means of subsistence in any country just equal to the easy support of its inhabitants. The constant effort towards population, which is found to act even in the most vicious societies, increases the number of people before the means of subsistence are increased. The food therefore which before supported seven millions must now be divided among seven millions and a half or eight millions. The poor consequently must live much worse, and many of them be reduced to severe distress. The number of labourers also being above the proportion of the work in the market, the price of labour must tend toward a decrease, while the price of provisions would at the same time tend to rise. The labourer therefore must work harder to earn the same as he did before. During this season of distress, the discouragements to marriage, and the difficulty of rearing a family are so great that population is at a stand. In the meantime the cheapness of labour, the plenty of labourers, and the necessity of an increased industry amongst them, encourage cultivators to employ more labour upon their land, to turn up fresh soil, and to manure and improve more completely what is already in tillage, till ultimately the means of subsistence become in the same proportion to the population as at the period from which we set out. The situation of the labourer being then again tolerably comfortable, the restraints to population are in some degree loosened, and the same retrograde and progressive movements with respect to happiness are repeated.

This sort of oscillation will not be remarked by superficial observers, and it may be difficult even for the most penetrating mind to calculate its periods. Yet that in all old states some such vibration does exist, though from various transverse causes, in a much less marked, and in a much more irregular manner than I have described it, no reflecting man who considers the subject deeply can well doubt.

Many reasons occur why this oscillation has been less obvious, and less decidedly confirmed by experience, than might naturally be expected.

One principal reason is that the histories of mankind that we possess are histories only of the higher classes. We have but few accounts that can be depended upon of the manners and customs of that part of mankind where these retrograde and progressive movements chiefly take place. A satisfactory history of this kind, on one people, and of one period, would require the constant and minute attention of an observing mind during a long life. Some of the objects of inquiry would be, in what proportion to the number of adults was the number of marriages, to what extent vicious customs prevailed in consequence of the restraints upon matrimony, what was the comparative mortality among the children of the most distressed part of the community and those who lived rather more at their ease, what were the variations in the real price of labour, and what were the observable differences in the state of the lower classes of society with respect to ease and happiness, at different times during a certain period.

Such a history would tend greatly to elucidate the manner in which the constant check upon population acts and would probably prove the existence of the retrograde and progressive movements that have been mentioned, though the times of their vibrations must necessarily be rendered irregular from the operation of many interrupting causes, such as the introduction or failure of certain manufactures, a greater or less prevalent spirit of agricultural enterprise, years of plenty, or years of scarcity, wars and pestilence, poor laws, the invention of processes for shortening labour without the proportional extension of the market for the commodity, and, particularly, the difference between the nominal and real price for labour, a circumstance which has perhaps more than any other contributed to conceal this oscillation from common view.

It very rarely happens that the nominal price of labour universally falls, but we well know that it frequently remains the same, while the nominal price of provisions has been gradually increasing. This is, in effect, a real fall in the price of labour, and during this period the condition of the lower orders of the community must gradually grow worse and worse. But the farmers and capitalists are growing rich from the real cheapness of labour. Their increased capitals enable them to employ a greater number of men. Work therefore may be plentiful, and the price of labour would consequently rise. But the want of freedom in the market of labour, which occurs more or less in all communities, either from parish laws, or the more general cause of the facility of combination among the rich, and its difficulty among the poor, operates to prevent the price of labour from rising at the natural period, and keeps it down some time longer; perhaps till a year of scarcity, when the clamour is too loud and the necessity too apparent to be resisted.

The true cause of the advance in the price of labour is thus concealed, and the rich affect to grant it as an act of compassion and favour to the poor, in consideration of a year of scarcity, and, when plenty returns, indulge themselves in the most unreasonable of all complaints, that the price does not again fall, when a little reflection would shew them that it must have risen long before but from an unjust conspiracy of their own. But though the rich by unfair combinations contribute frequently to prolong a season of distress among the poor, yet no possible form of society could prevent the almost constant action of misery upon a great part of mankind, if in a state of inequality, and upon all, if all were equal.

The theory on which the truth of this position depends appears to me so extremely clear that I feel at a loss to conjecture what part of it can be denied.

That population cannot increase without the means of subsistence is a proposition so evident that it needs no illustration.

That population does invariably increase where there are the means of subsistence, the history of every people that have ever existed will abundantly prove.

And that the superior power of population cannot be checked without producing misery or vice, the ample portion of these too bitter ingredients in the cup of human life and the continuance of the physical causes that seem to have produced them bear too convincing a testimony.

POPULATION PRESSURE ON THE ENVIRONMENT

BY FRANCES MOORE LAPPÉ
AND JOSEPH COLLINS

The followers of Malthus attributed many of the world's environmental problems to pressures caused by the excess of people, but not everyone agreed with them. Frances Moore Lappé and her colleague Joseph Collins took a very different view, from a very different political perspective, in their book *Food First*, from which this extract is taken, first published in 1975.

The deterioration of our global ecosystem and its agricultural resources coincides with an increase in the population of human beings and livestock. Yet is there a *necessary* causal link? We have had to conclude there is not.

Much of the current destruction of the ecosystem in underdeveloped countries began with colonialism. The plantations established by the British, Spanish and other colonial powers put a double burden on the land. First, they expropriated the best land for continuous cultivation of crops for export. Second, they usually pushed the local farmers on to marginal, often hilly, land not at all suitable for intensive farming. Land that otherwise might have served for grazing, forestry, or recreation soon became ravaged by erosion.

This double burden – cash cropping for export and squeezing the majority of farmers on to erosion-prone lands – is being reinforced today. Take a Central American country like El Salvador. The country is mostly steep hills and mountains. The most fertile and productive lands are the middle volcanic slopes, some scattered interior river basins, and the coastal plain. Beginning with the Spanish conquest, these prime lands have been owned by large estates devoted to exports: cotton, sugar, and coffee crops and cattle ranches. Less than one in a hundred farms in El Salvador has more than 250 acres;

but those few that do, together take up *half* of the total farming land of the country, including all of the prime land.

The land left over, now mainly barren hills, is all that some 350,000 *campesinos* have on which to scratch out a subsistence living for their families. Much of the land they are forced to cultivate is so steep, it has to be planted with a stick. The erosion can be so devastating – one study concluded 77 per cent of the nation's land is suffering from accelerated erosion – that the *campesinos* must abandon a slope after a single year's meagre yield. Where they will go in the future is not at all clear. Already the rapid soil depletion has set off a heavy migration of Salvadorians into neighbouring Honduras. This land search by desperate Salvadorians helped precipitate a war between the two countries in 1969. And we were told that this was the first war in history caused by the population explosion.

It is tempting to look at an area such as the Caribbean, where semitropical forests have been destroyed and soil badly eroded, and simply diagnose the problem as too many people. Currently, local farms feed only one third of the Caribbean population and 70 per cent of the children are malnourished.

But before accepting 'too many people' as the cause, consider some figures on Caribbean land use. Over half of all the arable land is made to produce crops and cattle for export. In individual countries the usurpation of the best land for export crops is even more dramatic. In Guadaloupe over 66 per cent of the arable land produces sugar cane, cocoa, and bananas. In Martinique over 70 per cent is planted with sugar cane, cocoa, bananas, and coffee. In Barbados, 77 per cent of the arable land grows sugar cane alone.

'Haiti,' comments environmental writer Erik Eckholm, 'is among the few countries that already rival or perhaps surpass El Salvador in nationwide environmental destruction'. Not coincidentally, only a few people own the country's farmland. The best valley lands belong to a handful of elites and their foreign partners, who produce endless vistas of sugar cane, coffee trees, and cattle – all for export. We were particularly struck to see the miserable shacks of the landless along the edge of fertile irrigated fields growing feed for thousands of pigs that wind up as sausages for Chicago's Servbest Foods. Meanwhile the majority of Haitians are left to ravage the once-green mountain slopes in near futile efforts to grow food. In desperation thousands flee to the United States, where they compete with the poorest paid Americans for minimum wage jobs.

In Africa it is colonialism's cash crops and their continuing legacy, not the pressure of its population, that are destroying soil resources. Vast tracts of geologically old sediments perfectly suitable for permanent crops such as grazing grasses or trees have instead been torn up for planting cotton and peanuts. The soil becomes rapidly poor in humus and loses its cohesiveness. The wind, quite strong in the dry season, then easily erodes the soils. Soil deterioration leads to declining crop yields and consequently to an expansion of cultivated land, often on to marginal soils.

In dramatic contrast to cash-cropping monoculture, the traditional self-provisioning agriculture that it replaces is often quite sound ecologically. It is a long-evolved adaptation to tropical soil and climate. It reflects a sophisticated understanding of the complex rhythms of the local ecosystem. The mixing of crops, sometimes of more than twenty different species, means harvests are staggered and provides maximum security against wholesale losses due to unseasonable weather, pests, or disease. Moreover, mixed cropping provides the soil with year-round protection from the sun and rain.

The problem of soil erosion *is* serious. But soil erosion occurs largely because fertile land is monopolized by a few, forcing the majority of farmers to overuse vulnerable soils. Moreover, soil impoverishment results, not from an effort to meet the basic food needs of expanding populations, but increasingly from the pressure to grow continuously non-food and luxury export crops over large areas to the neglect of traditional techniques that once protected the soil.

Overgrazing is another sure way to ruin marginal lands. But to get at the cause one must ask, Who is overgrazing and why? And does it follow that marginal lands can never be suitable for livestock? Finally, since overgrazing means too many cattle on the land, must we conclude this reflects too many people?

Some outsiders see Africa's nomadic pastoralists as the culprits. We have come to learn, however, that nomadic pastoralists have traditionally made efficient use of vast stretches of semi-arid land that otherwise would remain unproductive. While their migrations might look random to the outsider, they are, in reality, patterned to take advantage of variations in rainfall and vegetation. The nomads may herd their livestock over hundreds of miles from rainy season pastures to oases of perennial grasses in dry seasons. Pastoral nomadism, then, is a rational response to an environment characterized by the scarcity of water, seasonal drought, and widely scattered seasonal fodder resources. The nomads' tactics make use of resources that others would not even consider as resources.

Another adaptation technique of traditional pastoralists is keeping a herd that consists of different types of livestock: camels, sheep, goats, donkeys, as well as cattle. A mixed herd can exploit a variety of ecological niches. Cattle and sheep graze on grasslands; and goats browse on shrubs and low parts of trees. Valuable protein for human consumption is thus produced by plants that humans cannot eat. Different species also have different reproductive cycles; staggered breeding seasons ensure some type of milk throughout the year. The hardiness of goats and camels make them good animals to fall back on in times of drought when cattle die off. A varied herd also acts as a walking storehouse for food, either directly or in exchange for grain, during annual dry spells and periodic droughts.

Pastoralists traditionally produced enough meat and dairy products to exchange with farmers for grain. In addition, the pastoralists' herds annually manured the fallow fields of the farmers. The animals thus gained good grazing land and the fertility of the farmers' soils improved. This symbiotic relationship allowed for remarkably dense populations to comfortably inhabit seemingly inhospitable lands.

If raising livestock has been and can be such an excellent way to make marginal lands productive, what has gone wrong? What is behind the many reports of overgrazing in regions like the African Sahel, that vast stretch of semi-arid land along the southern border of the Sahara?

To answer such questions we have to go back to the beginning of this century. The French colonial administration created arbitrary 'national' borders (today enforced by the newly independent governments) without regard to the need of the nomads to migrate. Endless restrictions have made it increasingly difficult for the nomads to shift their herds in response to the short- and long-term cycles of nature.

The French also slapped a head tax on each nomad. The tax had to be paid in French francs even though most nomads lived within a barter economy. The nomads needed, therefore, to raise more livestock, so that some could be sold for cash. Over the years, their need for money has been compounded by the growing lure of imported consumer goods.

Higher market prices also prompted pastoralists to build up their herds beyond the carrying capacity of the lands.

The expansion of lands for peanut and cotton production sharply decreased the amount of pasture available to herders. Farmers also began to keep small herds near their houses. These herds, kept in such a confined space, resulted in localized overgrazing. Moreover, the urban and export demand for beef induced the pastoralists to upset the natural balance of a diversified herd in favour of cattle. Modern inoculations against disease also facilitated the build-up of herds beyond the carrying capacity of the grazing lands. Medicine that was meant to save these herds ultimately contributed to the death by starvation of tens of thousands of animals.

Aid agencies, including the United States Agency for International Development (AID), drilled deep water wells in the late 1950s and early 1960s. – When the rains began to fail, the nomads started to move their cattle en masse to these wells.–

Before long on average in the Sahel, 6,000 head of cattle were milling about wells surrounded by grazing lands that at best could feed 600. After the cattle ate out the areas around the wells and trampled down the soil, the caked earth could no longer even absorb the scarce rains.–

You have probably read that the plight of the pastoralists proves that these countries are overpopulated and have exhausted their resources. Does more cattle mean there are too many people? We think the answer is by now obvious: not necessarily. But there is no need to romanticize nomads. Undoubtedly they must come into a new ecological balance within the context of the rest of society.–

Like the wildlife areas of Africa, the Amazon River basin has long been seen as one of the world's few remaining great natural preserves. Recently the public has become vaguely aware that it too is being threatened. The Amazon basin *is* being 'ravaged', but is the cause overpopulation?

Since the mid-1960s Brazil's largest government project is the 'colonization' of this extraordinary region. The plans call for sweeping clean tens of millions of acres of tropical forest. Already legions of Caterpillar Tractors' gargantuan 35-ton D-9s, mounted with angle ploughs weighing 2,500 pounds each, are bulldozing the forest at 2,700 yards an hour, uprooting everything in sight. In some areas the job calls for two D-9s with a heavy chain between them rolling a huge hollow steel ball eight feet in diameter and weighing 6,000 pounds. As the tractors move forward, the chain jerks out the trees, destroying the extensive matted root system and exposing the thin tropical soil. Fires visible for miles devour the debris. Such massive deforestation is, according to the President of the Brazilian Academy of Science, Warwick Kerr, 'taking place at a faster pace than Brazil and perhaps the world has ever known before. The Amazon forest will disappear in 35 years if it continues to be destroyed at the present rate.'

Is it really Brazil's expanding population behind those unrelenting D-9 'jungle crushers'? No, the truth is that Brazil with 2.3 acres of already cropped land per person (slightly better than the ratio in the United States) hardly needs to invade its tropical forests in order to feed its people.

The Amazon forest is earmarked for destruction for two entirely different reasons. Settlement or 'colonization' schemes historically have been safety valves – primarily a way to sidestep the urgent need for land redistribution. In Brazil, a mere one per cent of the farms take up over 43 per cent of the country's total farmland, and the best land at that. In brutal contrast, 50 per cent of the farms are left with less than 3 per cent of the land. In addition, at least 7 million rural families own no land at all – in a country where, even without taking the Amazon region into consideration, there are potentially ten cultivable acres for every family. Four out of five rural families, even if they do find work on a large estate, earn less than $33 a month. Yet a family of three needs at least $65 a month to buy food alone. It all translates into a massive waste of human life. Almost 200 of every 1,000 babies born in rural north-east Brazil die in their first year of life.

To avoid provoking Brazil's most powerful families by dividing up the large, generally export-oriented estates, the military government announced an absurd solution: move the rural poor to the Amazon basin, a tropical region totally unsuited for intensive and continuous farming. Thus the pressure on the Amazon forest comes *not* from Brazil's population growth but from a government's efforts to diffuse pressures for a just redistribution of land.

Ten years after much self-serving fanfare, the government has resettled a mere 10,000 small farmers. Even then, despite enormous bureaucratic expenditures, many of these farms have been soon abandoned, in part since their tropical soils cannot support intensive cultivation. Far from being concerned, the government has added insult to injury. Only a few years after trumpeting that prosperity for the rural poor was just a thousand or so miles down a not yet completed road, the government opted for a different type of pioneer. Kingdom-sized concessions, none smaller than 125,000 acres, were the new order of the day – mainly for export-oriented ranching and pulpwood production.

The 'pioneers' are some of Brazil's richest families, already among the country's largest landholders, a number of Brazilian corporations, and, for good measure, a few television stars. Also quick to find out what Brazil can do for them are many of the world's largest multinational corporations. – The 'homesteads' of these pioneers run as large as 3.7 million acres, half the size of Holland.–

In 1975 a United States reconnaisance satellite's heat sensor detected a sudden and intense warming of the earth in the Amazon basin usually associated with an imminent volcanic eruption. A special alert mission was dispatched. And what did they find? A German multinational corporation burning down one million acres of tropical forest for a cattle ranch.–

Some justify the whole Amazon scheme as necessitated by Brazil's or the world's population problem. In reality the scheme is a public relations fraud by the Brazilian government at the expense of the landless, a devastation of the country's natural resources to provide a fleeting profit for the rich. It is also, in the opinion of many noted environmental scientists, an ecological disaster in the making not only for Brazil but for the entire world.–

It is not, then, growing population that threatens to destroy the environment, either here or abroad, but a system that promotes the utilization of food-producing resources according to narrow profit-seeking criteria. Taking advantage of this system are land monopolizers growing non-food and luxury crops and colonial patterns of taxation and cash-cropping that force the rural majority to abuse marginal land.

Of course there are areas where population density exacerbates environmental deterioration. But – what is most critical is to distinguish exacerbating factors from the root cause. Where environmental destruction is most severe, halving the population would not solve the problem. Basic changes in the control of wealth remain the only path to an ecologically sane use of land.

THE TRUE HUNGER GAP AND THE CALORIE SWINDLE

BY GEORG BORGSTROM

The old nineteenth century fear of mass starvation caused by the Malthusian imbalance between population growth and agricultural production was revived by modern environmentalists and pursued along two lines, those of population growth and of food production. Georg Borgstrom, Professor of Food Science and Geography at Michigan State University, was one of the earliest and most forceful writers on the limits to food production and his first book, *The Hungry Planet*, went through several editions following its publication in 1965. Although his analysis differs from that of Lappé and Collins, the extract here illustrates that Borgstrom's anger at the injustice and dishonesty he saw in the treatment of the poor by the rich is no less intense than theirs.

Most writers on the subject of the world's food supplies confine themselves to calculating man's total calorie requirements and the capability of agriculture to meet these demands. This dangerous oversimplification is also encountered in most textbooks on agriculture, economic geography, and nutrition. Figures are presented that give a reassuring picture of the world abundance in food and how much more can be raised. These rosy analyses completely overlook the fact that, despite two postwar decades of tremendous efforts, we have not been able to satisfy even the minimum needs of the human race. Only a minor fraction of those now living come close to opulence.

Taking Denmark and Holland as patterns for the world, these 'experts' offer entirely unrealistic calculations of the enormous quantities of food that would be obtained if, all over the world, the production level of agriculture were to be raised to that of these two countries. They completely disregard the obvious fact that neither of these two countries would be able to manage as they do without importing considerable quantities of feed, or without their fisheries. If the world really were to follow such foolish advice and copy Holland, for instance – a net-importing (imports exceed exports) country – the earth would need to acquire a food- and feed-producing satellite larger in size (148 per cent) than the present globe. Furthermore, world fisheries would have to 35-fold their present catch to provide the human household with a corresponding amount of fish as feed. (Calculated on the basis of 1966-67 figures.) Although indisputable facts refute the validity of such evasive reference to Dutch accomplishments, this argument is nonetheless repeatedly brought forth to support the contention that the world could feed twelve to fifteen billion people. The truth of the matter is that most of the world would be starving if it were to allow itself the present Dutch extravagance.

– Only one-tenth of what the human race eats in terms of calories consists of animal products – meat, milk, eggs, and fish - yet such delicacies are, by and large, the privilege of a few hundred million.

A number of striking examples could be set forth to demonstrate what could be achieved if one could concern oneself merely with filling the calorie requirements of man. The United States, for instance, could dispense with much of its agriculture and convert the land thus freed into parks for the recreation of its zooming population. The present corn acreage would in effect suffice to provide ample and adequate amounts of calories to fill the present US needs. The total tilled land in the United States could easily supply the world's present population, now exceeding three and a half billion, with all the calories it needs if the northern zone were to grow sugar beets and the southern region sugar cane.

This kind of reasoning is oversimplification and as such grossly misleading. It should be obvious even to the layman, that apart from the intolerable monotony of such a diet, it would inevitably lead to a nutritional catastrophe. People, as living beings, are certainly not mere internal-combustion engines. Recognizing only the fuel value of our food is an error and greatly misleading. Of course man needs energy, but that need has never been the really serious obstacle of man, despite what atomic physicists try to make us believe. Energy is not a limiting factor in food production. In three days the sun supplies the earth with more energy than is totally accumulated in all the deposits of coal, oil, and uranium.

In his food man needs protein – the living substrate of the cell's protoplasm – and in addition his protein intake has to satisfy very narrow specifications as to molecular structure. Man, furthermore, requires a number of vitamins, also special fats and, it would appear, certain specified carbohydrates. The proteins, however, are key compounds. It is more than a coincidence that, during recent decades, protein deficiency diseases have come to prevail in most continents and must be regarded as the chief nutritional deficiency of the world. Before we make an effort to outline in more realistic terms the true dimension of the protein shortage situation, we must deal with another aspect of what might be designated the calorie fallacy.

The average calorie intake of the hungry masses of India is said to be about 1,900 calories a day per person, while contemporary expert opinion puts the normal requirement of a full-grown person of 154 pounds (70 kilograms) weight at about 3,000 calories, recognizing that some of this is inevitably wasted and some is never used up by the body. Taking into consideration the fact that the East Indians are relatively shorter in stature (consequently weigh less) and also that there is a greater proportion of children among them as compared to the United States and Western Europe, the actual requirement of an average East Indian at the present time may be estimated as from 2,400 to 2,500 calories. Thus, the gap between the present underconsumption and an adequate but still minimal diet requires an additional 500 to 600 calories a day per person. This would involve an increase of approximately 30 to 35 per cent in the amount of grain grown in that country.

We will not discuss at this stage whether or not it would be feasible for India to do this and to what degree this extra grain could be raised; instead, let us scrutinize these figures and see if they hold true. Even the Indians consume certain animal products, above all milk and fish, and a little meat and eggs as well. Now, for every calorie of animal foodstuffs produced, five to eight primary calories are required, represented by plant products and other feeding-stuffs that the animals need for their maintenance as well as for their food-producing activities. On such a simplified basis, the number of calories required to feed the various categories of livestock, in terms of primary calories, can be computed. The intake of an East Indian is therefore not restricted to the 1,900 calories he actually puts into his mouth, but comprises also the primary calories needed to procure these animal products. In this way the total amount of calories disposed per day reaches around 2,900. The most telling aspect of this, however, is not so much the fact that India's figure has to be readjusted in this way, but that the corresponding data for Americans and West Europeans must be revised upward in a similar way and this has much more far-reaching consequences.

The calorie consumption of most of the peoples of the Western world is thus not confined to the 3,000 calories they eat every day, but is more in the region of 8,000 to 10,000. The average American disposes of about 10,870 primary calories a day, while the New Zealander requires 12,430. The Mexican figure is 4,820 with 14 per cent of the direct calorie intake referring to animal products as compared to 42 per cent for the United States. Here we encounter the true disparity among the peoples of the world – the true Hunger Gap.

It should be obvious that in order to fill such a gap, far greater efforts are called for. Measures are needed of quite another magnitude and scope than those generally indicated. It can safely be said that discrepancies of such tremendous dimensions could never be eliminated even if agricultural miracles and worldwide equalization of distribution were accomplished.–

There is an upper class of some 450 million, out of the world's 3.7 billion, which occupies a privileged position as far as nutrition goes. We like to think that we owe our abundance to our greater skill and ingenuity, completely forgetting that we owe it equally, or maybe even to a greater extent, to our good fortune in the great lottery of history, which has given us a disproportionate share of the world's agricultural land resources. When the Europeans overflowed their boundaries, they took possession of this vast double continent of North and South America, as well as of Australia, parts of Southeast Asia and South Africa. Millions of acres in developing countries are devoted to providing this luxury client with such items as sugar, cotton, coffee, tea, oilseeds, and bananas.

These extravagant nations, to which the United States clearly belongs, constitute the privileged countries of the world. At present, their peoples dispose of as many calories per day or per year, as do the 1,500 millions at the lower end of the scale, such as the peoples of China, India, Indonesia, etc. Politically, this enormous chasm between the two groups provides an explosive situation, while economically the repercussions of this widening gap will become more and more serious. Wages and prices cannot in the long run remain unaffected by the fact that it costs three times as much to maintain a Westerner, whether he be professor, labourer, or engineer, than it does to feed even adequately an East Indian or Chinese. It is worth noting that most students of these calorie needs – have not recognized the true relationship between calories and man's nutritional needs, but have satisfied themselves with using simple, standardized consumption figures, the real validity of which they have made no attempt to examine.–

Most significant is the fact that West European food standard to such a surprising degree is depending on Peruvian-Chilean crutches. The influx of animal protein through the backdoor in the form of anchoveta fish meal constitutes a major factor in the animal production of the Netherlands, West Germany, Italy, and others. This support constitutes a decisive leverage not only toward a high nutritional standard but also as to animal production, both yet to be recognized in world economy.

It is urgent that the public be alerted to this deceptive calorie and quantity thinking. Even the layman would understand that a person cannot live on sugar and flour and remain healthy. Western agriculture has been dominated by this yield concept based on quantity. Progress has been gauged in terms of increased yields per acre or in tons per working hour. These are important measurements but they are far from enough, especially when it comes to the decisive question of food production and nutritional needs. It is most unfortunate that higher yields to such a great degree have been attained at the expense of quality. This is particularly true with regard to protein. Quality has frequently deteriorated considerably, showing up in declining protein levels. Both grain, potato, and root crops have been made to fill up their cells with more starch and sugar, while on the whole the relative content of protein has dropped, even when in a few cases the acre-yield may have been sustained or has even been raised. This trend becomes particularly hazardous when the protein level falls below the acknowledged nutritive minimum of approximately 12 per cent, which is a must for both man and non-ruminant animals.–

The high-yielding US crops of corn and wheat have to be supplemented with approximately two-thirds of the present soybean production in order to fill in the protein content of these two crops to equal what was common twenty-five years ago. Hybrid corn has to be sent to a feed mill in order to be mixed with protein foods to make it into an acceptable hog food. The West European of today has to put a slice of cheese on *his* bread and butter to make it as nourishing as his grandfather's. Postwar wheat yields in the United States, frequently the highest ever recorded in this country, and the resultant surpluses, are partly due to new wheat varieties, most of which contain 20-25 per cent less protein compared with the wheats grown when World War II ended.

Many of the yield increases registered by modern-day agriculture have similarly been attained at the expense of something else. We would have been better aware of this deterioration if we had substituted one crop for another, rather than filling up grain with more carbohydrates and thereby 'diluting' its proteins and arriving at less relative amounts. In some cases the nitrogen as well as the protein level has been raised, but only rarely at the same rate as total yield, and this generally only in the initial phases of improvements in a low-yielding agriculture. One additional complication is the fact that such extra protein in most instances is inferior to 'normal' protein as to its amino-acid composition, i.e., nutritive value, and in extreme cases simple nitrogenous compounds, such as nitrate, glutamine, etc., pile up in the cells. –

A new phase in this deceptive procedure are the exaggerated claims now attached to high-yielding wheat and rice varieties. In most of the countries hit by this alleged 'green revolution', protein is already critically short and the protein intake close to or below the minimum level of 12 per cent. Most of these higher yields are in starch and what these countries need more than anything else is expanded acreages for beans and other pulses, peanuts, and other nuts, to reduce the alarming protein gap. –

The dissatisfaction exhibited by many colonial peoples can also be traced back to the same kind of hazardous thinking in terms of calories. These people were often supplied with cheap fats and sugar by the colonizers, but at the same time they were frequently deprived of protein foods or meat-producing pastures. The expensive but valuable animal products were placed beyond reach of the purchasing power of the new proletariat. –

Mankind should benefit by its errors and gradually employ more constructive methods, but we persist in placing quantity ahead of quality, as though more tons per acre were more important than what kind of tons are obtained. The calorie swindle is no feat in the history of mankind; in fact it is inflicting major sufferings on the human race through diseases and hunger.

MALTHUS AND THE
PRODUCTIVITY OF FARMS
BY PETR ALEKSEEVICH KROPOTKIN

Distress at modern farming methods, combined with disgust at the artificiality of many aspects of contemporary life, led groups of environmentally-minded people to establish rural communes which became a feature of the later 1970s. Politically, most of the 'communards' regarded themselves as anarchists in the tradition of P.A. Kropotkin (1842-1921). A Russian aristocrat who lived for a time in England, and a distinguished geographer and geologist, Kropotkin's political vision, gentle, yet carefully constructed and argued, turned him into an almost saintly figure and certainly one deserving our admiration. The gentleness came from a rejection of 'social Darwinism', for his own studies led him to suppose collaboration among animals to be more usual and more important than competition (a view that commands much modern scientific support) and consequently he rejected the Malthusianism on which social Darwinism is based. This extract is taken from what is perhaps his most popular book, *Fields, Factories and Workshops*, first published in 1898.

Few books have exercised so pernicious an influence upon the general development of economic thought as Malthus's *Essay on the Principle of Population* exercised for three consecutive generations. It appeared at the right time, like all books which have had any influence at all, and it summed up ideas already current in the minds of the wealth-possessing minority. It was precisely when the ideas of equality and liberty, awakened by the French and American revolutions, were still permeating the minds of the poor, while the richer classes had become tired of their amateur excursions into the same domains, that Malthus came to assert, in reply to Godwin, that no equality is possible; that the poverty of the many is not due to institutions, but is a natural *law*. Population, he wrote, grows too rapidly and the new-comers find no room at the feast of nature; and that law cannot be altered by any change of institutions.–

Science, down to the present day, remains permeated with Malthus's teachings. Political economy continues to base its reasoning upon a tacit admission of the impossibility of rapidly increasing the productive powers of a nation, and of thus giving satisfaction to all wants. – Political economy never rises above the hypothesis of a *limited and insufficient supply of the necessities of life*; it takes it for granted.–

True, the formidable growth of the productive powers of man in the industrial field, since he tamed steam and electricity, has somewhat shaken Malthus's doctrine. Industrial wealth *has* grown at a rate which no possible increase of population could attain, and it *can* grow with still greater speed. But agriculture is still considered a stronghold of Malthusian pseudo-philosophy. The recent achievements of agriculture and horticulture are not sufficiently well known; and while our gardeners defy climate and latitude, acclimatize sub-tropical plants, raise several crops a year instead of one, and themselves make the soil they want for each special culture, the economists nevertheless continue saying that the surface of the soil is limited, and still more its productive powers; they still maintain that a population which should double each thirty years would soon be confronted by a lack of the necessities of life!–

The deeper one goes into the subject, the more new and striking data does he discover, and the more Malthus's fears appear groundless.–

While we are so often told that wheat-growing does not pay, and England consequently reduces from year to year the area of its wheat fields, the French peasants steadily increase the area under wheat, and the greatest increase is due to those peasant families which themselves cultivate the land they own. In the course of the nineteenth century they have nearly doubled the area under wheat, as well as the returns from each acre, so as to increase almost fourfold the amount of wheat grown in France.

At the same time, the population has only increased by 41 per cent, so that the ratio of the increase of the wheat crop has been six times greater than the ratio of increase of population, although agriculture has been hampered all the time by a series of serious obstacles – taxation, military service, poverty of the peasantry, and even, up to 1884, a severe prohibition of all sorts of association among the peasants.–

The ratio of progress in agriculture is still better seen from the rise of the standard of requirement as regards cultivation of land. Some thirty years ago the French considered a crop very good when it yielded 22 bushels to the acre; but with the same soil the present requirement is at least 33 bushels, while in the best soils the crop is good only when it yields from 43 to 48 bushels, and occasionally they produce as much as 55 bushels to the acre.–

The small island of Jersey, eight miles long and less than six miles wide, still remains a land of open-field culture; but, although it comprises only 28,707 acres, rocks included, it nourishes a population of about two inhabitants to each acre, or 1,300 inhabitants to the square mile, and there is not one writer on agriculture who, after having paid a visit to this island, did not praise the well-being of the Jersey peasants and the admirable results which they obtain in their small farms of from 5 to 20 acres – very often less than 5 acres – by means of a rational and intensive culture.

Most of my readers will probably be astonished to learn that the soil of Jersey, which consists of decomposed granite, with no organic matter in it, is not at all of astonishing fertility, and that its climate, though more sunny than the climate of these isles, offers many drawbacks on account of the small amount of sun-heat during the summer and of the cold winds in spring. But so it is in reality, and at the beginning of the nineteenth century the inhabitants of Jersey lived chiefly on imported food. The successes accomplished lately in Jersey are entirely due to the amount of labour which a dense population is putting into the land; to a system of land-tenure, land-transference and inheritance very different from those which prevail elsewhere; to freedom from state taxation; and to the fact that communal institutions have been maintained, down to quite a recent period, while a number of communal habits and customs of mutual support, derived therefrom, are alive to the present time.–

The more we study the modern achievements of agriculture, the more we see that the limits of productivity of the soil are not attained, even in Jersey. New horizons are continually unveiled.–

Potatoes are largely used in Germany and Belgium for distilleries; consequently the distillery owners try to obtain the greatest possible amounts of starch from the acre. Extensive experiments have lately been made for that purpose in Germany, and the crops were: 9 tons per acre for the poor sorts, 14 tons for the better ones, and 32 and 4/10ths tons for the best varieties of potatoes.

Three tons to the acre and more than 30 tons to the acre are thus the ascertained limits; and one necessarily asks oneself: Which of the two requires *less labour* in tilling, planting, cultivating and digging, and less expenditure in manure – 30 tons grown on 10 acres, or the same 30 tons grown on 1 acre? If labour is of no consideration, while every penny spent in seeds and manure is of great importance, as is unhappily very often the case with the peasant – he will perforce choose the first method. But is it the most economic?

Again, in the Saffelare district and Jersey they succeed in keeping one head of horned cattle to each acre of green crops, meadows and pasture land, while elsewhere 2 or 3 acres are required for the same purpose.–

It is evident that in a book which is not intended to be a manual of agriculture, all I can do is to give only a few hints to set people thinking for themselves upon this subject. But the little that has been said is sufficient to show that we have no right to complain of over-population, and no need to fear it in the future. Our means of obtaining from the soil whatever we want, under *any* climate and upon *any* soil, have lately been improved at such a rate that we cannot foresee yet what is the limit of productivity of a few acres of land. The limit vanishes in proportion to our better study of the subject, and every year makes it vanish further and further from our sight.

SMOKELESS FUEL

BY JOHN EVELYN

If population and pressure on resources form two strands of the environmentalist debate, pollution caused, perhaps, by the processing of resources forms a third. Concern about pollution is not new. Air pollution by smoke was becoming a problem in medieval London as 'sea-coal' (so-called because it was carried by sea from north-east England to London) became more popular. From that time the use of coal increased steadily and the use of wood declined. By the seventeenth century ways were being sought to process coal into a fuel that would burn at temperatures high enough for iron-smelting. John Evelyn observed one of these experiments on the 11th April, 1656, and recorded it in his diary, adding a further note later (here in parenthesis). What impressed him was the possibility of producing not an improved fuel, so much as a cleaner one.

Came home by Greenwich ferry, where I saw Sir J. Winter's project of charring sea-coal, to burn out the sulphur, and render it sweet. He did it by burning the coals in such earthen pots as the glass-men melt their metal, so firing them without consuming them, using a bar of iron in each crucible, or pot, which bar has a hook at one end, that so the coals being melted in a furnace with other crude sea-coals under them, may be drawn out of the pots sticking to the iron, whence they are beaten off in great half-exhausted cinders, which being re-kindled, make a clear pleasant chamber-fire, deprived of their sulphur and arsenic malignity. What success it may have, time will discover. (Many years ago, Lord Dundonald revived the project, with the proposed improvement of extracting and saving the tar. Unfortunately, he did not profit by it. The coal thus charred is sold as *coke*, a very useful fuel.)

COKETOWN

BY CHARLES DICKENS

We associate the worst of the damage inflicted by heavy industry on the natural environment and on people with the factory towns of the nineteenth century, and many of our images of that world are derived from the writings of Charles Dickens (1812-70). In his later years, Dickens became more severely critical of the conditions he saw about him. He satirized the Court of Chancery in *Bleak House*, published in 1853, and a year later published *Hard Times*, the book from which the following description of an imaginary Lancashire mill town is taken. The 'hard times' of the title refer to the periodic trade slumps of the period.

Coketown, to which Messrs Bounderby and Gradgrind now walked, was a triumph of fact; it had no greater taint of fancy in it than Mrs Gradgrind herself. Let us strike the key-note, Coketown, before pursuing our tune.

It was a town of red brick, or of brick that would have been red if the smoke and ashes had allowed it; but, as matters stood it was a town of unnatural red and black like the painted face of a savage. It was a town of machinery and tall chimneys, out of which interminable serpents of smoke trailed themselves for ever and ever, and never got uncoiled. It had a black canal in it, and a river that ran purple with ill-smelling dye, and vast piles of building full of windows where there was a rattling and a trembling all day long, and where the piston of the steam-engine worked monotonously up and down, like the head of an elephant in a state of melancholy madness. It contained several large streets all very like one another, and many small streets still more like one another, inhabited by people equally like one another, who all went in and out at the same hours, with the same sound upon the same pavements, to do the same work, and to whom every day was the same as yesterday and tomorrow, and every year the counterpart of the last and the next.

These attributes of Coketown were in the main inseparable from the work by which it was sustained; against them were to be set off, comforts of life which found their way all over the world, and elegancies of life which made, we will not ask how much of the fine lady, who could scarcely bear to hear the place mentioned. The rest of its features were voluntary, and they were these.

You saw nothing in Coketown but what was severely workful. If the members of a religious persuasion built a chapel there – as the members of eighteen religious persuasions had done – they made it a pious warehouse of red brick, with sometimes (but this only in highly ornamented examples) a bell in a bird-cage on the top of it. The solitary exception was the New Church; a stuccoed edifice with a square steeple over the door, terminating in four short pinnacles like florid wooden legs. All the public inscriptions in the town were painted alike, in severe characters of black and white. The jail might have been the infirmary, the infirmary might have been the jail, the town-hall might have been either, or both, or anything else, for anything that appeared to the contrary in the graces of their construction. Fact, fact, fact, everywhere in the material aspect of the town; fact, fact, fact, everywhere in the immaterial. The M'Choakumchild school was all fact, and the relations between master and man were all fact, and everything was fact between the lying-in hospital and the cemetery, and what you couldn't state in figures, or show to be purchaseable in the cheapest market and saleable in the dearest, was not, and never should be, world without end, Amen.

A town so sacred to fact, and so triumphant in its assertion, of course got on well? Why no, not quite well. No? Dear me!

No. Coketown did not come out of its own furnaces, in all respects like gold that had stood the fire. First, the perplexing mystery of the place was, Who belonged to the eighteen denominations? Because, whoever did, the labouring people did not. It was very strange to walk through the streets on a Sunday morning, and note how few of *them* the barbarous jangling of bells that was driving the sick and nervous mad, called away from their own quarter, from their own close rooms, from the corners of their own streets, where they lounged listlessly, gazing at all the church and chapel going, as at a thing with which they had no manner of concern. Nor was it merely the stranger who noticed this, because there was a native organization in Coketown itself, whose members were to be heard of in the House of Commons every session, indignantly petitioning for acts of parliament that should make those people religious by main force. Then, came the Teetotal Society, who complained that these people *would* get drunk, and showed in tabular statements that they did get drunk, and proved at tea parties that no inducement, human or Divine (except a medal), would induce them to forego their custom of getting drunk. Then, came the chemist and druggist, with other tabular statements, showing that when they didn't get drunk, they took opium. Then, came the experienced chaplain of the jail, with more tabular statements, outdoing all the previous tabular statements, and showing that the same people *would* resort to low haunts, hidden from the public eye, where they heard low singing and saw low dancing, and mayhap joined in it; and where A.B., aged twenty-four next birthday, and committed for eighteen months' solitary, had himself said (not that he had ever shown himself particularly worthy of belief) his ruin began, as he was perfectly sure and confident that otherwise he would have been a tip-top moral specimen. Then, came Mr Gradgrind and Mr Bounderby, the two gentlemen at this present moment walking through Coketown, and both eminently practical, who could, on occasion, furnish more tabular statements derived from their own personal experience, and illustrated by cases they had known and seen, from which it clearly appeared – in short it was the only clear thing in the case – that these same people were a bad lot altogether, gentlemen; that do what you would for them they were never thankful for it, gentlemen; that they were restless, gentlemen; that they never knew what they wanted; that they lived upon the best, and bought fresh butter, and insisted on Mocha coffee, and rejected all but prime parts of meat, and yet were eternally dissatisfied and unmanageable. In short it was the moral of the old nursery fable:

> There was an old woman, and what do you think?
> She lived upon nothing but victuals and drink;
> Victuals and drink were the whole of her diet,
> And yet this old woman would NEVER be quiet.

A MORNING BATH

BY WILLIAM MORRIS

The nineteenth century was an age of protest, reform, and dreams of what the world and society might be like, dreams of Utopia. These Utopias were founded in an unshakeable belief in 'progress', the essentially optimistic idea that with appropriate adjustments the continued production of material goods, based on the mastery of nature, and of knowledge to assist that mastery, could be induced to lead to a world freed from war, social unrest, poverty, injustice, and the unfair exploitation of working people. William Morris (1834-96) described such a Utopia in *News from Nowhere*, from which these extracts are taken. The story appeared in instalments in *Commonweal*, the journal of the Socialist League, which he founded, and edited between 1885 and 1890, and it was published in book form in 1891.

I had by no means shaken off the feeling of oppression, and wherever I might have been should scarce have been quite conscious of the place; so it was no wonder that I felt rather puzzled in despite of the familiar face of the Thames. Withal I felt dizzy and queer; and remembering that people often got a boat and had a swim in mid-stream, I thought I would do no less. It seems very early, quoth I to myself, but I daresay I shall find someone at Biffin's to take me. However, I didn't get as far as Biffin's, or even turn to my left thitherward, because just then I began to see that there was a landing-stage right before me in front of my own house: in fact, on the place where my next-door neighbour had rigged one up, though somehow it didn't look like that either. Down I went to it, and sure enough among the empty boats moored to it lay a man on his sculls in a solid-looking tub of a boat clearly meant for bathers. He nodded to me, and bade me good morning as if he expected me, so I jumped in without any words, and he paddled away quietly as I peeled for my swim. As we went, I looked down on the water, and couldn't help saying:

'How clear the water is this morning!'

'Is it?' said he; 'I didn't notice it. You know the flood-tide always thickens it a bit.'

'H'm,' said I, 'I have seen it pretty muddy even at half-ebb.'

He said nothing in answer, but seemed rather astonished; and as he now lay just stemming the tide, and I had my clothes off, I jumped in without more ado. Of course when I had my head above water again I turned towards the tide, and my eyes naturally sought for the bridge, and so utterly astonished was I by what I saw, that I forgot to strike out, and went spluttering under water again, and when I came up made straight for the boat; for I felt that I must ask some questions of my waterman, so bewildering had been the half-sight I had seen from the face of the river with the water hardly out of my eyes; though by this time I was quit of the slumbrous and dizzy feeling, and was wide-awake and clear-headed.

As I got in up the steps which he had lowered, and he held out his hand to help me, we went drifting speedily up towards Chiswick; but now he caught up the sculls and brought her head round again, and said:

'A short swim, neighbour; but perhaps you find the water cold this morning, after your journey. Shall I put you ashore at once, or would you like to go down to Putney before breakfast?'

He spoke in a way so unlike what I should have expected from a Hammersmith waterman, that I stared at him, as I answered, 'Please to hold her a little; I want to look about me a bit.'

'All right,' he said; 'it's no less pretty in its way here than it is off Barn Elms; it's jolly everywhere this time in the morning. I'm glad you got up early; it's barely five o'clock yet.' –

I felt that I must make some conversation; so I pointed to the Surrey bank, where I noticed some light plank stages running down the foreshore, with windlasses at the landward end of them, and said, 'what are they doing with those things here? If we were on the Tay, I should have said that they were for drawing the salmon-nets; but here – '

'Well,' said he, smiling, 'of course that is what they *are* for. Where there are salmon, there are likely to be salmon-nets, Tay or Thames; but of course they are not always in use; we don't want salmon *every* day of the season.'

I was going to say, 'But is this the Thames?' but held my peace in my wonder, and turned my bewildered eyes eastward to look at the bridge again, and thence to the shores of the London river; and surely there was enough to astonish me. For though there was a bridge across the stream and houses on its banks, how all was changed from last night! The soap-works with their smoke-vomiting chimneys were gone; the engineer's works gone; the lead-works gone; and no sound of riveting and hammering came down the west wind from Thorneycroft's. Then the bridge! I had perhaps dreamed of such a bridge, but never seen such an one out of an illuminated manuscript; for not even the Ponte Vecchio at Florence came anywhere near it. It was of stone arches, splendidly solid, and as graceful as they were strong; high enough also to let ordinary river traffic through easily. Over the parapet showed quaint and fanciful little buildings, which I supposed to be booths or shops, beset with painted and gilded vanes and spirelets. The stone was a little weathered, but showed no marks of the grimy sootiness which I was used to on every London building more than a year old. In short, to me a wonder of a bridge.

The sculler noted my eager astonished look, and said, as if in answer to my thoughts:

'Yes, it *is* a pretty bridge, isn't it? Even the up-stream bridges, which are so much smaller, are scarcely daintier, and the down-stream ones are scarcely more dignified and stately.'

I found myself saying, almost against my will, 'How old is it?'

'O, not very old,' he said: 'it was built, or at least opened, in 2003. There used to be a rather plain timber bridge before then.'

The date shut my mouth as if a key had been turned in a padlock fixed to my lips; for I saw that something inexplicable had happened, and that if I said much, I should be mixed up in a game of cross questions and crooked answers. So I tried to look unconcerned, and to glance in a matter-of-course way at the banks of the river, though this is what I saw up to the bridge and a little beyond; say as far as the site of the soap-works. Both shores had a line of very pretty houses, low and not large, standing back a little way from the river; they were mostly built of red brick and roofed with tiles, and looked, above all, comfortable, and as if they were, so to say, alive and sympathetic with the life of the dwellers in them. There was a continuous garden in front of them, going down to the water's edge, in which flowers were now blooming luxuriantly, and sending delicious waves of summer scent over the eddying stream. Behind the houses, I could see great trees rising, mostly planes, and looking down the water there were the reaches towards Putney almost as if they were a lake with a forest shore, so thick were the big trees; and I said aloud, but as if to myself:

'Well, I'm glad that they have not built over Barn Elms.'

I blushed for my fatuity as the words slipped out of my mouth, and my companion looked at me with a half smile which I thought I understood; so to hide my confusion I said, 'Please take me ashore now: I want to get my breakfast.'

QUESTIONS AND ANSWERS

BY WILLIAM MORRIS

'Tell me in detail,' said I, 'what lies east of Bloomsbury now?'
Said he: 'There are but few houses between this and the
outer part of the old city; but in the city we have a thickly
dwelling population. Our forefathers, in the first clearing of the slums
were not in a hurry to pull down the houses in what was called at the
end of the nineteenth century the business quarter of the town, and
what later got to be known as the Swindling Kens. You see, these
houses, though they stood hideously thick on the ground, were
roomy and fairly solid in building, and clean, because they were not
used for living in, but as mere gambling booths; so the poor people
from the cleared slums took them for lodgings and dwelt there, till the
folk of those days had time to think of something better for them; so
the buildings were pulled down so gradually that people got used to
living thicker on the ground there than in most places; therefore it
remains the most populous part of London, or perhaps of all these
islands. But it is very pleasant there, partly because of the splendour
of the architecture, which goes further than what you will see
elsewhere. However, this crowding, if it may be called so, does not go
further than a street called Aldgate, a name which perhaps you have
heard of. Beyond that the houses are scattered wide about the
meadows there, which are very beautiful, especially when you get on
to the lovely river Lea (where old Isaak Walton used to fish, you know)
about the places called Stratford and Old Ford, names which of
course you will not have heard of, though the Romans were busy
there once upon a time.'

Not heard of them! thought I to myself. How strange! that I who
had seen the very last remnant of the pleasantness of the meadows
by the Lea destroyed, should have heard them spoken of with
pleasantness come back to them in full measure.

Hammond went on: 'When you get down to the Thames side you

come on the Docks, which are works of the nineteenth century, and are still in use, although not so thronged as they once were, since we discourage centralization all we can, and we have long ago dropped the pretension to be the market of the world. About these Docks are a good few houses, which, however, are not inhabited by many people permanently; I mean, those who use them come and go a good deal, the place being too low and marshy for pleasant dwelling. Past the Docks eastward and landward it is all flat pasture, once marsh, except for a few gardens, and there are very few permanent dwellings there: scarcely anything but a few sheds, and cots for the men who come to look after the great herds of cattle pasturing there. But however, what with the beasts and the men, and the scattered red-tiled roofs and the big hayricks, it does not make a bad holiday to get a quiet pony and ride about there on a sunny afternoon of autumn, and look over the river and the craft passing up and down, and on to Shooters' Hill and the Kentish uplands, and then turn round to the wide green sea of the Essex marshland, with the great domed line of the sky, and the sun shining down in one flood of peaceful light over the long distance. There is a place called Canning's Town, and further out, Silvertown, where the pleasant meadows are at their pleasantest: doubtless they were once slums, and wretched enough.'

The names grated on my ear, but I could not explain why to him. So I said: 'And south of the river, what is it like?'

He said: 'You would find it much the same as the land about Hammersmith. North, again, the land runs up high, and there is an agreeable and well-built town called Hampstead, which fitly ends London on that side. It looks down on the north-western end of the forest you passed through.'

I smiled. 'So much for what was once London,' said I. 'Now tell me about the other towns of the country.'

He said: 'As to the other big murky places which were once, as we know, the centres of manufacture, they have, like the brick and mortar desert of London, disappeared; only, since they were centres of nothing but "manufacture", and served no purpose but that of the gambling market, they have left less signs of their existence than London. Of course, the great change in the use of mechanical force made this an easy matter, and some approach to their break-up as centres would possibly have taken place, even if we had not changed our habits so much: but they being such as they were, no sacrifice would have seemed too great a price to pay for getting rid of the "manufacturing districts", as they used to be called. For the rest, whatever coal or mineral we need is brought to grass and sent whither it is needed with as little as possible of dirt, confusion, and the distressing of quiet people's lives. One is tempted to believe from what one has read of the conditions of those districts in the nineteenth century, that those who had them under their power worried, befouled, and degraded men out of malice prepense: but it was not so; like the miseducation of which we were talking just now, it came out of their dreadful poverty. They were obliged to put up with everything, and even pretend that they liked it; whereas we can now deal with things reasonably, and refuse to be saddled with what we do not want.'

TAMING TECHNOLOGY

BY ALVIN TOFFLER

In 1970, Alvin Toffler published *Future Shock*, a long book in which he dealt with a vast range of issues he saw emerging as people faced a world whose rate of change was accelerating dramatically. As this extract shows, he was alert to what others were beginning to call the 'environmental crisis', and he saw dangers not only in the 'crisis' itself, but in some reactions to it.

Future shock – the disease of change – can be prevented. But it will take drastic social, even political action. No matter how individuals try to pace their lives, no matter what psychic crutches we offer them, no matter how we alter education, the society as a whole will still be caught on a runaway treadmill until we capture control of the accelerative thrust itself.

The high velocity of change can be traced to many factors. Population growth, urbanization, the shifting proportions of young and old – all play their part. Yet technological advance is clearly a critical node in the network of causes; indeed, it may be the node that activates the entire net. One powerful strategy in the battle to prevent mass future shock, therefore, involves the conscious regulation of technological advance.

We cannot and must not turn off the switch of technological progress. Only romantic fools babble about returning to a 'state of nature'. A state of nature is one in which infants shrivel and die for lack of elementary medical care, in which malnutrition stultifies the brain, in which, as Hobbes reminded us, the typical life is 'poor, nasty, brutish, and short'. To turn our back on technology would be not only stupid but immoral.

Given that a majority of men still figuratively live in the twelfth century, who are we even to contemplate throwing away the key to economic advance? Those who prate anti-technological nonsense in the name of some vague 'human values' need to be asked 'which humans?'. To deliberately turn back the clock would be to condemn billions to enforced and permanent misery at precisely the moment in history when their liberation is becoming possible. We clearly need not less but more technology.

At the same time, it is undeniably true that we frequently apply new technology stupidly and selfishly. In our haste to milk technology for immediate economic advantage, we have turned our environment into a physical and social tinderbox.

The speed-up of diffusion, the self-reinforcing character of technological advance, by which each forward step facilitates not one but many additional further steps, the intimate link-up between technology and social arrangements – all these create a form of psychological pollution, a seemingly unstoppable acceleration of the pace of life.

This psychic pollution is matched by the industrial vomit that fills our skies and seas. Pesticides and herbicides filter into our foods. Twisted automobile carcasses, aluminium cans, non-returnable glass bottles and synthetic plastics form immense kitchen middens in our midst as more and more of our detritus resists decay. We do not even begin to know what to do with our radioactive wastes – whether to pump them into the earth, shoot them into outer space, or pour them into the oceans.

Our technological powers increase, but the side effects and potential hazards also escalate. We risk thermopollution of the oceans themselves, overheating them, destroying immeasurable quantities of marine life, perhaps even melting the polar icecaps. On land we concentrate such large masses of population in such small urban-technological islands, that we threaten to use up the air's oxygen faster than it can be replaced, conjuring up the possibility of new Saharas where the cities are now. Through such disruptions of the natural ecology, we may literally, in the words of biologist Barry Commoner, be 'destroying this planet as a suitable place for human habitation'.

As the effects of irresponsibly applied technology become more grimly evident, a political backlash mounts. An offshore drilling accident that pollutes 800 square miles of the Pacific triggers a shock wave of indignation all over the United States. A multi-millionaire industrialist in Nevada, Howard Hughes, prepares a lawsuit to prevent the Atomic Energy Commission from continuing its underground nuclear tests. In Seattle, the Boeing Company fights growing public clamour against its plans to build a supersonic jet

114

transport. In Washington, public sentiment forces a reassessment of missile policy. At MIT, Wisconsin, Cornell, and other universities, scientists lay down test tubes and slide rules during a 'research moratorium' called to discuss the social implications of their work. Students organize 'environmental teach-ins' and the President lectures the nation about the ecological menace. Additional evidences of deep concern over our technological course are turning up in Britain, France and other nations.

We see here the first glimmers of an international revolt that will rock parliaments and congresses in the decades ahead. This protest against the ravages of irresponsibly used technology could crystallize in pathological form – as a future-phobic fascism with scientists substituting for Jews in the concentration camps. Sick societies need scapegoats. As the pressures of change impinge more heavily on the individual and the prevalence of future shock increases, this nightmarish outcome gains plausibility. It is significant that a slogan scrawled on a wall by striking students in Paris called for 'death to the technocrats!'

The incipient worldwide movement for control of technology, however, must not be permitted to fall into the hands of irresponsible technophobes, nihilists and Rousseauian romantics. For the power of the technological drive is too great to be stopped by Luddite paroxysms. Worse yet, reckless attempts to halt technology will produce results quite as destructive as reckless attempts to advance it.

Caught between these twin perils, we desperately need a movement for responsible technology. We need a broad political grouping rationally committed to further scientific research and technological advance – but on a selective basis only. Instead of wasting its energies in denunciations of The Machine or in negativistic criticism of the space programme, it should formulate a set of positive technological goals for the future.

Such a set of goals, if comprehensively and well worked out, could bring order to a field now in total shambles. By 1980, according to Aurelio Peccei, the Italian economist and industrialist, combined research and development expenditures in the United States and Europe will run to $73 billion per year. This level of expense adds up to three-quarters of a trillion dollars per decade. With such large sums at stake, one would think that governments would plan their technological development carefully, relating it to broad social goals, and insisting on strict accountability. Nothing could be more mistaken.

'No one – not even the most brilliant scientist alive today - really knows where science is taking us,' says Ralph Lapp, himself a scientist-turned-writer. 'We are aboard a train which is gathering speed, racing down a track on which there are an unknown number of switches leading to unknown destinations. No single scientist is in the engine cab and there may be demons at the switch. Most of society is in the caboose looking backward.'

It is hardly reassuring to learn that when the Organization for Economic Cooperation and Development issued its massive report on science in the United States, one of its authors, a former premier of Belgium, confessed: 'We came to the conclusion that we were looking for something – which was not there: a science policy'. The committee could have looked even harder, and with still less success, for anything resembling a conscious technological policy.

Radicals frequently accuse the 'ruling class' or the 'establishment' or simply 'they' of controlling society in ways inimical to the welfare of the masses. Such accusations may have occasional point. Yet today we face an even more dangerous reality: many social ills are less the consequence of oppressive control than of oppressive lack of control. The horrifying truth is that, so far as much technology is concerned, no one is in charge.

OF THE NATURAL CONDITION OF MANKIND

BY THOMAS HOBBES

Alvin Toffler referred to Thomas Hobbes's famous description of 'primitive' life as being 'poor, nasty, brutish, and short'. Other writers in the 1970s took up this theme, but chose to show that, contrary to Hobbes's view, the life of primitive people is actually rather pleasant. Of course, so far from being 'savages' primitive peoples dwell at peace with themselves, among themselves, and with their natural surroundings. This was the view of the 'noble savage' favoured by Jean-Jacques Rousseau (1712-78), not as an attainable goal for modern people, but as a kind of original state from which civilization had irreversibly departed. Since Hobbes (1588-1679) is mentioned so often, the following extract is included. This is what he actually wrote, in chapter XIII of *Leviathan*, published in 1651. He maintained that society consists in the binding together of individuals under the laws of an absolute ruler, the 'sovereign', and that only thus can people be free and at peace. It is worth remembering that Hobbes lived through the turmoil of the English Civil War and Restoration.

During the time men live without a common power to keep them all in awe, they are in that condition which is called war; and such a war, as is of every man, against every man. For WAR, consisteth not in battle only, or in the act of fighting; but in a tract of time, wherein the will to contend by battle is sufficiently known: and therefore the notion of *time*, is to be considered in the nature of war; as it is in the nature of weather. For as the nature of foul weather, lieth not in a shower or two of rain; but in an inclination thereto of many days together: so the nature of war, consisteth not in actual fighting; but in the known disposition thereto, during all the time there is no assurance to the contrary. All other time is PEACE.

Whatsoever therefore is consequent to a time of war, where every man is enemy to every man; the same is consequent to the time, wherein men live without other security, than what their own strength, and their own invention shall furnish them withal. In such condition, there is no place for industry; because the fruit thereof is uncertain: and consequently no culture of the earth; no navigation, nor use of the commodities that may be imported by sea; no commodious building; no instruments of moving, and removing, such things as require much force; no knowledge of the face of the earth; no account of time; no arts; no letters; no society; and which is worst of all, continual fear, and danger of violent death; and the life of man, solitary, poor, nasty, brutish, and short.

A BLUEPRINT
FOR
SURVIVAL

The 'Blueprint' appeared as the entire January, 1972, issue of *The Ecologist* magazine. The document was written fairly quickly, as most such documents are, and the contributions from the various authors (Edward Goldsmith, Robert Allen, Michael Allaby, John Davoll, and Sam Lawrence) assembled in what was then the editorial office of the magazine, in Edward Goldsmith's home at Kew Green, London. While it was still in its proof stage Robert Allen circulated it to a number of eminent academics, inviting them to endorse its main argument by attaching their names to it. By the time it was published, the inside front cover of the magazine carried the following 33 supporting names: Prof. Don Arthur, King's College, London; Prof. D. Bryce-Smith, University of Reading; Sir Frank Fraser Darling; Prof. G.W. Dimbleby, Institute of Archaeology, University of London; Prof. George Dunnet, University of Aberdeen; Dr. P.N. Edmunds, Fife District Laboratory; Prof. R.W. Edwards, University of Wales Institute of Science and Technology; Dr. S.R. Eyre, University of Leeds; Prof. Douglas Falconer, University of Edinburgh; Prof. John Friend, University of Hull; Prof. F.W. Grimes, Institute of Archaeology, University of London; Prof. John Hawthorn, University of Strathclyde; Prof. G. Melvyn Howe, University of Strathclyde; Sir Julian Huxley, FRS; Dr. David Lack, FRS, University of Oxford; Dr. J.P. Lester, British Medical Association; Dr. John A. Loraine, MRC Clinical Endocrinology Unit, Edinburgh; Diana G.M. Loraine; Dr. Aubrey Manning, University of Edinburgh; Prof. Vincent Marks, University of Surrey; Prof. Ivor Mills, University of Cambridge; Dr. E. Mishan, American University, Washington; Prof. P.J. Newbould, New University of Ulster; Prof. Forbes W. Robertson, University of Aberdeen; Prof. W.A. Robson, London School of

Economics; Dr. J. Rose; Sir Edward Salisbury, FRS; Dr. R. Scorer, Imperial College, London; Peter Scott; Dr. Malcolm Slesser, University of Strathclyde; Prof. C.H. Waddington, FRS, University of Edinburgh; Dr. Watson, University of Strathclyde; and Prof. V.C. Wynne-Edwards, FRS, University of Aberdeen and chairman of the Natural Environment Research Council. With such a pedigree it is hardly surprising that the press conference held to launch the Blueprint was packed. For a little while after it appeared it was actually difficult to get into the Goldsmith house for the reporters and photographers crowding the doorway. Predictably, the issue of the magazine sold out and was reprinted several times. Then it appeared in book form and was translated into many languages. The extract I reproduce here consists of the whole of the introduction, in which the central proposition is outlined.

The principal defect of the industrial way of life with its ethos of expansion is that it is not sustainable. Its termination within the lifetime of someone born today is inevitable – unless it continues to be sustained for a while longer by an entrenched minority at the cost of imposing great suffering on the rest of mankind. We can be certain, however, that sooner or later it will end (only the precise time and circumstances are in doubt), and that it will do so in one of two ways: either against our will, in a succession of famines, epidemics, social crises and wars; or because we want it to – because we wish to create a society which will not impose hardship and cruelty upon our children – in a succession of thoughtful, humane and measured changes. We believe that a growing number of people are aware of this choice, and are more interested in our proposals for creating a sustainable society than in yet another recitation of the reasons why this should be done. We will therefore consider these reasons only briefly, reserving a fuller analysis for the four appendices which follow the Blueprint proper.

Radical change is both necessary and inevitable because the present increases in human numbers and *per capita* consumption, by disrupting ecosystems and depleting resources, are undermining the very foundations of survival. At present the world population of 3,600 million is increasing by 2 per cent per year (72 million), but this overall figure conceals crucially important differences between countries. The industrialised countries with one-third of the world population have annual growth rates of between 0.5 and 1.0 per cent; the underdeveloped countries on the other hand, with two-thirds of the world population, have annual growth rates of between 2 and 3 per cent, and from 40 to 45 per cent of their population is under 15. It is commonly overlooked that in countries with an unbalanced age structure of this kind the population will continue to increase for many years even after fertility has fallen to the replacement level. As the Population Council has pointed out: 'If replacement is achieved in the developed world by 2000 and in the developing world by 2040, then the world's population will stabilise at nearly 15.5 billion (15,500 million) about a century hence, or well over four times the present size'.

The *per capita* use of energy and raw materials also shows a sharp division between the developed and the underdeveloped parts of the world. Both are increasing their use of these commodities, but consumption in the developed countries is so much higher that, even with their smaller share of the population, their consumption may well represent over 80 per cent of the world total. For the same reason, similar percentage increases are far more significant in the developed countries; to take one example, between 1957 and 1967 *per capita* steel consumption rose by 12 per cent in the US and by 41 per cent in India, but the actual increases (in kg per year) were from 568 to 634 and from 9.2 to 13 respectively. Nor is there any sign that an eventual end to economic growth is envisaged, and indeed industrial economies appear to break down if growth ceases or even slows, however high the absolute level of consumption. Even the US still aims at an annual growth of GNP of 4 per cent or more. Within this overall figure much higher growth rates occur for the use of particular resources, such as oil.

The combination of human numbers and *per capita* consumption has a considerable impact on the environment, in terms of both the resources we take from it and the pollutants we impose on it. A distinguished group of scientists, who came together for a 'Study of Critical Environmental Problems' (SCEP) under the auspices of the Massachusetts Institute of Technology, state in their report the clear need for a means of measuring this impact, and have coined the term 'ecological demand', which they define as 'a summation of all man's demands on the environment, such as the extraction of resources and the return of wastes'. Gross Domestic Product (GDP), which is population multiplied by material standard of living appears to provide the most convenient measure of ecological demand, and according to the UN *Statistical Yearbook* this is increasing annually by 5 to 6 per cent, or doubling every 13.5 years. If this trend should continue, then in the time taken for world population to double (which is estimated to be by just after the year 2000), total ecological demand will have increased by a factor of six. SCEP estimate that 'such demand-producing activities as agriculture, mining and industry have global annual rates of increase of 3.5 per cent and 7 per cent respectively. An integrated rate of increase is estimated to be between 5 and 6 per cent per year, in comparison with an annual rate of population increase of only 2 per cent'.

It should go without saying that the world cannot accommodate this continued increase in ecological demand. *Indefinite* growth of whatever type cannot be sustained by *finite* resources. This is the nub of the environmental predicament. It is still less possible to maintain indefinite *exponential* growth – and unfortunately the growth of ecological demand is proceeding exponentially (i.e. it is increasing geometrically, by compound interest).

The implications of exponential growth are not generally appreciated and are well worth considering. As Professor Forrester explains it, '. . . pure exponential growth possesses the characteristic of behaving according to a 'doubling time'. Each fixed time interval shows a doubling of the relevant system variable. Exponential growth is treacherous and misleading. A system variable can continue through many doubling intervals without seeming to reach significant size. But then in one or two more doubling periods, still following the same law of exponential growth, it suddenly seems to become overwhelming'.

Thus, supposing world petroleum reserves stood at 2,100 billion barrels, and supposing our rate of consumption was increasing by 6.9 per cent per year, then demand will exceed supply by the end of the century. What is significant, however, is not the speed at which such vast reserves can be depleted, but that as late as 1975 there will appear to be reserves fully ample enough to last for considerably longer. Such a situation can easily lull one into a false sense of security and the belief that a given growth rate can be sustained, if not indefinitely, at least for a good deal longer than is actually the case. The same basic logic applies to the availability of any resource including land, and it is largely because of this particular dynamic of exponential growth that the environmental predicament has come upon us so suddenly, and why its solution requires radical measures, many of which run counter to values which, in our industrial society we have been taught to regard as fundamental.

If we allow the present growth rate to persist, total ecological demand will increase by a factor of 32 over the next 66 years – and there can be no serious person today willing to concede the possibility, or indeed the desirability, of our accommodating the pressures arising from such growth. For this can be done only at the cost of disrupting ecosystems and exhausting resources, which must lead to the failure of food supplies and the collapse of society. It is worth briefly considering each in turn.

We depend for our survival on the predictability of ecological processes. If they were at all arbitrary, we would not know when to reap or sow, and we would be at the mercy of environmental whim. We could learn nothing about the rest of nature, advance no hypotheses, suggest no 'laws'. Fortunately, ecological processes *are* predictable, and although theirs is a relatively young discipline, ecologists have been able to formulate a number of important 'laws', one of which in particular relates to environmental predictability: namely, that all ecosystems tend towards stability, and further that the more diverse and complex the ecosystem the more stable it is; that is, the more species there are, and the more they interrelate, the more stable is their environment. By stability is meant the ability to return to the original position after any change, instead of being forced into a totally different pattern – and hence predictability.

Unfortunately, we behave as if we knew nothing of the environment and had no conception of its predictability, treating it instead with scant and brutal regard as if it were an idiosyncratic and extremely stupid slave. We seem never to have reflected on the fact that a tropical rain forest supports innumerable insect species and yet is never devastated by them; that its rampant luxuriance is not contingent on our overflying it once a month and bombarding it with insecticides, herbicides, fungicides, and what-have-you. And yet we tremble over our wheatfields and cabbage patches with a desperate battery of synthetic chemicals, in an absurd attempt to impede the operation of the immutable 'law' we have just mentioned – that all ecosystems tend towards stability, therefore diversity and complexity, therefore a growing number of different plant and animal species until a climax or optimal condition is achieved. If we were clever, we would recognise that successful long-term agriculture demands the achievement of an artificial climax, an imitation of the pre-existing ecosystem, so that the level of unwanted species could be controlled by those that did no harm to the crop-plants.

Instead we have put our money on pesticides, which although they have been effective, have been so only to a limited and now diminishing extent: according to SCEP, the 34 per cent increase in world food production from 1951 to 1966 required investments in nitrogenous fertilisers of 146 per cent and in pesticides of 300 per cent. At the same time they have created a number of serious problems, notably resistance – some 250 pest species are resistant to one group of pesticides or another, while many others require increased applications to keep their populations within manageable proportions – and the promotion of formerly innocuous species to pest proportions, because predators that formerly kept them down have been destroyed. The spread of DDT and other organochlorines in the environment has resulted in alarming population declines among woodcock, grebes, various birds of prey and seabirds, and in a number of fish species, principally the sea trout. SCEP comments: 'the oceans are an ultimate accumulation site of DDT and its residues. As much as 25 per cent of the DDT compounds produced to date may have been transferred to the sea. The amount in the marine biota is estimated to be in the order of less than 0.1 per cent of total production and has already produced a demonstrable impact upon the marine environment. ... The decline in productivity of marine food fish and the accumulation of levels of DDT in their tissues which are unacceptable to man can only be accelerated by DDT's continued release to the environment...')

There are half a million man-made chemicals in use today, yet we cannot predict the behaviour or properties of the greater part of them (either singly or in combination) once they are released into the environment. We know, however, that the combined effects of pollution and habitat destruction menace the survival of no less than 280 mammal, 350 bird, and 20,000 plant species. To those who regret these losses but greet them with the comment that the survival of *Homo sapiens* is surely more important than that of an eagle or a primrose, we repeat that *Homo sapiens* himself depends on the continued resilience of those ecological networks of which eagles and primroses are integral parts. We do not need to utterly destroy the ecosphere to bring catastrophe upon ourselves: all we have to do is to carry on as we are, clearing forests, 'reclaiming' wetlands, and imposing sufficient quantities of pesticides, radioactive materials, plastics, sewage, and industrial wastes upon our air, water and land systems to make them inhospitable to the species on which their continued stability and integrity depend. Industrial man in the world today is like a bull in a china shop, with the single difference that a bull with half the information about the properties of china as we have about those of ecosystems would probably try and adapt its behaviour to its environment rather than the reverse. By contrast, *Homo sapiens industrialis* is determined that the china shop should adapt to him, and has therefore set himself the goal of reducing it to rubble in the shortest possible time.

Increases in food production in the undeveloped world have barely kept abreast of population growth. Such increases as there have been are due not to higher productivity but to the opening up of new land for cultivation. Unfortunately this will not be possible for much longer: all the good land in the world is now being farmed, and according to the FAO, at present rates of expansion none of the marginal land that is left will be unfarmed by 1985 – indeed some of the land now under cultivation has been so exhausted that it will have to be returned to permanent pasture.

For this reason, FAO's programme to feed the world depends on a programme of intensification, at the heart of which are the new high-yielding varieties of wheat and rice. These are highly responsive to inorganic fertilisers and quick-maturing, so that up to ten times present yields can be obtained from them. Unfortunately, they are highly vulnerable to disease, and therefore require increased protection by pesticides, and of course they demand massive inputs of fertilisers (up to 27 times present ones). Not only will these disrupt local ecosystems, thereby jeopardising long-term productivity, but they force hard-pressed undeveloped nations to rely on the agro-chemical industries of the developed world.

Whatever their virtues or faults, the new genetic hybrids are not intended to solve the world food problem, but only to give us time to devise more permanent and realistic solutions. It is our view, however, that these hybrids are not the best means of doing this, since their use is likely to bring about a reduction in overall diversity, when the clear need is to develop an agriculture diverse enough to have long-term potential. We must beware of those 'experts' who appear to advocate the transformation of the ecosphere into nothing more than a food-factory for man. The concept of a world consisting solely of man and a few favoured food plants is so ludicrously impracticable as to be seriously contemplated only by those who find solace in their own wilful ignorance of the real world of biological diversity.

We in Britain must bear in mind that we depend on imports for half our food, and that we are unlikely to improve on this situation. The 150,000 acres which are lost from agriculture each year are about 70 per cent more productive than the average for all enclosed land, while we are already beginning to experience diminishing returns from the use of inorganic fertilisers. In the period 1964-9, applications of phosphates have gone up by 2 per cent, potash by 7 per cent, and nitrogen by 40 per cent, yet yields per acre of wheat, barley, lucerne and temporary grass have levelled off and are beginning to decline, while that of permanent grass has risen only slightly and may be levelling off. As *per capita* food availability declines throughout the rest of the world, and it appears inevitable it will, we will find it progressively more difficult and expensive to meet our food requirements from abroad. The prospect of severe food shortages within the next thirty years is not so much a fantasy as that of the continued abundance promised us by so many of our politicians.

As we have seen, continued exponential growth of consumption of materials and energy is impossible. Present reserves of all but a few metals will be exhausted within 50 years, if consumption rates continue to grow as they are. Obviously there will be new discoveries and advances in mining technology, but these are likely to provide us with only a limited stay of execution. Synthetics and substitutes are likely to be of little help, since they must be made from materials which themselves are in short supply; while the hoped-for availability of unlimited energy would not be the answer, since the problem is the ratio of useful metal to waste matter (which would have to be disposed of without disrupting ecosystems), not the need for cheap power. Indeed, the availability of unlimited power holds more of a threat than a promise, since energy use is inevitably pollution, and in addition we would ultimately have to face the problem of disposing of an intractable amount of waste heat.

The developed nations consume such disproportionate amounts of protein, raw materials and fuels that unless they considerably reduce their consumption there is no hope of the undeveloped nations markedly improving their standards of living. This vast differential is a cause of much and growing discontent, made worse by our attempts at cultural uniformity on behalf of an expanding market economy. In the end, we are altering people's aspirations without providing the means for them to be satisfied. In the rush to industrialise we break up communities, so that the controls which formerly regulated behaviour are destroyed before alternatives can be provided. Urban drift is one result of this process, with a consequent rise in anti-social practices, crime, deliquency, and so on, which are so costly for society in terms both of money and of well-being.

At the same time, we are sowing the seeds of massive unemployment by increasing the ratio of capital to labour so that the provision of each job becomes ever more expensive. In a world of fast diminishing resources, we shall quickly come to the point when very great numbers of people will be thrown out of work, when the material compensations of urban life are either no longer available or prohibitively expensive, and consequently when whole sections of society will find good cause to express their considerable discontent in ways likely to be anything but pleasant for their fellows.

It is worth bearing in mind that the barriers between us and epidemics are not so strong as is commonly supposed. Not only is it

126

increasingly difficult to control the vectors of disease, but it is more than probable that urban populations are being insidiously weakened by overall pollution levels, even when they are not high enough to be incriminated in any one illness. At the same time international mobility speeds the spread of disease. With this background, and at a time of widespread public demoralisation, the collapse of vital social services such as power and sanitation, could easily provoke a series of epidemics – and we cannot say with confidence that we would be able to cope with them.

At times of great distress and social chaos, it is more than probable that governments will fall into the hands of reckless and unscrupulous elements, who will not hesitate to threaten neighbouring governments with attack, if they feel that they can wrest from them a larger share of the world's vanishing resources. Since a growing number of countries (an estimated 36 by 1980) will have nuclear power stations, and therefore sources of plutonium for nuclear warheads, the likelihood of a whole series of local (if not global) nuclear engagements is greatly increased.

There will be those who regard these accounts of the consequences of trying to accommodate present growth rates as fanciful. But the imaginative leap from the available scientific information to such predictions is negligible, compared with that required for those alternative predictions, laughably considered 'optimistic', of a world of 10,000 to 15,000 million people, all with the same material standard of living as the US, on a concrete replica of this planet, the only moving parts being their machines and possibly themselves. Faced with inevitable change, we have to make decisions, and we must make these decisions *soberly* in the light of the best information, and not as if we were caricatures of the archetypal mad scientist.

By now it should be clear that the main problems of the environment do not arise from temporary and accidental malfunctions of existing economic and social systems. On the contrary, they are the warning signs of a profound incompatibility between deeply rooted beliefs in continuous growth and the dawning recognition of the earth as a space ship, limited in its resources and vulnerable to thoughtless mishandling. The nature of our response to these symptoms is crucial. If we refuse to recognise the cause of our trouble the result can only be increasing disillusion and growing strain upon the fragile institutions that maintain external peace and internal social cohesion. If, on the other hand, we can respond to this unprecedented challenge with informed and constructive action the rewards will be as great as the penalties for failure.

We are sufficiently aware of 'political reality' to appreciate that many of the proposals we will make will be considered impracticable. However, we believe that if a strategy for survival is to have any chance of success, the solutions must be formulated in the light of the problems and not from a timorous and superficial understanding of what may or may not be immediately feasible. If we plan remedial action with our eyes on political rather than ecological reality, then very reasonably, very practically, and very surely, we will muddle our way to extinction.

A measure of political reality is that government has yet to acknowledge the impending crisis. This is to some extent because it has given itself no machinery for looking at energy, resources, food, environmental disruption and social disruption as a whole, as part of a general, global pattern, preferring instead to deal with its many aspects as if they were self-contained analytical units. Lord Rothschild's Central Policy Review Staff in the Cabinet Office, which is the only body in government which might remedy the situation, appears not to think it worthwhile: at the moment at least, they are undertaking 'no specific studies on the environment that would require an environmentalist or ecologist'. There is a strong element of positive feedback here, in that there can be no appreciation of our predicament unless we view it in totality, and yet government can see no cause to do so unless it can be shown that such a predicament exists.

Possibly because government sees the world in fragments and not as a totality, it is difficult to detect in its actions or words any coherent general policy, although both major political parties appear to be mesmerised by two dominating notions: that economic expansion is essential for survival and is the best possible index of progress and well-being; and that unless solutions can be devised that do not threaten this notion, then the problems should not be regarded as existing. Unfortunately, government has an increasingly powerful incentive for continued expansion in the tendency for economic growth to create the need for more economic growth. This it does in six ways:

Firstly, the introduction of technological devices, i.e. the growth of the technosphere, can only occur to the detriment of the ecosphere, which means that it leads to the destruction of natural controls which must then be replaced by further technological ones. It is in this way that pesticides and artificial fertilisers create the need for yet more pesticides and artificial fertilisers.

Secondly, for various reasons, industrial growth, particularly in its earlier phases, promotes population growth. Even in its later phases, this can still occur at a high rate (0.5 per cent in the UK). Jobs must constantly be created for the additional people – not just any jobs, but those that are judged acceptable in terms of current values. This basically means that the capital outlay per person employed must be maintained, otherwise the level of 'productivity' per man will fall, which is a determinant of both the 'viability' of economic enterprise and of the 'standard of living'.

Thirdly, no government can hope to survive widespread and protracted unemployment, and without changing the basis of our industrial society, the only way government can prevent it is by stimulating economic growth.

Fourthly, business enterprises, whether state-owned or privately owned, tend to become self-perpetuating, which means that they require surpluses for further investment. This favours continued growth.

Fifthly, the success of a government and its ability to obtain support is to a large extent assessed in terms of its ability to increase the 'standard of living' as measured by *per capita* gross national product (GNP).

Finally, confidence in the economy, which is basically a function of its ability to grow, must be maintained to ensure a healthy state of the stock market. Were confidence to fall, stock values would crash, drastically reducing the availability of capital for investment and hence further growth, which would lead to further unemployment. This would result in a further fall in stock-market values and hence give rise to a positive-feedback chain-reaction, which under the existing order might well lead to social collapse.

For all these reasons, we can expect our government (whether Conservative or Labour) to encourage further increases in GNP regardless of the consequences, which in any case tame 'experts' can be found to play down. It will curb growth only when public opinion demands such a move, in which case it will be politically expedient, and when a method is found for doing so without creating unemployment or excessive pressure on capital. We believe this is possible only within the framework of a fully integrated plan.

The emphasis must be on integration. If we develop relatively clean technologies but do not end economic growth then sooner or later we will find ourselves with as great a pollution problem as before but without the means of tackling it. If we stabilise our economies and husband our non-renewable resources without stabilising our populations we will find we are no longer able to feed ourselves. As Forrester and Meadows convincingly make clear [in *Limits to Growth*], daunting though an integrated programme may be, a piecemeal approach will cause more problems than it solves.

Our task is to create a society which is sustainable and which will give the fullest possible satisfaction to its members. Such a society by definition would depend not on expansion but on stability. This does not mean to say that it would be stagnant – indeed it could well afford more variety than does the state of uniformity at present being imposed by the pursuit of technological efficiency. We believe that the stable society, as well as removing the sword of Damocles which hangs over the heads of future generations, is much more likely than the present one to bring the peace and fulfilment which hitherto have been regarded, sadly, as utopian.

OF THE STATIONARY STATE

BY JOHN STUART MILL

The attainment of a 'stable society' became the goal of the more radical environmentalists, and in the more limited sense of a society in which the size of the human population remained steadily at some sustainable level, of many who would not regard themselves as political radicals. New ideas, however, have an uncomfortable habit of turning out to be less original than they seem. The next extract, from *The Principles of Political Economy*, was written by J.S. Mill and published in 1848.

There is room in the world, no doubt, and even in old countries, for a great increase of population, supposing the arts of life to go on improving, and capital to increase. But even if innocuous, I confess to see very little reason for desiring it. The density of population necessary to enable mankind to obtain, in the greatest degree, all the advantages both of co-operation and of social intercourse, has, in all the most populous countries, been attained. A population may be too crowded, though all be amply supplied with food and raiment. It is not good for man to be kept perforce at all times in the presence of his species. A world from which solitude is extirpated, is a very poor ideal. Solitude, in the sense of being often alone, is essential to any depth of meditation or of character; and solitude in the presence of natural beauty and grandeur, is the cradle of thoughts and aspirations which are not only good for the individual, but which society could ill do without. Nor is there much satisfaction in contemplating the world with nothing left to the spontaneous activity of nature; with every rood of land brought into cultivation, which is capable of growing food for human beings; every flowery waste or natural pasture ploughed up, all quadrupeds or birds which are not domesticated for man's use exterminated as his rivals for food, every hedgerow or superfluous tree rooted out, and scarcely a place left where a wild shrub or flower could grow without being eradicated as a weed in the name of improved agriculture. If the earth must lose that great portion of its pleasantness which it owes to things that the unlimited increase of wealth and population would extirpate from it, for the mere purpose of enabling it to support a larger, but not a better or a happier population, I sincerely hope, for the sake of posterity, that they will be content to be stationary, long before necessity compels them to it.

It is scarcely necessary to remark that a stationary condition of capital and population implies no stationary state of human improvement. There would be as much scope as ever for all kinds of mental culture, and moral and social progress; as much room for improving the Art of Living, and much more likelihood of its being improved, when minds cease to be engrossed by the art of getting on. Even the industrial arts might be as earnestly and as successfully cultivated, with this sole difference, that instead of serving no purpose but the increase of wealth, industrial improvements would produce their legitimate effect, that of abridging labour. Hitherto it is questionable if all the mechanical inventions yet made have lightened the day's toil of any human being. They have enabled a greater population to live the same life of drudgery and imprisonment, and an increased number of manufacturers and others to make fortunes. They have increased the comforts of the middle classes. But they have not yet begun to effect those great changes in human destiny, which it is in their nature and in their futurity to accomplish. Only when in addition to just institutions, the increase of mankind shall be under the deliberate guidance of judicious foresight, can the conquests made from the powers of nature by the intellect and energy of scientific discoverers, become the common property of the species, and the means of improving and elevating the universal lot.

THE ECONOMICS OF THE COMING SPACESHIP EARTH

BY KENNETH E. BOULDING

Former Professor of Economics at the University of Michigan, Kenneth E. Boulding devoted much attention to the economic implications of the crisis being defined by environmentalists. The essay reprinted here is taken from the proceedings of one of a series of forums held by Resources for the Future and it was first published in 1966.

The closed earth of the future requires economic principles which are somewhat different from those of the open earth of the past. For the sake of picturesqueness, I am tempted to call the open economy the 'cowboy economy', the cowboy being symbolic of the illimitable plains and also associated with reckless, exploitative, romantic, and violent behaviour, which is characteristic of open societies. The closed economy of the future might similarly be called the 'spaceman' economy, in which the earth has become a single spaceship, without unlimited reservoirs of anything, either for extraction or for pollution, and in which, therefore, man must find his place in a cyclical ecological system which is capable of continuous reproduction of material form even though it cannot escape having inputs of energy. The difference between the two types of economy becomes most apparent in the attitude towards consumption. In the cowboy economy, consumption is regarded as a good thing and production likewise; and the success of the economy is measured by the amount of the throughput from the 'factors of production', a part of which, at any rate, is extracted from the reservoirs of raw materials and noneconomic objects, and another part of which is output into the reservoirs of pollution. If there are infinite reservoirs from which material can be obtained and into which effluvia can be deposited, then the throughput is at least a plausible measure of the success of the economy. The gross national product is a rough measure of this total throughput. It should be possible, however, to distinguish that part of the GNP which is derived from exhaustible and that which is derived from reproducible resources, as well as that part of consumption which represents effluvia and that which represents input into the productive system again. Nobody, as far as I know, has ever attempted to break down the GNP in this way, although it would be an interesting and extremely important exercise, which is unfortunately beyond the scope of this paper.

By contrast, in the spaceman economy, throughput is by no means a desideratum, and is indeed to be regarded as something to be minimized rather than maximized. The essential measure of the success of the economy is not production and consumption at all, but the nature, extent, quality, and complexity of the total capital stock, including in this the state of the human bodies and minds included in the system. In the spaceman economy, what we are primarily concerned with is stock maintenance, and any technological change which results in the maintenance of a given total stock with a lessened throughput (that is, less production and consumption) is clearly a gain. This idea that both production and consumption are bad things rather than good things is very strange to economists, who have been obsessed with the income-flow concepts to the exclusion, almost, of capital-stock concepts.

There are actually some very tricky and unsolved problems involved in the questions as to whether human welfare or well-being is to be regarded as a stock or a flow. Something of both these elements seems actually to be involved in it, and as far as I know there have been practically no studies directed towards identifying these two dimensions of human satisfaction. Is it, for instance, eating that is a good thing, or is it being well fed? Does economic welfare involve having nice clothes, fine houses, good equipment, and so on, or is it to be measured by the depreciation and the wearing out of these things? I am inclined myself to regard the stock concept as most fundamental, that is, to think of being well fed as more important than eating, and to think even of so-called services as essentially involving the restoration of a depleting psychic capital. Thus I have argued that we go to a concert in order to restore a psychic condition which might be called 'just having gone to a concert', which, once established, tends to depreciate. When it depreciates beyond a certain point, we go to another concert in order to restore it. If it depreciates rapidly, we go to a lot of concerts; if it depreciates slowly, we go to few. On this view, similarly, we eat primarily to restore bodily homoeostasis, that is, to maintain a condition of being well fed, and so on. On this view, there is nothing desirable in consumption at all. The less consumption we can maintain a given state with, the better off we are. If we had clothes that did not wear out, houses that did not depreciate, and even if we could maintain our bodily condition without eating, we would clearly be much better off.

It is this last consideration, perhaps, which makes one pause. Would we, for instance, really want an operation that would enable us to restore all our bodily tissues by intravenous feeding while we slept? Is there not, that is to say, a certain virtue in throughput itself, in activity itself, in production and consumption itself, in raising food and in eating it? It would certainly be rash to exclude this possibility. Further interesting problems are raised by the demand for variety. We certainly do not want a constant state to be maintained; we want fluctuations in the state. Otherwise there would be no demand for variety in food, for variety in scene, as in travel, for variety in social contact, and so on. The demand for variety can, of course, be costly, and sometimes it seems to be too costly to be tolerated or at least legitimated, as in the case of marital partners, where the maintenance of a homoeostatic family is usually regarded as much more desirable than the variety and excessive throughput of the libertine. There are problems here which the economics profession has neglected with astonishing singlemindedness. My own attempts to call attention to some of them, for instance, in two articles, as far as I can judge, produced no response whatever; and economists continue to think and act as if production, consumption, throughput, and the GNP were the sufficient and adequate measure of economic success.

It may be said, of course, why worry about all this when the spaceman economy is still a good way off (at least beyond the lifetimes of any now living), so let us eat, drink, spend, extract and pollute, and be as merry as we can, and let posterity worry about the spaceship earth. It is always a little hard to find a convincing answer to the man who says, 'What has posterity ever done for me?' and the conservationist has always had to fall back on rather vague ethical principles postulating identity of the individual with some human community or society which extends not only back into the past but forward into the future. Unless the individual identifies with some community of this kind, conservation is obviously 'irrational'. Why should we not maximize the welfare of this generation at the cost of posterity? *Après nous, le déluge* has been the motto of not insignificant numbers of human societies. The only answer to this, as far as I can see, is to point out that the welfare of the individual depends on the extent to which he can identify himself with others, and that the most satisfactory individual identity is that which identifies not only with a community in space but also with a community extending over time from the past into the future. If this kind of identity is recognized as desirable, then posterity has a voice, even if it does not have a vote; and in a sense, if its voice can influence votes, it has votes too. This whole problem is linked up with the much larger one of the determinants of the morale, legitimacy, and 'nerve' of a society, and there is a great deal of historical evidence to suggest that a society which loses its identity with posterity and which loses its positive image of the future loses also its capacity to deal with present problems, and soon falls apart.

Even if we concede that posterity is relevant to our present problems, we still face the question of time-discounting and the closely related question of uncertainty-discounting. It is a well known phenomenon that individuals discount the future, even in their own lives. The very existence of a positive rate of interest may be taken as at least strong supporting evidence of this hypothesis. If we discount our own future, it is certainly not unreasonable to discount posterity's future even more, even if we do give posterity a vote. If we discount this at five per cent per annum, posterity's vote or dollar halves every fourteen years as we look into the future, and after even a hundred years it is pretty small – only about one-and-a-half cents on the dollar. If we add another five per cent for uncertainty, even the vote of our grandchildren reduces almost to insignificance. We can argue, of course, that the ethical thing to do is not to discount the future at all, that time-discounting is mainly the result of myopia and perspective, and hence is an illusion which the moral man should not tolerate. It is a very popular illusion, however, and one that must certainly be taken into consideration in the formulation of policies. It explains, perhaps, why conservationist policies almost have to be sold under some other excuse which seems more urgent, and why, indeed, necessities which are visualized as urgent, such as defence, always seem to hold priority over those which involve the future.

All these considerations add some credence to the point of view which says that we should not worry about the spaceman economy at all, and that we should just go on increasing the GNP and indeed the gross world product, or GWP, in the expectation that the problems of the future can be left to the future, that when scarcities arise, whether this is of raw materials or of pollutable reservoirs, the needs of the then present will determine the solutions of the then present, and there is no use giving ourselves ulcers by worrying about problems that we really do not have to solve. There is even high ethical authority for this point of view in the New Testament, which advocates that we should take no thought for tomorrow and let the dead bury their dead. There has always been something rather refreshing in the view that we should live like the birds, and perhaps posterity is for the birds in more senses than one; so perhaps we should call it a day and go out and pollute something cheerfully. As an old taker of thought for the morrow, however, I cannot quite accept this solution; and I would argue, furthermore, that tomorrow is not only very close, but in many respects it is already here. The shadow of the future spaceship, indeed, is already falling over our spendthrift merriment. Oddly enough, it seems to be in pollution rather than in exhaustion that the problem is first becoming salient. Los Angeles has run out of air, Lake Erie has become a cesspool, the oceans are filling up with lead and DDT, and the atmosphere may become man's major problem in another generation, at the rate at which we are filling it up with gunk. It is, of course, true that at least on a microscale, things have been worse at times in the past. The cities of today, with all their foul air and polluted waterways, are probably not as bad as the filthy cities of the pretechnical age. Nevertheless, that fouling of the nest which has been typical of man's activity in the past on a local scale now seems to be extending to the whole world society; and one certainly cannot view with equanimity the present rate of pollution of any of the natural reservoirs, whether the atmosphere, the lakes, or even the oceans.

PROBLEMS AND MODELS

BY DONELLA H. MEADOWS,
DENNIS L. MEADOWS,
JØRGEN RANDERS, AND
WILLIAM W. BEHRENS III

In the spring of 1968, a group of thirty people met in Rome at the invitation of Dr Aurelio Peccei to discuss the impending crisis. From this meeting there developed the Club of Rome, eventually with some seventy members. The Club of Rome is an 'invisible college'. Membership is limited in size and is by invitation only, although the identity of members is not kept a secret. The Club inaugurated a project on 'the predicament of mankind' and in 1970, with financial support from the Volkswagen Foundation, it sponsored a team at the Massachusetts Institute of Technology, led by Professor Dennis Meadows, to construct a computer model of the world and to run it into the future. A popular summary of the results was published in the spring of 1972 and a much longer technical document describing the modelling techniques used appeared some time later. The extract here is taken from the popular summary, a book called simply *The Limits to Growth*. At the time, the work was novel in that it was the first attempt to simulate the entire world in this way, and it used what was then one of the most powerful computers in the world. As a measure of the rate at which computer technology developed, within ten years it was possible to run the 'Limits' programs on a home computer.

Every person approaches his problems, wherever they occur on the space-time graph, with the help of models. A model is simply an ordered set of assumptions about a complex system. It is an attempt to understand some aspect of the infinitely varied world by selecting from perceptions and past experience a set of general observations applicable to the problem at hand. A farmer uses a mental model of his land, his assets, market prospects, and past weather conditions to decide which crops to plant each year. A surveyor constructs a physical model – a map – to help in planning a road. An economist uses mathematical models to understand and predict the flow of international trade.

Decision-makers at every level unconsciously use mental models to choose among policies that will shape our future world. These mental models are, of necessity, very simple when compared with the reality from which they are abstracted. The human brain, remarkable as it is, can only keep track of a limited number of the complicated, simultaneous interactions that determine the nature of the real world.

We, too, have used a model. Our is a formal, written model of the world. It constitutes a preliminary attempt to improve our mental models of long-term, global problems by combining the large amounts of information that is already in human minds and in written records with the new information-processing tools that mankind's increasing knowledge has produced – the scientific method, systems analysis, and the modern computer.

Our world model was built specifically to investigate five major trends of global concern – accelerating industrialization, rapid population growth, widespread malnutrition, depletion of non-renewable resources, and a deteriorating environment. These trends are all interconnected in many ways, and their development is measured in decades or centuries, rather than in months or years. With the model we are seeking to understand the causes of these trends, their interrelationships, and their implications as much as one hundred years in the future.

The model we have constructed is, like every other model, imperfect, oversimplified, and unfinished. We are well aware of its shortcomings, but we believe that it is the most useful model now available for dealing with problems far out on the space-time graph. To our knowledge it is the only formal model in existence that is truly global in scope, that has a time horizon longer than thirty years, and that includes important variables such as population, food production, and pollution, not as independent entities, but as dynamically interacting elements, as they are in the real world.

Since ours is a formal, or mathematical, model it also has two important advantages over mental models. First, every assumption we make is written in a precise form so that it is open to inspection and criticism by all. Second, after the assumptions have been scrutinized, discussed, and revised to agree with our best current knowledge, their implications for the future behaviour of the world system can be traced without error by a computer, no matter how complicated they become.

We feel that the advantages listed above make this model unique among all mathematical and mental world models available to us today. But there is no reason to be satisfied with it in its present form. We intend to alter, expand, and improve it as our own knowledge and the world data base gradually improve.

In spite of the preliminary state of our work, we believe it is important to publish the model and our findings now. Decisions are being made every day, in every part of the world, that will affect the physical, economic, and social conditions of the world system for decades to come. These decisions cannot wait for perfect models and total understanding. They will be made on the basis of some model, mental or written, in any case. We feel that the model described here is already sufficiently developed to be of some use to decision-makers. Furthermore, the basic behaviour modes we have already observed in this model appear to be so fundamental and general that we do not expect our broad conclusions to be substantially altered by further revisions.

It is not the purpose of this book to give a complete, scientific description of all the data and mathematical equations included in the world model. Such a description can be found in the final technical report of our project. Rather, in *The Limits to Growth* we summarize the main features of the model and our findings in a brief, non-technical way. The emphasis is meant to be not on the equations or the intricacies of the model, but on what it tells us about the world. We have used a computer as a tool to aid our own understanding of the causes and consequences of the accelerating trends that characterize the modern world, but familiarity with computers is by no means necessary to comprehend or to discuss our conclusions. The implications of those accelerating trends raise issues that go far beyond the proper domain of a purely scientific document. They must be debated by a wider community than that of scientists alone. Our purpose here is to open that debate.

The following conclusions have emerged from our work so far. We are by no means the first group to have stated them. For the past several decades, people who have looked at the world with a global, long-term perspective have reached similar conclusions. Nevertheless, the vast majority of policy-makers seem to be actively pursuing goals that are inconsistent with these results.

Our conclusions are:

1. If the present growth trends in world population, industrialization, pollution, food production, and resource depletion continue unchanged, the limits to growth on this planet will be

reached sometime within the next one hundred years. The most probable result will be a rather sudden and uncontrollable decline in both population and industrial capacity.

2. It is possible to alter these growth trends and to establish a condition of ecological and economic stability that is sustainable far into the future. The state of global equilibrium could be designed so that the basic material needs of each person on earth are satisfied and each person has an equal opportunity to realize his individual human potential.

3. If the world's people decide to strive for this second outcome rather than the first, the sooner they begin working to attain it, the greater will be their chances of success.

These conclusions are so far-reaching and raise so many questions for further study that we are quite frankly overwhelmed by the enormity of the job that must be done. We hope that this book will serve to interest other people, in many fields of study and in many countries of the world, to raise the space and time horizons of their concerns and to join us in understanding and preparing for a period of great transition – the transition from growth to global equilibrium.

THE TECHNOLOGICAL DEMANDS OF NUCLEAR POWER

BY WALTER C. PATTERSON

In the late 1970s opposition to nuclear power emerged as a new environmentalist cause. Later, the main popular worry about this source of energy related to its safety, but discussion of the issue did not begin with safety as the dominant theme. Walt Patterson, a Canadian-born physicist, is perhaps the best informed, most moderate, and most articulate representative of the British antinuclear movement. This extract is taken from his contribution to a forum on the subject held under the auspices of the Royal Institution in 1978, at which time Patterson represented Friends of the Earth. (Since it was written the name 'Windscale' has been changed to 'Sellafield', but the two are the same.)

In the summer of 1977, a young New Yorker scaled the entire 110-storey vertical exterior of the World Trade Centre. His exploit confirms that human beings have never refused to do anything merely on the basis that it is too risky. Nothing is too difficult if it is thought to be worth doing. However, what an individual considers worth doing may not be what the whole society would consider worth doing. As members of the community we do not - or should not – pursue a course of action simply 'because it is there'. We have to decide what is worth doing by comparison with other courses of action.

When we consider 'The Technological Demands of Nuclear Power' we must do so not 'because it is there' but to fulfill some agreed objective.

Let us at the outset discard as spurious the belief that nuclear technology is inherently arcane, requiring understanding vouchsafed to only a handful of initiates. It is long since clear that nothing about nuclear technology is in itself more esoteric than, say, computers or colour television. The nuclear mystique arose rather from the secrecy which shrouded the weapons programmes, and was carried over from them into the civil programmes.

The development of civil nuclear technology within the weapons programme was prompted at least in part by the desire to demonstrate that nuclear discoveries would ultimately benefit – not threaten – humanity. As an objective, this implied a powerful emotional commitment to nuclear technology, a commitment which still persists. Under such a stimulus, civil nuclear development was pursued for its own sake, and the pursuit was premature, both in time and scale. In Britain the initial civil nuclear policy proposals of the mid 1950s received only limited discussion, on the basis of even more limited information, largely provided by the interested parties. It was accepted then that the nature of nuclear technology required highly specialized expertise for its evaluation. The same pattern of nuclear decision-making behind the scenes has prevailed ever since. Only in the past two years has it begun to alter, with consequences as yet unclear.

The original decision to establish civil nuclear technology in Britain was taken by the government, which provided all the necessary support, financial and otherwise, to meet the 'technological demands'. The transition from military to civil was gradual, via the Calder Hall and Chapelcross stations, built to produce weapons-plutonium, generating electricity as a by-product. The civil Magnox stations, in their early years, were likewise credited with the plutonium they produced, although it had no civil application at the time. The government also provided all the necessary back-up, technical and financial, research and development, fuel cycle services, insurance, regulation, and safeguards. As a result, the technological demands of nuclear power were tackled in a context of economic unreality. Without the nuclear weapons programme, and if normal commercial criteria had been applied, it is doubtful if a civil nuclear industry would ever have arisen. It seems profoundly improbable that private finance and industry would have been willing to undertake the necessary commitments to launch a nuclear programme. Only a government could have pressed on along the nuclear route when there were easier avenues to similar goals. Nevertheless, despite delays, cost over-runs, technical lapses, and commercial disappointments, and although some unfortunates fell by the wayside, nuclear optimism remained unshaken, for more than two decades, sailing blithely above the trammels of everyday economics.

It is ironic that most of the recent public reaction against nuclear technology has likewise ignored the usual economic ground-rules. Public concern about nuclear hazards has tended to couch itself in absolutes: insistence on absolute safety of plant, absolute assurances against environmental degradation by radioactivity, absolute guarantees of eternal isolation of high level wastes. This reaction is doubly ironic since it is undeniably true that nuclear planners in Britain have always been acutely conscious of the potential hazards involved. The evidence on public record supports the view that exemplary foresight has always been exercised by nuclear designers and engineers in Britain. The availability of unstinting government support made it possible to take a 'belt and braces' approach wherever designers thought it necessary. Nuclear technology now in place in Britain may well be massively overdesigned, with working margins unnecessarily generous. From the standpoint of safety, such scruples are obviously welcome. They do, however, complicate matters when the economics of the real world begin to intrude. Any attempt to reduce tolerances and eliminate margins now deemed superfluous is bound to evoke qualms in some places.

It is the view of Friends of the Earth that there is only one hazard of nuclear technology which is qualitatively different from hazards arising in other industries, and that is that no absolute barrier can ever be erected to separate civil nuclear activities from their military counterpart. – It is a hazard for which no technical solution exists.–

The attribute unique to the nuclear industry is, of course, the radiation and the quantity of radioactivity produced by the fission process. The biological effects of radiation have been intensively studied for decades; it is probably true to say that much more is known about the consequences of exposure to radiation than about most other environmental hazards. It does not, however, follow that we know all there is to know about radiation hazards. On the contrary, much of the information we would like to have may be inherently unattainable. For some pathological effects, the latency period may be more than twenty years; such effects may be impossible to identify, either individually or statistically. Genetic consequences of low-level exposure of large populations may likewise be impossible to identify. Certainly if they are identified it will be much too late to rectify them. It is true that other environmental hazards may have similar effects; indeed it is possible that such hazards may interact synergistically with radiation exposure. To suggest that other environmental insults are not blameless is not to exculpate radiation, merely to compound the problem.

In the nuclear industry as in others, routine procedures once in a while go awry. The radioactive inventory of an operating power-reactor, reprocessing plant, or waste facility could cause death and injury, immediate and delayed, over a considerable area if it were to escape. It is therefore necessary to be assured that such escape will not occur. This is the category of hazard which has caused most controversy, with bitter disagreement about the probability and consequences of a major nuclear accident.

The most serious nuclear accident which has occurred in Britain was the fire which destroyed the Windscale Number One plutonium production reactor twenty years ago this week. It was of course not a civil facility. Neither, strictly spaeking, is the Chapelcross nuclear station in Scotland, one of whose reactors experienced an expensive and messy fuel channel meltdown in 1967. Even the 1973 ruthenium blow-back in Building B204 at Windscale took place in a converted weapons-programme plant. The civil nuclear programme in Britain, however, has a site safety record which many other industries should envy.

But, as an industry, it is still young; it will only attain its calendar majority next week, on 17 October, the twenty-first anniversary of the Queen's formal opening of Calder Hall in 1956. The body of experience thus far acquired, both here and abroad, is a limited data base on which to prognosticate future performance. Designs have changed too fast to permit much extrapolation from one to another; and the increase in scale of nuclear facilities has been breath-takingly swift. The generation of gigawatt-plus reactors now being commissioned internationally has recorded as yet only a few reactor-years of operation, but no means all of it reassuring.

The British programme has thus far been less headlong than most; scales and power densities have increased only comparatively gradually, with the exception of the leap from Oldbury to Wylfa, which led to five years of headaches. The debacle of the Advanced Gas-Cooled Reactors has been a sobering lesson for more recent policy. Accordingly, Friends of the Earth have always been less concerned about the safety of British thermal reactor designs than about light-water reactors. Again, however, it is necessary to add a proviso. The evaluation of the safety of British designs has always been carried out behind closed doors, in secret discussions between the builders, the customers and the Nuclear Installations Inspectorate. It would be easier to be reassured about the soundness of safety analyses if they were made public.

This past summer we have had the opportunity, unparalleled in Britain, of the Windscale inquiry, offering for the first time a detailed insight into the way the British nuclear industry approaches technical and economic issues. It has been a fascinating and illuminating experience. To Friends of the Earth the most striking aspect of the inquiry has been the asymmetry of the evaluations applied by British Nuclear Fuels Ltd., depending on whether they do or do not wish to do something. If they wish to do it, they exude confidence that all the technological demands can be fulfilled. They wave aside any inferences from the past unimpressive record. On the other hand, if they do not wish to do something, in their view it presents almost insuperable technical obstacles. Similar asymmetries have arisen concerning comparative economics, political implications, indeed virtually at every stage of the inquiry. It is conceivable that BNFL, Japan, and the British electricity supply industry might all be able to fulfill the purely technological demands of oxide fuel reprocessing; however, it remains far from clear why they should want to.

We know now that we face yet another inquiry, into the future use of the fast breeder reactor. In safety, as in other aspects, the fast breeder reactor is a different kettle of sodium. Again it is not easy to assess the present status of FBR safety analysis in Britain; too much takes place out of public view. But analyses and correspondence made public in the US indicate that there remains a stubborn expert disagreement about the severity of possible accidents in an FBR. Such hazards are not the primary cause of Friends of the Earth's opposition to the fast breeder reactor; its plutonium-based fuel cycle is, in our view, a more fundamental and intractable problem.

It is now regularly said that we should proceed forthwith to the construction of a full-scale demonstration plant, in the attempt to resolve these uncertainties. However, at this point, the discussion of 'technological demand' purely in terms of 'risk' becomes inadequate. It is necessary to step back and survey the broader context. It should not be assumed that we need to resolve the issue of fast reactor safety simply 'because it is there'. We have to ask whether this is really a problem worth solving.

Indeed, we have to ask whether all the problems of technological risk and hazard arising in civil nuclear technology are worth solving. If we were to solve them one and all, to the universal 'satisfaction' of the populace, what would we have accomplished? What goal would we have attained? Would this goal universally satisfy?—

One of the most immediate 'technological demands of nuclear power' is that it can be conveniently used only to generate electricity in very large base-load stations for distribution by a grid. Increasing reliance on nuclear power therefore implies increasing reliance on grid electricity; the 'technological demands' of nuclear power thus encompass the technical demands of grid electricity supply.

Electricity is not a fuel – it cannot be stored. An electricity system is a means of delivering to customers the energy from other sources – falling water, coal, oil, uranium, and so on. An electricity system is a natural monopoly like water supply or main drainage. Electricity suppliers and customers now expect a guaranteed supply of electricity at power points and switches at all times. Since the amount of electricity being used must match instantaneously the amount being generated, the system must be able to vary its output continuously throughout the day and throughout the year – a criterion to which nuclear generation is ill-adapted. To meet the brief annual peak of demand at a cold dinnertime in January with some capacity out of service, the system must have generating capacity which will lie idle much of the rest of the year, plus additional redundancy throughout the system. Electricity suppliers have always accepted this costly aspect of their operation, a direct result of the inability to store electricity; it is in passing curious that they should lay so much stress on the storage problems arising from postulated interruptions of solar, wind, or wave energy.

The trend in electricity supply has been toward increasing centralization coupled with 'economies of scale'. The result has been more monolithic inflexibility, beginning with the planning process and extending throughout the development and operation of the system. Because grid electricity is a monopoly providing an essential commodity, it escapes the ultimate sanction of bankruptcy, however disastrous its planning. Nevertheless, faulty decisions in an inflexible system are stubbornly difficult to rectify; their effects may persist for decades.

The sorry record of electricity demand forecasting for the past two decades underlines an important corollary: policy influences forecasts, had long done so and – if present plans are fulfilled – will in the future do so definitively. It now takes ten years to plan, construct and commission a new base-load station of the size considered 'economic'. Even the Electricity Council would probably admit that forecasts of demand more than six years hence are not much better than guesses. It is thus necessary to order a station four years or more before anyone can be sure it will be required. Planning becomes not an act of foresight but an act of faith.–

Yet the UK Atomic Energy Authority continues to put forward programmes for future nuclear electric generating capacity, which they are almost forthwith compelled to disown as an embarrassment. The basis of such demands seems to be the technological demand of keeping the nuclear industry busy.–

147

The inflexibility of electronuclear technology means that management can much more readily adjust the job structure than the capital structure of the industry. The constraint with which they must reckon is that of the trade unions. But the union leadership is centralized and remote from its shop-floor members, making control of shop-floor discipline difficult. In an industrial dispute the high 'productivity' of electricity supply workers can be matched by an equivalent high 'unproductivity'; a few dissatisfied workers may be able to cause a sudden and widespread interruption of the entire grid supply. The nature of the technology – the impossibility of storing electricity and the need to maintain continuous guaranteed supply – thus comes up against a fundamental vulnerability which might in due course present a desperately unpleasant problem in industrial relations, especially if the country were to become dependent on grid electricity for most of its energy supply.–

Central authority, faced with the responsibility to forestall such eventualities, will have to take a variety of measures affecting planning, finance and employment, to minimize the risks. These measures will be difficult and expensive, and probably unpopular – and they may not work.–

Electronuclear advocates may be correct. It may be possible to move toward an energy supply predominantly generated by base-load nuclear stations and delivered as grid electricity. It may be possible to do so without exposing the population to insidious injury from radioactivity in the environment, or to the consequences of disastrous nuclear accidents. But is it worth attempting? The technological demands of nuclear power make the electronuclear route a perversely difficult, expensive and potentially dangerous way to reach a destination we may deeply regret reaching – and there may be no way back.

SOFT ENERGY TECHNOLOGIES

BY AMORY B. LOVINS

Friends of the Earth was founded in the United States, but a British branch opened soon afterwards and Amory Lovins, an American, resigned from his post as a junior research fellow at Merton College, Oxford, to join its staff as a specialist in energy-related issues. He developed the concept of 'soft energy paths', and coined the term. This extract is taken from his book of that title.

There exists today a body of energy technologies that have certain specific features in common and that offer great technical, economic, and political attractions, yet for which there is no generic term. For lack of a more satisfactory term, I shall call them 'soft' technologies: a textural description, intended to mean not vague, mushy, speculative, or ephemeral, but rather flexible, resilient, sustainable, and benign. Energy paths dependent on soft technologies – will be called 'soft' energy paths, and the 'hard' technologies – constitute a 'hard' path (in both senses). The distinction between hard and soft energy paths rests not on how much energy is used, but on the technical and sociopolitical *structure* of the energy system, thus focusing our attention on consequent and crucial political differences.

– The social structure is significantly shaped by the rapid deployment of soft technologies. These are defined by five characteristics:

1. They rely on renewable energy flows that are always there whether we use them or not, such as sun and wind and vegetation: on energy income, not on depletable energy capital.

2. They are diverse, so that as a national treasury runs on many small tax contributions, so national energy supply is an aggregate of

very many individually modest contributions, each designed for maximum effectiveness in particular circumstances.

3. They are flexible and relatively low technology – which does not mean unsophisticated, but rather, easy to understand and use without esoteric skills, accessible rather than arcane.

4. They are matched in *scale* and in geographic distribution to end use needs, taking advantage of the free distribution of most natural energy flows.

5. They are matched in *energy quality* to end-use needs: a key feature that deserves immediate explanation.

People do not want electricity or oil, nor such economic abstractions as 'residential services', but rather comfortable rooms, light, vehicular motion, food, tables, and other real things. Such end-use needs can be classified by the physical nature of the task to be done. In the United States today, about 58 per cent of all energy at the point of end-use is required as heat, split roughly 23-35 between temperatures above and below the boiling point of water. (In Western Europe the low temperature heat alone is often a half of all end-use energy.) Another 38 per cent of all US end-use energy provides mechanical motion: 31 per cent in vehicles, 3 per cent in pipelines, 4 per cent in industrial electric motors. The rest, a mere 4 per cent of delivered energy, represents *all* lighting, electronics, telecommunications, electrometallurgy, electrochemistry, arc welding, electric motors in home appliances and in railways, and similar end-uses that now *require* electricity.

Some 8 per cent of all US energy end-use, then, and similarly little abroad, requires electricity for purposes other than low temperature heating and cooling. Yet, since we actually use electricity for many such low grade purposes, it now meets 13 per cent of US end-use needs – and its generation consumes 29 per cent of all US fossil fuels. A hard energy path would increase this 13 per cent figure to 20-40 per cent (depending on assumptions) by the year 2000, and far more thereafter. But this is wasteful because the laws of physics require, broadly speaking, that a power station change three units of fuel into two units of almost useless waste heat plus one unit of electricity. This electricity can do more difficult kinds of work than the original fuel, but unless this extra quality and versatility are used to advantage, the costly process of upgrading the fuel – and losing two-thirds of it – is all for naught.

Plainly we are using premium fuels and electricity for many tasks for which their high energy quality is superfluous, wasteful, and expensive, and a hard path would make this inelegant practice even more common. Where we want only to create temperature differences of tens of degrees, we should meet the need with sources whose potential is tens or hundreds of degrees, not with a flame temperature of thousands or a nuclear reaction temperature equivalent to trillions – like cutting butter with a chainsaw.

For some applications, electricity is appropriate and indispensable: electronics, smelting, subways, most lighting, some kinds of mechanical work, and a few more. But these uses are already oversupplied, and for the other, dominant, uses remaining in our energy economy this special form of energy cannot give us our money's worth.– Indeed, in probably no industrial country today can additional supplies of electricity be used to thermodynamic advantage that would justify their high cost in money and fuels.

So limited are the US end uses that really require electricity that by applying careful technical fixes to them we could reduce their 8 per cent total to about 5 per cent (mainly by reducing commercial overlighting), whereupon we could probably cover all those needs with present US hydroelectric capacity plus the cogeneration capacity available in the mid to late 1980s. Thus an affluent industrial economy could advantageously operate with no central power stations at all! In practice we would not necessarily want to go that far, at least not for a long time; but the possibility illustrates how far we are from supplying energy only in the quality needed for the task at hand.

Just as soft technologies' matching of energy quality to end-use needs virtually eliminates the costs and losses of secondary energy conversion, so the appropriate scale of soft technologies can virtually eliminate the costs and losses of energy distribution. Matching scale to end-uses can indeed achieve at least five important types of economies not available to larger, more centralized systems. The first type is reduced and shared overheads. At least half your electricity bill is fixed distribution costs to pay the overheads of a sprawling energy system: transmission lines, transformers, cables, meters and people to read them, planners, headquarters, billing computers, interoffice memos, advertising agencies. For electrical and some fossil fuel systems, distribution accounts for more than half of total capital cost, and administration for a significant fraction of total operating cost. Local or domestic energy systems can reduce or even eliminate these infrastructure costs. The resulting savings can far outweigh the extra costs of the dispersed maintenance infrastructure that the small systems require, particularly where that infrastructure already exists or can be shared (e.g., plumbers fixing solar heaters as well as sinks).

Small scale brings further savings by virtually eliminating

distribution losses, which are cumulative and pervasive in centralized energy systems (particularly those using high quality energy). Small systems also avoid direct diseconomies of scale, such as the frequent unreliability of large units and the related need to provide instant 'spinning reserve' capacity on electrical grids to replace large stations that suddenly fail. Small systems with short lead times greatly reduce exposure to interest, escalation, and mistimed demand forecasts – major indirect diseconomies of large scale.

The fifth type of economy available to small systems arises from mass production. Consider – the 100-odd million cars in the US. In round numbers, each car probably has an average cost of less than $4,000 and a shaft power over 100 kilowatts (134 horsepower). Presumably a good engineer could build a generator and upgrade an automobile engine to a reliable, 35 per cent efficient diesel at no greater total cost, yielding a mass-produced diesel generator unit costing less than $40 per kW. In contrast, the motive capacity in US central power stations – currently totalling about one-fortieth as much as in US cars – costs perhaps ten times more per kW, partly because it is not mass produced. This is not to argue for the widespread use of diesel generators; rather, to suggest that if we could build power stations the way we build cars, they would cost at least ten times less than they do, but we can't because they're too big. In view of this scope for mass-producing small systems, it is not surprising that at least one European car maker hopes to go into the wind machine and heat pump business. Such a market can be entered incrementally, without the billions of dollars' investment required for, say, liquefying natural gas or gasifying coal. It may require a production philosophy oriented toward technical simplicity, low replacement cost, slow obsolescence, high reliability, high volume, and low mark-up; but these are familiar concepts in mass production. Industrial resistance would presumably melt when – as with pollution abatement equipment – the scope for profit was perceived.

This is not to say that all energy systems need be at domestic scale. The object is to crack nuts with nutcrackers and drive pilings with triphammers, not the reverse: to use the most appropriately scaled tool for the job and so minimize costs, including social costs. In some cases this will require big systems, chiefly the existing hydroelectric dams. In most cases the scale needed will be smaller. For example, the medium scale of urban neighbourhoods and rural villages offers fine prospects for solar collectors – especially for adding collectors to existing buildings of which some (perhaps with large flat roofs) can take excess collector area while others cannot take any. They could be joined via communal heat storage systems, saving on labour cost and on heat losses. The costly craftwork of remodelling existing systems – 'backfitting' or 'retrofitting' idiosyncratic houses with individual collectors – could thereby be greatly reduced. Despite these advantages, medium-scale solar technologies are currently receiving little attention apart from a condominium village project in Vermont sponsored by the Department of Housing and Urban Development and the one-hundred dwelling unit Méjannes-le-Clap project in France.

The schemes that dominate ERDA's solar research budget – such as making electricity from huge collectors in the desert, or from temperature differences in the oceans, or from Brooklyn Bridge-like satellites in outer space – do not satisfy our criteria, for they are ingenious high technology ways to supply energy in a form and at a scale inappropriate to most end-use needs. Not all solar technologies are soft. Nor, for the same reason, is nuclear fusion a soft technology. But many genuine soft technologies are now available and are now economic. What are some of them?

Solar heating and, imminently, cooling head the list. They are incrementally cheaper than electric heating, and far more inflation-proof, practically anywhere in the world. In the United States (with fairly high average sunlight levels), they are cheaper than present electric heating virtually anywhere, cheaper than oil in many parts, and cheaper than gas and coal in some. Even in the least favourable parts of the continental United States, far more sunlight falls on a typical building than is required to heat and cool it without supplement; whether this is considered economic depends on how the accounts are done. The difference in solar input between the most and least favourable parts of the lower forty-nine states is generally less than twofold, and in cold regions, the long heating season can improve solar economics.

Ingenious ways of backfitting existing urban and rural buildings (even large commercial ones) or their neighbourhoods with efficient and exceedingly reliable solar collectors are being rapidly developed in both the private and public sectors. In some recent projects, the lead time from ordering to operation has been only a few months. Good solar hardware, often modular, is going into pilot or full scale production over the next few years, and will increasingly be integrated into buildings as a multipurpose structural element, thereby sharing costs. – Some novel types of very simple collectors with far lower costs also show promise in current experiments. Indeed, solar hardware *per se* is necessary only for backfitting existing buildings. If we build new buildings properly in the first place, they can use 'passive' solar collectors – large south windows or glass-covered black south walls – rather than special collectors. If we did this to all new houses in the next twelve years, we would save about as much energy as we expect to recover from the Alaskan North Slope.

Second, exciting developments in the conversion of agricultural, forestry, and urban wastes to methanol and other liquid and gaseous fuels now offer practical, economically interesting technologies sufficient to run an efficient US transport sector. Some bacterial and enzymatic routes under study look even more promising, but presently proved processes already offer sizeable contributions without the inevitable climatic constraints of fossil fuel combustion. Organic conversion technologies must be sensitively integrated with agriculture and forestry so as not to deplete the soil; most current methods seem suitable in this respect, though they may change the farmer's priorities by making his whole yield of biomass (vegetable matter) saleable.

The required scale of organic conversion can be estimated. Each year the US beer and wine industry, for example, microbiologically produces 5 per cent as many gallons (not all alcohol, of course) as the US oil industry produces gasoline. Gasoline has 1.5 to 2 times the fuel value of alcohol per gallon. Thus a conversion industry roughly ten to fourteen times the physical scale (in gallons of fluid output per year) of US cellars and breweries, albeit using different processes, would produce roughly one-third of the present gasoline requirements of the United States. If one assumes a transport sector with three times today's average efficiency – a reasonable estimate for early in the next century – then the whole of the transport needs could be met by organic conversion. The scale of effort required does not seem unreasonable, since it would replace in function half the present refinery capacity.

Additional soft technologies include wind hydraulic systems (especially those with a vertical axis), which already seem likely in many design studies to compete with nuclear power in much of North America and Western Europe. But wind is not restricted to making electricity: it can heat, pump, heat-pump, or compress air. Solar process heat, too, is coming along rapidly as we learn to use the 5800°C potential of sunlight (much hotter than a boiler). Finally, high and low temperature solar collectors, organic converters, and wind machines can form symbiotic hybrid combinations more attractive than the separate components.

Energy storage is often said to be a major problem of energy income technologies. But this 'problem' is largely an artefact of trying to recentralize, upgrade and redistribute inherently diffuse energy flows. Directly storing sunlight or wind – or, for that matter, electricity from any source – is indeed difficult on a large scale. But it is easy if done on a scale and in an energy quality matched to most end-use needs. Daily, even seasonal, storage of low and medium temperature heat at the point of use is straightforward with water tanks, rock beds, or perhaps fusible salts. Neighbourhood heat storage is even cheaper. In industry, wind-generated compressed air can easily (and, with due care, safely) be stored to operate machinery: the technology is simple, cheap, reliable, and highly developed. (Some European cities even used to supply compressed air as a standard utility.) Installing pipes to distribute hot water (or compressed air) tends to be considerably cheaper than installing equivalent electric distribution capacity. Hydroelectricity is stored behind dams, and organic conversion yields readily stored liquid and gaseous fuels. On the whole, therefore, energy storage is much less of a problem in a soft energy economy than in a hard one.

Recent research suggests that a largely or wholly solar economy can be constructed in the United States with straightforward soft technologies that are now demonstrated and now economic or nearly economic. Such a conceptual exercise does not require 'exotic' methods such as sea-thermal, hot-dry-rock geothermal, cheap (perhaps organic) photovoltaic, or solar-thermal electric systems. If developed, as some probably will be, these technologies could be convenient, but they are in no way essential for an industrial society operating solely on energy income.

THE CLEAN ANSWER TO KING COAL'S POISONOUS REIGN

BY ANDREW KENNY

Opposition to nuclear power continues to the present day. Many environmentalists prefer 'traditional' fuels, especially coal, and some still dream of the day when visionary 'soft energy paths' become reality, although that day seems to draw no nearer. Yet the antinuclear lobby does not speak for all environmentalists as Andrew Kenny's article demonstrates.

I am a vegetarian and therefore a supporter of nuclear power. I became a vegetarian 20 years ago because I believed that the farming and slaughter of animals was cruel and because I thought it was a shameful waste of food to take the grain that could feed ten people and give it to a beast to produce only enough meat to feed one person. My reasons, in short, for turning to vegetarianism were respect for man and nature. These are precisely my reasons for turning to nuclear power.

Rather late in life I changed careers, became an engineer and joined an electricity utility. They required me to spend one and a half years at a coal station before I could join the nuclear section. My stay at the coal station shocked me and greatly increased my zeal for nuclear power. I have taken a vow to myself that if I ever have children I shall not allow them to grow up near a coal station (I should be perfectly happy for them to grow up near a nuclear one). But distance from coal power is not enough to escape its menace.

I support nuclear power for one reason only: that it is cleaner and safer than other practicable large-scale sources of electricity. The best way to see this is in the question of waste. In the case of nuclear power, a small amount of uranium is dug out of the ground, refined, passed through a nuclear reactor, stored and then returned to the ground again. The original uranium lying in the ground is mildly dangerous in that it emits a radioactive gas, radon, that naturally seeps out of the ground, sometimes causing lung cancer. The nuclear waste is dangerous in the short term but in the long term, because of its shorter half-lives, it is less dangerous than what it came from.

In the case of coal power, a huge amount of coal is dug out of the ground, passed through a coal furnace and converted into dangerous substances which are then either poured into the atmosphere for plants and men to breathe or dumped on to ash tips, leaching their poisons into the water courses. The original coal is quite safe. The coal wastes are very dangerous, and unlike the nuclear wastes, many remain dangerous for ever.

Nuclear power produces only one form of pollution, radiation, and only two possible dangers, cancer and genetic disease. Even in these it is overshadowed by coal. Large amounts of radiation can certainly cause cancer but low levels of radiation are a natural and inescapable fact of life. Soil, milk, stone, wood, flesh – these are all radioactive and with the sun they give us a 'background radiation' massively larger than any radiation received even on the doorstep of a nuclear station.

Coal, too, is radioactive and, having heard that a coal station routinely emits more radiation than a nuclear one, I put radiation badges on the workers of our coal station and measured the levels there. Sure enough, the radiation next to the coal station was twice as high as that next to our nuclear station, although the levels were both very low.

Far more serious are the chemical cancer agents from coal. In the short term I lived in the small township at the coal station, two people, one the power station manager's wife, died grim deaths by cancer. Their deaths are doubtless of no statistical significance but the carcinogens in the coal wastes are a hard fact. They include organic carcinogens such as nitrosamines and benzopyrenes and, worse, heavy metals such as cadmium and arsenic.

Cadmium is normally locked safely into the coal but when the coal is burnt in the furnace the cadmium vaporizes, turns into tiny particles, passes through the smokestacks and spreads through the atmosphere to settle finely on the ground where it dissolves in water, enters human tissue and causes cancer. Cadmium has a half-life of infinity. When Chernobyl's ruined reactor has become less radioactive than the soil in your back garden, when the Pharoahs' mighty pyramids have crumbled into sand, when our sun has become a Red Giant and boiled our oceans dry, the cadmium from your local coal station will be as deadly as on the day it left the smokestack.

Radiation in large amounts is known to cause genetic damage in animals, but the curious fact is that it has never been observed to cause genetic damage in human beings. The first generation of survivors after the bombs on Hiroshima and Nagasaki was minutely studied but the babies born to them showed not the slightest increase in abnormality. Coal power stations emit many chemicals, such as the polycyclic aromatic hydrocarbons (PAH), known to cause genetic defects in animals. They may do the same in humans but this is not yet known. Those cartoons of two-headed children, so liked by the antinuclear brigade, apply at least as well to coal power.

By every measure the death rate from coal power is much larger than the death rate from nuclear power. Per unit of energy extracted, coal mining claims more than ten times as many deaths as uranium mining. Far worse are the civilian casualties. Study after study into the deaths caused by coal pollution agree that the figure is about 50 deaths per medium-sized coal station per year. This figure is necessarily tentative because coal pollution is diffuse and insidious in its effects. It translates into 25,000 deaths per year in America and 1,700 deaths per year in Britain.

The World Health Organization estimates that the Chernobyl accident may cause 1,600 premature deaths over the next 30 years. Thus coal power in the United Kingdom kills more civilians in one year than Chernobyl will kill in 30. And Chernobyl is the only civilian nuclear accident ever to claim a life. Three Mile Island killed nobody, injured nobody and exposed the nearest civilians to radiation less than one tenth of one dental X-ray.

The direct human casualties from coal power, although far larger than from nuclear power, are dwarfed by the devastation coal causes to the environment. Acid rain, caused by sulphur oxides (SOx) and nitrogen oxides (NOx) from coal stations and other burning of fossil fuel, has already caused vast damage to the planet's lakes and forests and the damage is spreading.

Even more ominous are the future consequences of the millions of tons of carbon dioxide that coal stations pour into the atmosphere. The 'greenhouse effect' has been much in the news recently. The global weather system is very complicated and very finely poised, and it is difficult to make short-term assessments.

What is absolutely certain is that the fragile balance depends crucially on the amount of carbon dioxide in the atmosphere and that amount is rising inexorably. We are sliding towards some immense change, perhaps a catastrophe. The human race is threatened by several rising trends – population growth, the demand for resources – but of all the graphs of doom none gives such apocalyptic warning as the rising level of carbon dioxide. The future of our civilization may well depend on reversing it. Nuclear stations produce not one drop of acid rain, not one breath of carbon dioxide.

There is no such thing as a clean coal power station. A 'clean stack' simply means that the visible pollution has been removed. But most coal pollution is invisible. Only a minority of advanced coal stations have chemical scrubbing and even these only attempt to reduce the SOx and NOx. None try to remove the heavy metals. It is impossible to remove the carbon dioxide.

The most fanatical antagonists of nuclear power are forced to admit that its safety record is without equal in power generation. But they cry, what if the really big nuclear power disaster happens? The really big disaster will not happen because it cannot happen. No nuclear power accident can match the damage done by the routine operation of coal power stations.

The superb safety record of nuclear power in the West is not because of any superhuman diligence by nuclear engineers – indeed many of them were hair-raisingly sloppy in the early days – but because the designs they have chosen are intrinsically safe. Chernobyl happened because the RMBK reactor was not intrinsically safe.

Nuclear power, unlike any other large industrial process I can think of, offers itself to inherent safety. There are nuclear reactor designs now on the drawing board in which safety is entirely passive: human operators will control the reactor only while it is running within safe limits; if it deviates from the limits, the laws of nature will overrule the operators and shut the reactor down safely. Nuclear power, safe now, offers yet more safety in the future.

A paradoxical reason for the fear of nuclear power is its unique ability to take precautions. Precautions scare people. An ambulance parked conspicuously on the beach and marked 'shark attack unit' would frighten bathers rather than reassure them. Nuclear power is able to take precautions and does so; coal is unable to take them and does not.

When you have been working near the reactor, you are scanned for radioactive contamination because it is so easy to do so; when you have been working in coal, you are not examined for particle penetration of the deep lung tissue because it is difficult to do so. It is quite easy to collect and store nuclear waste and so it is done. It is impossible to collect and store coal waste and so it is not done. The nuclear safety measures are highly visible and make people nervous.

There are passionate and articulate pro-nuclear voices within the nuclear industry but these voices are deliberately silenced by the industry itself. This was my biggest surprise on entering it. But it is easy to see why. The best argument for nuclear power is simply a comparison between its dangers and the dangers of all competitors, including the renewable sources, but mainly coal.

Nuclear stations usually belong to utilities, such as the CEGB, which make most of their electricity from coal. The dangers of coal are much greater than those of nuclear power but less well publicized and of course the utilities want to keep it that way. When I first joined our nuclear section, I was asked to write a publicity blurb to attract young people to a career in nuclear power. I did so, and included a comparison between nuclear waste and coal waste. My blurb was published in full, except that all reference to coal waste was removed.

Some people suspect that the power utilities are covering up a big secret about nuclear power. They are right. The big secret is that nuclear power is very much safer than coal.

Indeed if I were an engineer in the CEGB, I would be in trouble for this article. This is why I am coyly avoiding naming my country or utility. If privatization in Britain were to mean the nuclear power stations becoming independent of the coal ones and competing against them, then the proponents of nuclear power would be free to go on to the attack and the British people would soon hear what the people in the industry already know, that coal stations are ecological time bombs.

I am sure that coal's magnificent machines will remain in the folk memory long after they have been condemned to scrapyards and museums.

Nothing in nuclear power can match the romance and splendour of the coal age. Nuclear power is a bit of a bore but it has arrived, perhaps at the eleventh hour, to offer us salvation from looming ecological disaster. If we do not take up its offer, our grandchildren and their grandchildren will neither understand us nor forgive us.

STRATEGIES FOR SURVIVAL

BY BARBARA WARD AND RENÉ DUBOS

In June, 1972, the first of a series of United Nations 'megaconferences' was held in Stockholm. The UN Conference on the Human Environment (UNCHE) took place at several venues simultaneously and large numbers of unofficial meetings were held all over the city. White bicycles were supplied free to help people move around. The Conference issued a Declaration on the Human Environment, a long list of recommendations, and eventually the General Assembly translated these into authorization and funding for the establishment of the UN Environment Programme (UNEP), based in Nairobi, to coordinate national efforts and to sponsor a global monitoring system. In preparation for the Conference the UN arranged a series of meetings of scientists and intellectual leaders from many countries. Maurice Strong, Secretary-General of UNCHE and first executive director of UNEP, commissioned Barbara Ward and René Dubos to write a report based on ideas expressed at those meetings. The resulting book was called *Only One Earth*, which was also the motto for UNCHE. This extract is taken from the end of the book.

But we are not sleepwalkers or sheep. If men have not hitherto realized the extent of their planetary interdependence, it was in part at least because, in clear, precise, physical, and scientific fact, it did not yet exist. The new insights of our fundamental condition can also become the insights of our survival. We may be learning just in time.

There are three clear fields in which we can already begin to perceive the direction in which our planetary policies have to go. They match the three separate, powerful and divisive thrusts - of science, of markets, of nations – which have brought us, with such tremendous force, to our present predicament. And they point in the opposite direction – to a deeper and more widely shared knowledge of our environmental unity, to a new sense of partnership and sharing in our 'sovereign' economics and politics, to a wider loyalty which transcends the traditional limited allegiance of tribes and peoples. There are already pointers to these necessities. We have now to make them the new drives and imperatives of our planetary existence.

We can begin with knowledge.

The first step toward devising a strategy for Planet Earth is for the nations to accept a *collective* responsibility for discovering more – much more – about the natural system and how it is affected by man's activities and vice-versa. This implies cooperative monitoring, research and study on an unprecedented scale. It implies an intensive world-wide network for the systematic exchange of knowledge and experience. It implies a quite new readiness to take research wherever it is needed, with the backing of international financing. It means the fullest cooperation in converting knowledge into action – whether it involves placing research satellites in orbit, or reaching agreements on fishing, or introducing a new control for snail-borne disease.

But it is important not to make so much of our state of ignorance that we are inhibited from vigorous action now. For, while there is much that we do not yet understand, there are fundamental things that we *do* know. Above all, we know that there are limits to the burdens that the natural system and its components can bear, limits to the levels of toxic substances the human body can tolerate, limits to the amount of manipulation that man can exert upon natural balances without causing a break-down in the system, limits to the psychic shock that men and societies can absorb from relentlessly accelerating social change - or social degradation. In many cases we cannot yet define these limits. But wherever the danger signals are appearing – inland seas losing oxygen, pesticides producing resistant strains of pest, laterite replacing tropical forests, carbon dioxide in the air, poisons in the ocean, the ills of the inner cities – we must be ready to set in motion the cooperative international efforts of directed research which make available, with all possible speed, solutions for those most intimately concerned with the immediate problem and wider knowledge for all men of how our natural systems actually work.

To go blindly on, sharing, inadvertently, the risks and keeping to ourselves the knowledge needed for solutions can only mean more agonies than we can cope with and more danger than future generations deserve. A full and open sharing of new knowledge about the interdependence of the planetary systems on which we all depend can also help us, as it were, to creep up on the infinitely sensitive issues of divisive economic and political sovereignty.

Given our millenial habits of separate decision-making and the recent tremendous explosion of *national* power, how can any perception of the biosphere's essential unity and interdependence be combined with the acutely self-conscious separate sovereignty of more than 130 national governments?

In fact, for at least a century, some habits of cooperation have been accepted by states simply through recognition of their own self-interests. Ever since the world economy began to increase in extent and interdependence in the eighteenth and nineteenth centuries, sovereign states have shared some of their authority either by binding themselves to certain forms of cooperative behaviour or by delegating limited power to other bodies. Despite rhetorical insistence on absolute sovereignty, governments have recognized in practice that this is impossible in some cases and inordinately foolish in many more. It is no use claiming the sovereign right not to deliver other people's letters if they use their sovereign right to refuse yours. The alternative to international allocation of radio frequencies would be chaos in world communications to the disadvantage and danger of all states. In brief, when governments are faced with such realities, they have exercised their inherent sovereign right to share voluntarily their sovereignty with others in limited and agreed areas of activity.

In the twentieth century, as a consequence of an ever greater overlap between supposedly sovereign national interests, the number of international treaties, conventions, organizations, consultative forums, and cooperative programmes has multiplied rapidly. The growth of an intergovernmental community finds its most concrete expression in the United Nations and its family of specialized functional agencies and regional commissions. Outside the United Nations system, there has been an analogous growth of international organizations, governmental and non-governmental, especially on the regional level.

All inter-governmental institutions are still, ultimately, creatures of national governments, but a large amount of their day-to-day work is sufficiently and obviously useful that a measure of authority and initiative comes to rest with them. They acquire support within national governments from the relevant ministries and agencies which, in turn, find useful constituencies within the ranks of international organizations. This is, none of it, a formal departure from sovereignty. But a strict, literal definition of sovereignty gets blurred in practice and the existence of continuous forums for debate and bargaining helps instill the habit of cooperation into the affairs of reluctant governments.

It is on to this scene of ultimate national sovereignty and proliferating intermediate institutions that the new environmental imperatives have broken in the last few years. The first effect has undoubtedly been to complicate still further a very complicated situation. Quite suddenly, for a whole variety of reasons, a very wide range of institutions have added an environmental concern to their other interests. In some cases, traditional programmes and activities have been renamed to qualify them under the environmental rubric. In others a number of agencies have taken up the same environmental topic, though mainly from differing points of view. There has been some genuine innovation, and there is much ferment and groping as international organizations, to a greater or lesser degree, seek to comprehend and to adapt to the environmental imperative.

To give only one example of this combination of goodwill and overlap, one can cite the instance of air pollution, where it can be argued that the industrialized nations are the main polluters. Regional groupings such as the Organization for Economic Cooperation and Development – the successor to the old Marshall Plan bureaucracy, linking North America with Western Europe and, more recently, Japan – are setting up an Environment Committee to coordinate a number of its existing research activities, for instance, its Air Management Research Group. The regional Commissions of the United Nations are also beginning to move and the Economic Commission for Europe also has a Committee of Experts on Air Pollution. So has the North Atlantic Treaty Organization, which includes air pollution among a number of other research activities such as open waters and inland waters pollution, disaster relief and regional decision-making for environmental issues.

This picture of a somewhat uncoordinated and hence not fully focused activity, however, largely reflects the recentness of the environmental awareness. National governments, too, are trying to find means of adding an environmental angle of vision to institutions which have hitherto followed the traditional one-track approach to specialized problems through separate and usually uncoordinated administration. A rash of environmental councils and commissions is now appearing round the world to coordinate the activities of hitherto separate ministries. Several countries have taken the bolder step of bringing relevant ministries – housing, transport, technology – together in single Departments of the Environment. The various experiments are mostly not yet two years old, and it is too soon to say how well they may succeed in introducing an integrative view of man-environment relations into the national decision-making process. Certainly it will not be easy.

And certainly it will be still more difficult at the international than at national levels of decision-making. So locked are we within our tribal units, so possessive over national rights, so suspicious of any extension of international authority that we may fail to sense the need for dedicated and committed action over the whole field of planetary necessities. Nonetheless there are jobs to be done which perhaps require at this stage no more than a limited, special and basically self-interested application of the global point of view. For instance, it is only by forthright cooperation and action at the global level that nations can protect mankind from inadvertent and potentially disastrous modification in the planetary weather system over which no nation can assert sovereignty. Again, no sovereignty can hold sway over the single, inter-connected global ocean system which is nature's ultimate sink and man's favourite sewer.

Where pretensions to national sovereignty have no relevance to perceived problems, nations have no choice but to follow the course of common policy and coordinated action. In three vital, related areas this is now the undeniable case – the global atmosphere, the global oceans, and the global weather system. All require the adoption of a planetary approach by the leaders of nations, no matter how parochial their point of view toward matters that lie within national jurisdiction. A strategy for Planet Earth, undergirded by a sense of collective responsibility to discover more about man-environment relations, could well move, then, into operation on these three fronts: atmosphere, oceans and climate. It is no small undertaking, but quite possibly the very minimum required in defence of the future of the human race.

But it is not only the pollutions and degradations of the atmosphere and oceans that threaten the quality of life at the planetary level. There are threats, too, of disease spreading among under-nourished children, of protein deficiency maiming the intelligence of millions, of spreading illiteracy combined with rising numbers of unemployed intellectuals, of landless workers streaming to the squalid cities and worklessness growing there to engulf a quarter of the working force. An acceptable strategy for Planet Earth must, then, explicitly take account of the fact that the 'natural resource' most threatened with pollution, most exposed to degradation, most liable to irreversible damage is not this or that species, not this or that plant or biome or habitat, not even the free airs of the great oceans. It is man himself.

Here again, no one nation, not even groups of nations, can, acting separately, avoid the tragedy of increasing divisions between wealthy 'North' and poverty-stricken 'South' in our planet. No nations, acting singly or only with their own kind, rich or poor, can stave off the risk of unacceptable paternalism on the one hand or resentful rejection on the other. International policies are, in fact, within sight of the point reached by *internal* development in the mid nineteenth century. Either they will move on to a community based upon a more systematic sharing of wealth – through progressive income tax, through general policies for education, shelter, health and housing – or they will break down in revolt and anarchy. Many of today's proposals for development aid, through international channels, are a first sketch of such a system.

But at this point, if gloom is the psychological risk of all too many ecological forecasts, may we not go to the opposite extreme of Pollyanna optimism in forecasting any such growth of a sense of community in our troubled and divided planet? With war as mankind's oldest custom and divided sovereignty as his most treasured inheritance, where are the energies, the psychic force, the profound commitment needed for a wider loyalty?

Loyalty may, however, be the key. It is the view of many modern psychologists that man is a killer not because of any biological imperative but because of his capacity for misplaced loyalty. He will do in the name of a wider allegiance what he would shrink to do in his own nature. His massive, organized killings – the kind that distinguish him from all other animals – are invariably done in the name of faith and group of people or clan. And here, it is not wholly irrational to hope that the full realization of planetary interdependence – in biosphere and technosphere alike – may begin to affect man in the depths of his capacity for psychic commitment. All loyalty is based on two elements – the hope of protection and the hope of enhancement. On either count, the new ecological imperative can give a new vision of where man belongs in his final security and his final sense of dignity and identity.

At the most down-to-earth level of self-interest, it is the realization of the planet's totally continuous and interdependent systems of air, land and water that helps to keep a check on the ultimate lunacies of nuclear weaponry. When after the nuclear testing continued in 1969, the air above Britain was found to contain 20 per cent more strontium-90 and caesium-137, it is not a very sophisticated guess that the air above the testing states contained no less. It is the force of such recognition that lay behind the first global environmental agreement – the Test-Ban Treaty negotiated in 1963 – which has kept earlier nuclear powers out of competitive air testing and saved unnumbered children from leukaemia. Similar calculations of enlightened self-interest underlie the treaty to keep nuclear weapons out of space, off the seabeds and away from Antarctica.

Where negotiations continued – as in the treaty to prevent the spread of nuclear weapons, or the Soviet-American negotiations for a mutual limitation of strategic arms – the underlying rationale is still the same. As the airs and oceans flow round our little planet, there is not much difference between your strontium-90 and my strontium-90. They are lethal to us both.

It is even possible that recognition of our environmental interdependence can do more than save us, negatively, from the final folly of war. It could, positively, give us that sense of community, of belonging and living together, without which no human society can be built up, survive and prosper. Our links of blood and history, our sense of shared culture and achievement, our traditions, our faiths are all precious and enrich the world with the variety of scale and function required for every vital ecosystem. But we have lacked a wider rationale of unity. Our prophets have sought it. Our poets have dreamed of it. But it is only in our own day that astronomers, physicists, geologists, chemists, biologists, anthropologists, ethnologists and archaeologists have all combined in a single witness of advanced science to tell us that, in every alphabet of our being, we do indeed belong to a single system, powered by a single energy, manifesting a fundamental unity under all its variations, depending for its survival on the balance and health of the total system.

If this vision of unity – which is not a vision only but a hard and inescapable scientific fact – can become part of the common insight of all the inhabitants of Planet Earth, then we may find that, beyond all our inevitable pluralisms, we can achieve just enough unity of purpose to build a human world.

In such a world, the practices and institutions with which we are familiar inside our domestic societies would become, suitably modified, the basis of planetary order. In fact, in many of our present international institutions the sketch of such a system already exists. A part of the process would be the non-violent settlement of disputes with legal arbitral and policing procedures on an international basis. Part of it would be the transfer of resources from rich to poor through progressive world sharing – the system of which a 1 per cent standard of gross national product for aid-giving is the first faint sign. World plans for health and education, world investment in progressive farming, a world strategy for better cities, world action for pollution control and an enhanced environment would simply be seen as logical extensions of the practice of limited inter-governmental cooperation, already imposed by mutual functional needs and interests.

Our new knowledge of our planetary interdependence demands that the functions are now seen to be world-wide and supported with as rational a concept of self-interest. Governments have already paid lip-service to such a view of the world by setting up the whole variety of United Nations agencies whose duty it is to elaborate world-wide strategies. But the idea of authority and energy and resources to support their policies seems strange, visionary and Utopian at present, simply because world institutions are not backed by any sense of planetary community and commitment. Indeed, the whole idea of operating effectively at the world level still seems in some way peculiar and unlikely. The planet is not yet a centre of rational loyalty for all mankind.

But possibly it is precisely this shift of loyalty that a profound and deepening sense of our shared and inter-dependent biosphere can stir to life in us. That men can experience such transformations is not in doubt. From family to clan, from clan to nation, from nation to federation – such enlargements of allegiance have occurred without wiping out earlier loves. Today, in human society, we can perhaps hope to survive in all our prized diversity provided we can achieve an ultimate loyalty to our single, beautiful and vulnerable Planet Earth.

Alone in space, alone in its life-supporting systems, powered by inconceivable energies, mediating them to us through the most delicate adjustments, wayward, unlikely, unpredictable, but nourishing, enlivening and enriching in the largest degree – is this not a precious home for all of us earthlings? Is it not worth our love? Does it not deserve all the inventiveness and courage and generosity of which we are capable to preserve it from degradation and destruction and, by doing so, to secure our own survival?

THE MEDITERRANEAN ACTION PLAN

BY PETER S. THACHER

International cooperation on environmental issues has had its successes, none more impressive than that leading to the Barcelona Convention for the Protection of the Mediterranean Sea from Pollution, one of whose key elements is an Action Plan to protect the environment of the region. In 1977, Peter S. Thacher, deputy executive director of the UN Environment Programme (UNEP), described that Plan and the way it was produced.

B arring a major catastrophe, the rest of this century will almost certainly see continued rapid growth and change in the Mediterranean Basin. This will make heavy demands on the resources of the Sea itself as well as upon its shore areas. During the past ten years the population of the 18 littoral states increased by more than 50 million people, a significant portion of whom are concentrated in a coastal strip only a few kilometres wide. This is part of the historical movement of people towards the coastal area of the Mediterranean that has resulted in pressures on the natural system which are evidenced by visible deterioration, frequently in the form of pollution. –

In 1974 the [UNEP] Council singled out 'regional activities' for the protection of the marine environment as an area of programme concentration with specific reference to the Mediterranean.

Thus UNEP became directly concerned with the Mediterranean region and began to play a catalytic role as the focal point within the UN System for world environmental concerns, to bring together, in a cooperative search for solutions to the region's many pressing problems, the relevant United Nations system organizations and interested intergovernmental and nongovernmental organizations.

UNEP's first task was to draft a comprehensive action plan for the governments most concerned, the 18 coastal states bordering the Sea. Initial attention focused on the assessment functions, on devising authoritative means by which to diagnose the problem – how 'sick' was the Sea, what were the sources of the problems, the trends, the risks? But always assessment was seen as a means to an end – the management of man's actions in and around the Sea so as to assist the governments to protect the Sea. For both these functions national institutions and procedures were gradually identified and supporting measures – training, provision of equipment for laboratories – were initiated to get the process started.

There are several dimensions to the process by which UNEP drew up the draft Action Plan for the Mediterranean.

First, the need to secure government approval and commitment to put the plan into action meant that governments had to be involved in its design. As a creature of governments UNEP is dependent on their approval and funds for its work. But more important is the support which only governments can provide through national action and by committing resources to make an agreed plan effective.

Closely associated was the mixing of disciplines. The nature of environmental problems is such that conflicts are inherent between various governmental departments or agencies. The institutional aspects had been analyzed for the Stockholm Conference in such a way as to highlight the need for better coordination at both the national and international levels. Considerable care had to be exercised in the invitations to government experts to ensure a balance of disciplines, or viewpoints, in the process of drawing up the action plan.

Corresponding assignments of responsibility were made at the international level; to the Food and Agriculture Organization (FAO) and its General Fisheries Council for the Mediterranean (GFCM) to collect the national lawyers to draw up guidelines for a comprehensive treaty; to the Intergovernmental Oceanographic Commission (IOC) of the United Nations Educational, Social and Cultural Organization (UNESCO) to gather oceanographers for identification of research gaps in that Sea; to the Intergovernmental Maritime Consultative Organization (IMCO) to explore with national maritime authorities how to reduce ship-source pollutants and how to be better prepared in case of accidental spills.

Secondly, the process had to be dynamic, with provision made for constant flows of information, so that new scientific findings could be taken into account in legal negotiations, and it had to be comprehensive. For the purpose of organizing formal meetings a practice with precedents in the UN system was adopted: that of having parallel meetings of scientists and lawyers beneath a plenary at the political level. This was employed at UNEP's first intergovernmental meeting of the Mediterranean States at Barcelona in 1975. These interactions made it possible for the same meeting to approve a comprehensive plan embracing legal, scientific and other chapters, each of which was influenced by various disciplines.

But the preparations for each of the 'chapters' at such a meeting require considerable attention, especially in the avoidance of premature political representation.–

Another aspect of 'premature' politicization of the preparatory process refers to the need for quiet expert preparation of what may later become highly controversial proposals. Nothing is less conducive to the drawing up of a sound, well-founded proposal than premature publicity which encourages experts to defend their virtue, rather than exchange views in specialized fields. What is required is a careful weighing of risks and benefits and the setting of goals.–

The Mediterranean, like certain other semi-enclosed bodies of water, is threatened by a progressive accumulation of various forms of pollution. Such phenomena as tar-balls on beaches and algae blooms near sewage outfalls are highly visible. Other forms of pollution are less obvious, though perhaps more serious in the long run. Among the latter are the build-up of heavy metal compounds, and the eutrophication of bays and estuaries.

Much is known about the general movement of water entering the Mediterranean through the Strait of Gibraltar and the main rivers. There is a counter-clockwise current around its two main basins, and pollutants are centrifugally driven against the coasts. There are, however, no precise data available about pollutant levels, nor about the paths they travel in particular areas. Until recently, research and monitoring institutions in the coastal states used different methodologies and types of equipment, and were unable to compare results with one another.

Fortunately, a good deal of preliminary information was already available. In 1969 GFCM of FAO, in cooperation with the International Commission for the Scientific Exploration of the Mediterranean (ICSEM), formed a working party. Their 1972 report was the first comprehensive review of the state of pollution in the Mediterranean. A further important preparatory step was a UNEP-sponsored workshop held in Monaco in September 1974, organized by the IOC of UNESCO, and by GFCM and ICSEM. Forty scientists from Mediterranean research centres attended the workshop. Their principal conclusion was that pollution of coastal waters from land-based sources presented the main environmental problem of the Mediterranean. They attributed this to the general lack of adequate treatment and disposal systems for domestic and industrial wastes. Ninety per cent of all sewage entering the Mediterranean is either inadequately treated or not treated at all. The conclusions of the workshop were particularly interesting, since pollution from ships due to its high visibility, had until that time been widely regarded as the main issue. Coastal waters, however, were found to contain dangerously high concentrations of pesticides, hydrocarbons (not necessarily from ships) and pathogenic micro-organisms.

In accordance with the recommendations of the Monaco Workshop, UNEP prepared, and the Intergovernmental Meeting in Barcelona in 1975 approved, a *Mediterranean Pollution Monitoring and Research Programme* consisting of seven pilot projects –. UNEP is coordinating this programme in close cooperation with other members of the United Nations family, including FAO, IOC, the World Health Organization (WHO), the World Meteorological Organization (WMO), the International Atomic Energy Agency (IAEA) and the United Nations Development Programme (UNDP).

A number of other projects are under way in which many components of the UN are actively involved. These projects include the development of conceptual models of the biogeochemical cycle of selected pollutants, the assessment of land-based sources of pollution, the role of sedimentation in the pollution of the Mediterranean, the assessment of potential fisheries resources, and the development of guidelines and principles for the establishment and management of selected aquatic areas.

A meeting of legal experts was held in Rome, and at an intergovernmental meeting in Barcelona a preliminary draft convention developed by FAO with protocols and technical annexes was endorsed. Meetings of expert working groups followed in 1975 and early 1976, and in February 1976, UNEP convened a Conference of Plenipotentiaries, hosted by Spain in Barcelona. The Conference was able to approve and open for immediate signature three agreements: *Convention for the Protection of the Mediterranean Sea Against Pollution*; *Protocol for the Prevention of Pollution of the Mediterranean Sea by Dumping from Ships and Aircraft*; and *Protocol concerning Cooperation in Combating Pollution of the Mediterranean Sea by Oil and Other Harmful Substances in Cases of Emergency*.

These have now been signed by 15 states and by the European Economic Community, and will come into force when six states have deposited their instruments of ratification [they came into force in February, 1978. Ed.].–

Briefly, the Convention commits the coastal states to 'take all appropriate measures – to prevent, abate and combat pollution – and to protect and enhance the marine environment' of the Mediterranean region.

A further draft protocol on land-based sources of pollution was discussed and broadly agreed at a meeting in Athens early in 1977. Negotiations are currently under way for complete agreement and signature [it was signed in May, 1980. Ed.].

Many present and planned activities around the Mediterranean, where population is expected to double by the year 2000, have impacts on the quality of the environment. Efforts were launched in 1973-74 to identify these activities, and to learn how to evaluate the severity of their likely impacts and how to apply measures to reduce adverse effects.

UNEP recognizes the need for accelerated development, though it also lays stress on environmental safeguards. So, in partnership with other UN organizations, especially UNDP, UNEP began drawing up a programme of concerted action aimed at a better utilization of the region's resources. At the same time, a long-term planning exercise, known as the *Blue Plan*, has been undertaken –. At the initiative of the government of France, other interested governments and UNEP have considered proposals for studies by national research institutions to identify likely developments until the year 2000. These studies will cover a variety of developments, activities and sectors, including urbanization, industrialization, agriculture, transportation (maritime and on land), off-shore exploration and exploitation, and energy production and use. The results of these studies will put at the disposal of national decision-makers the information they need to plan socioeconomic development on an integrated basis, and in ways which will preserve and enhance the environment. Each proposal, whether it be to build a dam or an industrial complex, or to open up a new tourist area should, in its conceptual stage and in its execution, take full account of the damage it may do and the resources it may consume.

Representatives of 14 Mediterranean countries met in Split, Yugoslavia, early in 1977 and approved the three-phase programme of the Blue Plan, which will probably take four years to complete [it was signed in April, 1982, as a fourth protocol to the Convention. Ed.].

At Split the experts also decided on a Priority Actions Plan to carry out specific work in a number of fields: protection of soil, management of water resources, and of marine living resources (including aquaculture), human settlements, tourism, and the development of 'soft technologies' for energy, including solar energy.–

After reviewing suggestions put forward by UNEP, governments at Barcelona requested the Executive Director to establish 'simple coordinating mechanisms which use, to the greatest extent possible, existing international organizations –' and 'to keep under review, as the programme develops, the possible need for the strengthening of appropriate institutions in the region'. Foreseeing the possible need for 'specialized regional organizations', they asked that anything new be based on existing national institutions which could be strengthened and given a regional role.

In 1975 the most immediate institutional need was felt with regard to the scientific assessment activities. A survey showed that there were national institutions in the region capable of carrying out the research and monitoring programmes envisaged, but that a number of laboratories, especially in less wealthy coastal states, would need equipment and training if they were to participate in a meaningful way. The Action Plan called for a two-year pilot operation to be drawn up, and for first priority to be given to training and equipment to improve national capabilities, with in-service training confined within the region to the largest possible extent.

On this basis seven 'networks' of cooperating national institutions for the seven research and monitoring programmes were organized, each network supported through the Specialized Agency best equipped to assist, with one national laboratory designated as 'regional activity centre' to provide leadership and eventual coordination of each network. Contractual agreements were signed in 1975 and 1976.

A significant problem in this sector with special institutional implications is the need for intercalibration to ensure that comparable data are generated by different laboratories. This had been identified at the Stockholm Conference as a strategic weakness in all existing assessment activities, whether global or national; and was one to which UNEP gave early thought. The best work that had been done at the international level with regard to marine pollutants was a striking experiment carried out in 1970-71 at the IAEA's International Laboratory of Marine Radioactivity in Monaco on the basis of analysis by over 40 leading laboratories around the world of uniform samples of sea water.

Together with UNESCO, UNEP contributed funds to the Monaco Laboratory in order to take advantage of their experience and to broaden the scope of their work to marine pollutants beyond the field of radioactivity, specifically to include heavy metals and chlorinated hydrocarbons.

A conscious decision was made to seek broad participation in the assessment networks, rather than concentrating the effort only in those laboratories which could be counted on to produce high-quality data. Given the conflicts inherent in any environmental problem, and the special need to ensure that all Mediterranean governments treat the assesment data as authoritative – and take it into account in national decisions that affect the Sea – it was imperative to distribute leadership via the 'regional activity centres' to all sectors of the basin, rather than vest it in the traditional centres of competence and expertise on the northern shores.

Similarly, while 'outside' experience might be welcomed, the clear desire of Mediterranean scientists, as well as political leaders, was to retain in Mediterranean hands control over policy matters, especially the determination of scientific and other priorities. This perhaps reflects the failure of previous efforts at cooperative research programmes in which non-regional views were often paramount, yet ineffective in terms of generating cooperation by regional institutions in the form of dedicated equipment, personnel, and ship-time.

Because of the obvious risk of economic consequences from public presentation of detailed environmental assessments, UNEP and the cooperating agencies have approached the problem of data handling with special care. In the final analysis data will flow from cooperating national institutions only if there are assurances against its misuse or unauthorized disclosure, and for this purpose an appropriate international organization of high repute is a more likely repository than one under national control.

International machinery was also called for in the case of the Regional Oil Combating Centre, now established on Malta as part of the approved comprehensive Action Plan. In the related protocol, parties accept the obligation to communicate pertinent information about accidents or spills either directly, or through the regional Centre, to other parties likely to be affected, and to keep the Centre informed in any case. The primary objective of the Centre is not at this stage to deal with spills *per se*, but to strengthen national capacities and facilitate cooperation among the coastal states.–

The total cost of this plan to UNEP thus far has been about $5.6 million, in addition to which Specialized Agencies and other UN organizations have added more than $1 million. In the initial start-up phase, contributions by governments have been modest, but it has always been recognized by UNEP that governments will play the decisive role in protecting the Sea and hence that increasingly-significant costs will appear on national accounts. Similarly, as UNEP's catalytic function gives way to continuing national activities (e.g. as new equipment is installed, training completed, and national laboratories carry out continuing work cooperatively), the need will diminish for injection of UNEP's limited funds in the Mediterranean and this will allow their application elsewhere.

To finance the most ambitious, long-term Blue Plan component of the Action Plan, UNEP suggested that the governments of the region provide half the costs while UNEP and other international institutions divide the remainder. This formula was accepted by governments when they met at Split, Yugoslavia, in February 1977 and should provide a precedent for future financing by governments of a large share of the continuing expenses, especially after the entry-into-force of the Barcelona Convention and related protocols.–

The willingness of governments around the Mediterranean to put aside present differences in order to work together for the future is heartening. It shows how environmental concerns can serve as a unifying force, not only among scientists but also among economists and lawyers. Most significantly, it has united, in common action on common concerns, political leaders of the highly diverse coastal states of the Mediterranean region.

PUTTING GROWTH IN PERSPECTIVE

BY HERMAN KAHN, WILLIAM BROWN, AND LEON MARTEL

The gloomy prognoses of such documents as the 'Blueprint' and *The Limits to Growth* were not accepted by everyone and the staff of the Hudson Institute, led by Herman Kahn, developed a set of very different predictions for the future. The following passage is taken from a book published in 1976 to coincide with the United States Bicentennial: *The Next 200 Years.*

The scenario presented, elaborated and tested in this book can be summarized with the general statement that 200 years ago almost everywhere human beings were comparatively few, poor and at the mercy of the forces of nature, and 200 years from now, we expect, almost everywhere they will be numerous, rich and in control of the forces of nature. The 400-year period will thus have been as dramatic and important in the history of mankind as was the 10,000-year period that preceded it, a span of time that saw the agricultural revolution spread around the world, giving way finally to the birth of the Industrial Revolution. At the midway mark in the 400-year period we have just seen in the most advanced countries the initial emergence of superindustrial economies (where enterprises are extraordinarily large, encompassing and pervasive forces in both the physical and societal environments), to be followed soon by postindustrial economies (where the task of producing the necessities of life has become trivially easy because of technological advancement and economic development). We expect that almost all countries eventually will develop the characteristics of super- and postindustrial societies.

For the past several years many concerned, intelligent people have developed strongly pessimistic feelings about the evolution of economic, technological and industrial development. At first these feelings focused on glaring – and often growing – disparities in material well-being, not only between rich and poor nations, but within the rich nations themselves. More recently, rising concern about pollution and the possible exhaustion of many natural resources has increased the already serious doubts about the continuation of this 'disproportionate' consumption – doubts often expressed as questions about the moral right of the rich to use up so many 'non-renewable' or scarce resources and often at prices that are considered unfairly low.

On the other hand, concern is also growing about the possibility of a new economic order in which resource-rich nations of the Third World would combine in cartels to set high commodity prices. By thus preempting for themselves much of the surplus available in the production process, they might permanently diminish the prosperity of the wealthy nations and make life intolerable for the resource-poor nations or those unable to join a cartel.

Added to these feelings is a pervasive loss of confidence in the ability of national leaders in almost all developed countries to deal with the problems that beset the world today.–

Indeed, a consensus is emerging among many scholars and journalists that a turning point has been reached in world history, one that portends either a much more disciplined and austere - even bleak – future for mankind, or a dramatic and revolutionary change in domestic and international society, or perhaps both. These observers argue that contemporary trends – and the increasing threats that appear to accompany them – rule out any realistic possibility, through current or even reformed institutions, of continued worldwide economic development.–

Our preliminary findings suggest that the views described above may be based to a large extent on a misreading of certain current realities and their implications for the future. In fact, while Hudson's examination of these problems in historical perspective does reveal serious and potentially disastrous future possibilities, it also shows that many of them are more the growing pains of success (often accentuated by ill-timed bursts of mismanagement as well as the needlessly dire prophecies of doomsayers) than the inevitable precursors of doom.

In our view, the application of a modicum of intelligence and good management in dealing with current problems can enable economic growth to continue for a considerable period of time, to the benefit, rather than the detriment, of mankind. We argue that without such growth the disparities among nations so regretted today would probably never be overcome, that 'no growth' would consign the poor to indefinite poverty and increase the present tensions between 'haves' and 'have-nots'. Nevertheless, we do not expect economic growth to continue indefinitely; instead, its recent exponential rate will probably slow gradually to a low or zero rate. Our differences with those who advocate limits to growth deal less with the likelihood of this change than with the reasons for it.–

There are two basic and totally different images (or models) of the earth-centred perspective, which we have labelled the *neo-Malthusian* and the *technology-and-growth* positions. The first is a modern version of the analysis of the 19th-century English economist Thomas Malthus. – The opposite image stems from the premise that in the next 100 years material needs can be met so easily in the currently developed world that the more advanced nations will develop superindustrial and then postindustrial economies, and that the rest of the world will soon follow. Obviously these two basic images encompass a range of differing views and concepts, so to represent them fairly and without exaggeration, we have developed two detailed views for each of the two models – one of which in each case is a relatively extreme position, the other a moderate position. Thus, the neo-Malthusian model includes the views of a strong neo-Malthusian [A] and a moderate neo-Malthusian [B] (that is, a guarded pessimist); and for the contrasting model, we describe the positions taken by a moderate [C] (or guarded optimist) and an enthusiastic [D] advocate of technology and economic growth. Both of the moderate positions argue that we can expect serious problems in energy shortfalls, resource scarcities and food distribution. Both also raise the real possibility of cataclysmic or irreversible environmental damage. But both hold open the possibility (in one case barely and in the other relatively clearly) that with technological progress, wise policies, competent management and good luck, mankind can deal with these problems and survive into a future where, at the least, opportunity is not foreclosed and disaster is not foreordained. The guarded optimist's view goes even further, holding that we may still avert ultimate disaster even if the policies are not so wise, management not so competent and luck not so good, but the worse the policies, management and luck, the greater the potential for tragedy along the way and even for final cataclysm. –

In the last several years, the neo-Malthusian attitudes – A and B have gained great influence. Not too many years ago – not more than a decade – most educated Americans would have placed themselves in column C, leaning toward D. Today they tend to be in column B and leaning toward A, and many unreservedly support that column's full neo-Malthusian conclusions. It has become increasingly fashionable, especially among intellectuals at prestige universities and among spokesmen in the most respected newspapers and journals as well as on television, to attack economic growth, capitalism, industrialization, the consumer society and related values. Casual references are made to our vanishing resources, the end of the 'energy joyride', our increasingly 'suicidal' pollution, our 'self-destructive materialism', the poverty of our emotional and aesthetic lives, the disease of 'consumeritis' and the need to 'kick the energy habit'.–

We believe that the movement toward column A – propelled by a combination of compassion and guilt for the plight of the world's poor and the coincidental occurrence of worldwide crises in the supply of food and energy – has gone too far. Spurred now by well-publicized studies, it has acquired a momentum of its own which, if continued, will only deepen the malaise it depicts and make longer and more difficult the recovery that is required. We believe that plausible and realistic scenarios can be written consonant with a view that sees the world moving from column C toward column D. We argue that there is both need and opportunity for growth, and that because America and the rest of the nations of the developed world *do* use resources so intensely, there will be stimulation, not depression, for the economies of the less-developed countries. In fact, – the clearest moral and political argument for further growth in the developed world (and against artificial and forced limitation) is that it aids the poor both within and outside the developed countries.

Despite the confident tone of these last few pages – we would like to stress that in no sense do we wish to play down the importance of the issues raised by the neo-Malthusians or to assert that there are no serious problems. While we generally tend to be optimistic about many of them, we recognize that very unpleasant situations can arise – possibilities which must be dealt with competently and responsibly. We also believe not only that this can be done, but that in many cases it already is being done. Finally, we feel that even though the costs and risks are great, the effort to achieve a postindustrial society is on balance a worthwhile one; and further, that priorities which emphasize technological advancement and economic growth, but with prudence and care, are likely to be acceptable and largely beneficial.

Thus our disagreement with advocates of the limits-to-growth positions sometimes is that they raise false, non-existent or misformulated issues; equally often, perhaps, they pose as being basically insoluble real problems for which we believe rather straightforward and practical solutions can be found in most cases.

BUDDHIST ECONOMICS

BY E.F. SCHUMACHER

E.F. Schumacher attended one of the planning meetings for the 'Blueprint' but he did not contribute to its writing and did not endorse it; in fact he disapproved of it. He was especially critical of its emphasis on the impossibility of sustaining exponential growth, a matter he considered too self-evident to warrant such attention. The following year, 1973, he published his own book, *Small is Beautiful*, in which he collected articles he had written and lectures he had given over a number of years. His ideas inspired an entire movement within the broader environmental movement but they also reached and influenced politicians, including President Carter. The underlying theme of Schumacher's thought is outlined in 'Buddhist Economics', an article he wrote in 1966 for *Asia: A Handbook*, edited by Guy Wint and published by Anthony Blond, and reproduced in *Small is Beautiful*.

R ight Livelihood' is one of the requirements of the Buddha's Noble Eightfold Path. It is clear, therefore, that there must be such a thing as Buddhist economics.

Buddhist countries have often stated that they wish to remain faithful to their heritage. So Burma: 'The New Burma sees no conflict between religious values and economic progress. Spiritual health and material wellbeing are not enemies: they are natural allies.' Or: 'We can blend successfully the religious and spiritual values of our heritage with the benefits of modern technology.' Or: 'We Burmans have a sacred duty to conform both our dreams and our acts to our faith. This we shall ever do.'

All the same, such countries invariably assume that they can model their economic development plans in accordance with modern economics, and they call upon modern economists from so-called advanced countries to advise them, to formulate the policies to be pursued, and to construct the grand design for development, the Five-Year Plan or whatever it may be called. No one seems to think that a Buddhist way of life would call for Buddhist economics, just as the modern materialist way of life has brought forth modern economics.

Economists themselves, like most specialists, normally suffer from a kind of metaphysical blindness, assuming that theirs is a science of absolute and invariable truths, without any presuppositions. Some go as far as to claim that economic laws are as free from 'metaphysics' or 'values' as the law of gravitation. We need not, however, get involved in arguments of methodology. Instead, let us take some fundamentals and see what they look like when viewed by a modern economist and a Buddhist economist.

There is universal agreement that a fundamental source of wealth is human labour. Now, the modern economist has been brought up to consider 'labour' or work as little more than a necessary evil. From the point of view of the employer, it is in any case simply an item of cost, to be reduced to a minimum if it cannot be eliminated altogether, say, by automation. From the point of view of the workman, it is a 'disutility'; to work is to make a sacrifice of one's leisure and comfort, and wages are a kind of compensation for the sacrifice. Hence the ideal from the point of view of the employer is to have output without employees, and the ideal from the point of view of the employee is to have income without employment.

The consequences of these attitudes both in theory and in practice are, of course, extremely far-reaching. If the ideal with regard to work is to get rid of it, every method that 'reduces the work load' is a good thing. The most potent method, short of automation, is the so-called 'division of labour' and the classical example is the pin factory eulogised in Adam Smith's *Wealth of Nations*. Here it is not a matter of ordinary specialisation, which mankind has practised from time immemorial, but of dividing up every complete process of production into minute parts, so that the final product can be produced at great speed without anyone having had to contribute more than a totally insignificant and, in most cases, unskilled movement of his limbs.

The Buddhist point of view takes the function of work to be at least threefold: to give a man a chance to utilise and develop his faculties; to enable him to overcome his egocentredness by joining with other people in a common task; and to bring forth the goods and services needed for a becoming existence. Again, the consequences that flow from this view are endless. To organize work in such a manner that it becomes meaningless, boring, stultifying, or nerve-racking for the worker would be little short of criminal; it would indicate a greater concern with goods than with people, an evil lack of compassion and a soul-destroying degree of attachment to the most primitive side of this worldly existence. Equally, to strive for leisure as an alternative to work would be considered a complete misunderstanding of one of the basic truths of human existence, namely that work and leisure are complementary parts of the same living process and cannot be separated without destroying the joy of work and the bliss of leisure.

From the Buddhist point of view, there are therefore two types of mechanisation which must be clearly distinguished: one that enhances a man's skill and power and one that turns the work of man over to a mechanical slave, leaving man in a position of having to serve the slave. How to tell the one from the other? 'The craftsman himself,' says Ananda Coomaraswamy, a man equally competent to talk about the modern west as the ancient east, 'can always, if allowed to, draw the delicate distinction between the machine and the tool. The carpet loom is a tool, a contrivance for holding warp threads at a stretch for the pile to be woven round them by the craftsmen's fingers; but the power loom is a machine, and its significance as a destroyer of culture lies in the fact that it does the essentially human part of the work.' It is clear, therefore, that Buddhist economics must be very different from the economics of modern materialism, since the Buddhist sees the essence of civilisation not in a multiplication of wants but in the purification of human character. Character, at the same time, is formed primarily by a man's work. And work, properly conducted in conditions of human dignity and freedom, blesses those who do it and equally their products. The Indian philosopher and economist J.C. Kumarappa sums the matter up as follows:

'If the nature of the work is properly appreciated and applied, it will stand in the same relation to the higher faculties as food is to the physical body. It nourishes and enlivens the higher man and urges him to produce the best he is capable of. It directs his free will along the proper course and disciplines the animal in him into progressive channels. It furnishes an excellent background for man to display his scale of values and develop his personality.'

If a man has no chance of obtaining work he is in a desperate position, not simply because he lacks an income but because he lacks this nourishing and enlivening factor of disciplined work which nothing can replace. A modern economist may engage in highly sophisticated calculations on whether full employment 'pays' or whether it might be more 'economic' to run an economy at less than full employment so as to ensure a greater mobility of labour, a better stability of wages, and so forth. His fundamental criterion of success is simply the total quantity of goods produced during a given period of time. 'If the marginal urgency of goods is low,' says Professor Galbraith in *The Affluent Society*, 'then so is the urgency of employing the last man or the last million men in the labour force.' And again: 'If – we can afford some unemployment in the interest of stability – a proposition, incidentally, of impeccably conservative antecedents - then we can afford to give those who are unemployed the goods that enable them to sustain their accustomed standard of living.'

From a Buddhist point of view, this is standing the truth on its head by considering goods as more important than people and consumption as more important than creative activity. It means shifting the emphasis from the worker to the product of work, that is, from the human to the sub-human, a surrender to the forces of evil. The very start of Buddhist economic planning would be a planning for full employment, and the primary purpose of this would in fact be employment for everyone who needs an 'outside' job: it would not be the maximisation of employment nor the maximisation of production. Women, on the whole, do not need an 'outside' job, and the large-scale employment of women in offices or factories would be considered a sign of serious economic failure. In particular, to let mothers of young children work in factories while the children run wild would be as uneconomic in the eyes of a Buddhist economist as the employment of a skilled worker as a soldier in the eyes of a modern economist.

While the materialist is mainly interested in goods, the Buddhist is mainly interested in liberation. But Buddhism is 'The Middle Way' and therefore in no way antagonistic to physical well-being. It is not wealth that stands in the way of liberation but the attachment to wealth; not the enjoyment of pleasurable things but the craving for them. The keynote of Buddhist economics, therefore, is simplicity and non-violence. From an economist's point of view, the marvel of the Buddhist way of life is the utter rationality of its pattern – amazingly small means leading to extraordinarily satisfactory results.

For the modern economist this is very difficult to understand. He is used to measuring the 'standard of living' by the amount of annual consumption, assuming all the time that a man who consumes more is 'better off' than a man who consumes less. A Buddhist economist would consider this approach excessively irrational: since consumption is merely a means to human well-being, the aim should be to obtain the maximum of well-being with the minimum of consumption. Thus, if the purpose of clothing is a certain amount of temperature comfort and an attractive appearance, the task is to attain this purpose with the smallest possible effort, that is, with the smallest annual destruction of cloth and with the help of designs that involve the smallest possible input of toil. The less toil there is, the more time and strength is left for artistic creativity. It would be highly uneconomic, for instance, to go in for complicated tailoring, like the modern west, when a much more beautiful effect can be achieved by the skilful draping of uncut material. It would be the height of folly to make material so that it should wear out quickly and the height of barbarity to make anything ugly, shabby or mean. What has just been said about clothing applies equally to all other human requirements. The ownership and the consumption of goods is a means to an end, and Buddhist economics is the systematic study of how to attain given ends with the minimum means.

Modern economics, on the other hand, considers consumption to be the sole end and purpose of all economic activity, taking the factors of production – land, labour, and capital – as the means. The former, in short, tries to maximise human satisfactions by the optimal pattern of consumption, while the latter tries to maximise consumption by the optimal pattern of productive effort. It is easy to see that the effort needed to sustain a way of life which seeks to attain the optimal pattern of consumption is likely to be much smaller than the effort needed to sustain a drive for maximum consumption. We need not be surprised, therefore, that the pressure and strain of living is very much less in, say, Burma than it is in the United States, in spite of the fact that the amount of labour-saving machinery used in the former country is only a minute fraction of the amount used in the latter.

Simplicity and non-violence are obviously closely related. The optimal pattern of consumption, producing a high degree of human satisfaction by means of a relatively low rate of consumption, allows people to live without great pressure and strain and to fulfil the primary injunction of Buddhist teaching: 'Cease to do evil; try to do good.' As physical resources are everywhere limited, people satisfying their needs by means of a modest use of resources are obviously less likely to be at each other's throats than people depending upon a high rate of use. Equally, people who live in highly self-sufficient local communities are less likely to get involved in large-scale violence than people whose existence depends on world-wide systems of trade.

From the point of view of Buddhist economics, therefore, production from local resources for local needs is the most rational way of economic life, while dependence on imports from afar and the consequent need to produce for export to unknown and distant peoples is highly uneconomic and justifiable only in exceptional cases and on a small scale. Just as the modern economist would admit that a high rate of consumption of transport services between a man's home and his place of work signifies a misfortune and not a high standard of life, so the Buddhist economist would hold that to satisfy human wants from faraway sources rather than from sources nearby signifies failure rather than success. The former tends to take statistics showing an increase in the number of ton/miles per head of the population carried by a country's transport system as proof of economic progress, while to the latter – the Buddhist economist – the same statistics would indicate a highly undesirable deterioration in the *pattern* of consumption.

Another striking difference between modern economics and Buddhist economics arises over the use of natural resources. Bertrand de Jouvenal, the eminent French political philosopher, has characterised 'western man' in words which may be taken as a fair description of the modern economist:

'He tends to count nothing as an expenditure, other than human effort; he does not seem to mind how much mineral matter he wastes and, far worse, how much living matter he destroys. He does not seem to realise at all that human life is a dependent part of an ecosystem of many different forms of life. As the world is ruled from towns where men are cut off from any form of life other than human, the feeling of belonging to an ecosystem is not revived. This results in a harsh and improvident treatment of things upon which we ultimately depend, such as water and trees.'

The teaching of the Buddha, on the other hand, enjoins a reverent and non-violent attitude not only to all sentient beings but also, with great emphasis, to trees. Every follower of the Buddha ought to plant a tree every few years and look after it until it is safely established, and the Buddhist economist can demonstrate without difficulty that the universal observation of this rule would result in a high rate of genuine economic development independent of any foreign aid. Much of the economic decay of south-east Asia (as of many other parts of the world) is undoubtedly due to a heedless and shameful neglect of trees.

Modern economics does not distinguish between renewable and non-renewable materials, as its very method is to equalise and quantify everything by means of a money price. Thus, taking various alternative fuels, like coal, oil, wood, or water-power: the only difference between them recognised by modern economics is relative cost per equivalent unit. The cheapest is automatically the one to be preferred, as to do otherwise would be irrational and 'uneconomic'. From a Buddhist point of view, of course, this will not do; the essential difference between non-renewable fuels like coal and oil on the one hand and renewable fuels like wood and water-power on the other cannot be simply overlooked. Non-renewable goods must be used only if they are indispensable, and then only with the greatest care and the most meticulous concern for conservation. To use them heedlessly or extravagantly is an act of violence, and while complete non-violence may not be attainable on this earth, there is nonetheless an ineluctable duty on man to aim at the ideal of non-violence in all he does.

Just as a modern European economist would not consider it a great economic achievement if all European art treasures were sold to America at attractive prices, so the Buddhist economist would insist that a population basing its economic life on non-renewable fuels is living parasitically, on capital instead of income. Such a way of life could have no permanence and could therefore be justified only as a purely temporary expedient. As the world's resources of non-renewable fuels – coal, oil and natural gas – are exceedingly unevenly distributed over the globe and undoubtedly limited in quantity, it is clear that their exploitation at an ever-increasing rate is an act of violence against nature which must almost inevitably lead to violence between men.

This fact alone might give food for thought even to those people in Buddhist countries who care nothing for the religious and spiritual values of their heritage and ardently desire to embrace the materialism of modern economics at the fastest possible speed. Before they dismiss Buddhist economics as nothing better than a nostalgic dream, they might wish to consider whether the path of economic development outlined by modern economics is likely to lead them to places where they really want to be. Towards the end of his courageous book *The Challenge of Man's Future*, Professor Harrison Brown of the California Institute of Technology gives the following appraisal:

'Thus we see that, just as industrial society is fundamentally unstable and subject to reversion to agrarian existence, so within it the conditions which offer individual freedom are unstable in their ability to avoid the conditions which impose rigid organisation and totalitarian control. Indeed, when we examine all of the foreseeable difficulties which threaten the survival of industrial civilisation, it is difficult to see how the achievement of stability and the maintenance of individual liberty can be made compatible.'

Even if this were dismissed as a long-term view there is the immediate question of whether 'modernisation', as currently practised without regard to religious and spiritual values, is actually producing agreeable results. As far as the masses are concerned, the results appear to be disastrous – a collapse of the rural economy, a rising tide of unemployment in town and country, and the growth of a city proletariat without nourishment for either body or soul.

It is in the light of both immediate experience and long-term prospects that the study of Buddhist economics could be recommended even to those who believe that economic growth is more important than any spiritual or religious values. For it is not a question of choosing between 'modern growth' and 'traditional stagnation'. It is a question of finding the right path of development, the Middle Way between materialist heedlessness and traditionalist immobility, in short, of finding 'Right Livelihood'.

FROM UNDIFFERENTIATED TO ORGANIC GROWTH

BY MIHAIJLO MESAROVIC
AND EDUARD PESTEL

The second report of The Club of Rome, by Mihaijlo Mesarovic and Eduard Pestel, was published in 1975, as *Mankind at the Turning Point*. Like *The Limits to Growth* it was a popular exposition of an academic study. It, too, was concerned with 'growth', but as this extract shows, Professors Mesarovic and Pestel explored the difficulties arising from the casual use of that word.

Many of the global crises have been attributed to continuous and rapid growth. It has been argued, therefore, that growth must be stopped – or at the very least, deliberately retarded. Conversely, it has also been maintained that solutions of the world crises could be found only through continued growth. The fact is that both of these points of view require a great deal of qualification and more explicit definition before either one can be accepted as correct on a rational – rather than an ideological or emotional – basis. In other words, we need to know what is meant by 'growth', and in what sense that growth is considered as desirable or undesirable. Growth, after all, is a process, not an object; it cannot be pointed at physically, like a chair or table, for the sake of explication; rather, it must be conceptually defined.

But defining growth (especially in support of positions 'for' or 'against' growth) is not necessarily straightforward – as the confusion characteristic of current debate on growth or no-growth indicates. On certain growth issues there would seem to exist universal agreement. Consider, for example, the issue of population growth. Few would quarrel with the position that the global population cannot and should not be permitted to grow unchecked forever. That the population must level off some time, i.e., that population *growth should stop*, is the view gaining universal acceptance. On the other hand, none would argue against the growth in medical services leading to increased life expectancy and declining mortality rates; but this leads to increase rather than decline in population. The area of material consumption provides yet another example of the complexity of the growth issue and highlights the peril in taking a stand for or against growth as an abstract concept. It is a well-established fact that in the world's developed, industrialized regions materials consumption has reached proportions of preposterous waste. In those regions there must now be a relative decline in the use of various materials. On the other hand, in some other less fully developed world regions, there must be substantial growth in the use of some essential commodities, either for food production or for industrial production. The very existence of the population in those regions depends on such growth. Hence, unqualified arguments 'for' or 'against' growth are naive; *to grow or not to grow is neither a well-defined nor a relevant question until the location, sense, and subject of growing and the growth process itself are defined.*

To appreciate how rich and varied the concept of growth is one has to recall the growth processes as found in Nature. Two types of growth processes are of interest here: one is *undifferentiated growth*, the other is *organic growth*, or growth with differentiation. In the undifferentiated type, growth occurs through replication of cells by cell division: one cell divides into two, two into four, four into eight, and so on until, very rapidly, there are millions and billions of cells. For example, if the doubling time is one hour, the first cell will have become nearly 17 million cells after twenty-four hours, while after forty-eight hours there would be more than 280 trillion (280,000,000,000,000) cells. In undifferentiated growth all of the new cells are replicas of the first; growth is in quantity only. The result is a purely exponential increase in the cells' numbers.

Organic growth, in contrast, involves a process of differentiation, which means that various groups of cells begin to differ in structure and function. The cells become organ-specific according to the developmental process of the organism: liver cells become distinct from brain cells; brain cells are differentiated from the bone cells, etc. During and after differentiation, the number of cells can still increase, and the organs grow in size; but while some organs grow, others might decline.

The current discussion on the crisis in world development centres on growth as though it were necessarily the undifferentiated type. There is no reason, however, why parallels to organic growth should not be drawn upon: indeed, our analysis – points out the crucial importance of the organic growth concept for the future development of mankind.–

In the past the world community was merely a collection of fundamentally independent parts. Under such conditions each of the parts could grow – for better or worse – as it pleased. In the new conditions, exemplified by the global crises-syndrome, the world community has been transformed into a world system, i.e., a collection of functionally interdependent parts. Each part – whether a region or a group of nations – has its own contribution to make to the organic development of mankind: resources, technology, economic potential, culture, etc. In such a system the growth of any one part depends on the growth or non-growth of others. Hence the undesirable growth of any one part threatens not only that part but the whole as well. If the world system could embark on the path of organic growth, however, the organic interrelationships would act as a check against undifferentiated growth anywhere in the system.

If the concept of growth were restricted solely to undifferentiated growth, there would be no question but that the growth process – practically *all* growth processes – would have to stop. One does not need any complicated analysis to arrive at that conclusion. It is easy to see why. If, for example, an economy grows at a 5 per cent annual rate, it would, by the end of the next century, reach a level more than 500 times greater (or 50,000 per cent higher) than the current level. Even if the use of materials were to decline sharply in relation to the rise in economic output, the problems of acquiring, processing, and disposing of the materials would be staggering.– Growth for growth's sake in the sense of ever increasing numbers and larger size simply cannot continue forever.

On the basis of that irrefutable diagnosis, a prescription of no-growth administered immediately and worldwide might seem to be indicated. And, indeed, such a prescription might serve admirably – *if* the world were a uniform entity, which it is not; and *if* the world could be counted on to evolve into a uniform, one-world entity, which cannot and ought not to happen; and *if* growth and development could be measured along a single dimension for the entire world, which cannot be done. In fact growth occurs at varying rates along different paths in different parts of the world. While undifferentiated growth is assuming truly cancerous qualities in some parts of the world, the very existence of man is threatened daily in some other part by lack of growth; e.g., in regional food production.

It is this pattern of unbalanced and undifferentiated growth which is at the heart of the most urgent problems facing humanity - and a path which leads to a solution is that of organic growth.

In Nature organic growth proceeds according to a 'master plan', a 'blueprint'. According to this master plan diversification among cells is determined by the requirements of the various organs; the size and shape of the organs and, therefore, their growth processes are determined by their function, which in turn depends on the needs of the whole organism.

Such a 'master plan' is missing from the processes of growth and development of the world system. The master plan that regulates the growth of an organism has evolved through the process of natural selection; it is encoded in the genes and is given from the start to the growing organism, so that development of the organism is specified by it; the plan and the organism are inseparable. But the organic growth of mankind is *not* inherent in the present trend of world development. There is nothing to suggest that the transition from undifferentiated to organic growth will result from the present direction of development. Nor can it be assumed that such a plan will be injected by a *deus ex machina*. The master plan has yet to evolve through the exercise of options by the people who constitute the world system. To this extent *the options facing humanity contain the genesis of an organic growth*. And it is in this sense that mankind is at a turning point in its history: to continue along the path of cancerous undifferentiated growth or to start on the path of organic growth.

The transition from the present undifferentiated and unbalanced world growth to organic growth will lead to the creation of a new mankind. Such a transition would represent a dawn, not a doom, a beginning, not the end. Will mankind have the wisdom and will power to evolve a sound strategy to achieve that transition? In view of historical precedents, one might, legitimately, have serious doubts – *unless the transition evolves out of necessity. And this is where the current and future crises – in energy, food, materials, and the rest – can become error-detectors, catalysts for change, and as such blessings in disguise. The solutions of these crises will determine on which of the two paths mankind has chosen to travel.*

THE
BRANDT REPORT

The relationships between economic development, population growth and environmental quality were explored further in an even more prestigious study. Early in 1978, Willy Brandt drew together a team of 18 senior politicians, including Edward Heath from Britain and Olof Palme from Sweden, to investigate the political and economic systems that produced the sharp division between rich and poor countries. The Report of the Independent Commission on International Development Issues was published in 1980, with the title *North-South: A Programme for Survival*. The extract reproduced here omits the section dealing with migration and the need to protect the rights of migrant workers.

The present staggering growth of world population will continue for some considerable time. It will be one of the strongest forces shaping the future of human society. Over one million people are added to the population of the world every five days, and it will increase in the 1980s and 1990s by close to two billion, which is more than the total number of people in the world during the first decade of this century. Nine-tenths of the increase will take place in the Third World. In the industrial countries the prospects are more uncertain – there might be very small increases but in some of them the population may even decline somewhat.

It is true that the population explosion seems to be abating. Fertility is going down in many countries in the third World and their rate of population growth is no longer increasing. In some countries, including the People's Republic of China, birth rates have been reduced so much faster than death rates that growth rates have been cut in half. By the year 2000 world population is nonetheless likely to have grown from its present level of 4.3 billion to 6 or 6.5 billion. Rapid growth over a long time has produced a very young age structure in developing countries; the number of new families will grow so fast that even if each couple starting from today had only two children their population would increase by almost one-third.

The decline in fertility during the 1980s and 1990s is therefore not likely to make a great difference to the total numbers in the year 2000, but it is decisive to what happens after that. Depending on whether the decline in fertility accelerates or slows down, world population could, as projections show, stabilize – or possibly turn down – at levels anywhere between 8 and 15 billion in the course of the next century. Even on the assumption of continued fertility decline, the populations of most countries in the developing world are likely to reach at least twice their present size.–

It is easy to feel a sense of helplessness at these prospects. The growth of population at rates between 2 and 3 per cent per annum will produce a doubling of population in 25 to 35 years. This compounds the task of providing food, jobs, shelter, education and health services, of mitigating absolute poverty, and of meeting the colossal financial and administrative needs of rapid urbanization. It is also difficult to avoid the conclusion that a world of 15 billion people would be racked by a host of potentially devastating economic, social and political conflicts. Whether the nightmarish vision of a hopelessly overcrowded planet in the next century can be averted depends gravely on what is done now to hasten the stabilization of population.

Many countries have shown both that economic and social development itself helps to limit population growth and that public policies can contribute directly to the decline of birth rates. The countries where birth rates have recently most declined have usually been those which have managed to spread the benefits of development widely.–

There is a risk that the widespread trends of fertility decline may create the impression that the situation is taking care of itself. This could be unfortunate. International support for population policies is flagging at precisely the time when the commitment to, and political acceptance of, family planning policies is spreading in the Third World. Over sixty countries, with 95 per cent of the population of the Third World, have adopted family planning programmes, although the degree of commitment varies. The needs for population assistance are great – for example, the United Nations Fund for Population Activities (UNFPA) can only meet two-thirds of the requests it receives.–

We believe that development policies should include a national population programme aiming at an appropriate balance between population and resources, making family planning services freely available and integrated with other measures to promote welfare and social change. International support for population projects and programmes and for social and biomedical research needs to be greatly enlarged.–

A question we cannot overlook is whether the resources and the ecological system of the earth will suffice to meet the needs of a greatly increased world population at the economic standard that is hoped for. So far the bulk of the depletion of non-renewable resources and the pressure on the oceans and the atmosphere have been caused by the spectacular industrial growth of the developed countries where only one-fifth of the world's people live. But population growth in some parts of the Third World is already a source of alarming ecological changes, and its industrialization is bound to lead to greater pressure on resources and environment.

– The exhaustion of the world's oil supplies will force far-reaching change on the world economy in the foreseeable future, but most other mineral resources seem to be in relatively ample supply. The problems arising from their depletion stem largely from the character of their distribution and from the difficulties that may occur in their production and trade.

Renewable resources, however, may set narrower limits. The biological systems of the world are showing signs of strain. Thus the catch from ocean fishing has levelled off in spite of great improvements in modern fishing fleets. Depletion problems in relation to farming, water supplies and forestry are discussed in other parts of our Report. When the environment is overtaxed it does not harm only the countries directly faced with deterioration of the resource base but affects all countries through the ecosystem of the earth, as in the case of deforestation. The forests now covering about one-fifth of the earth's land surface are crucial to the stability of soil systems and to the survival of innumerable animal species and millions of human beings. They also help to absorb the excessive amounts of carbon dioxide emitted by the burning of fossil fuels, a process which threatens to warm up the atmosphere and could produce climatic change with potentially catastrophic consequences. The combined demand for firewood, farm land, and increased exports of forest products to industrial countries is causing a deforestation of 11 million hectares each year in the Third World. That is half the area of the United Kingdom. Deforestation also leads to impoverishment and erosion of the soil and increased flooding and silting up of rivers, reservoirs and harbours, as is happening in Panama, Bangladesh,

Nigeria and many other countries.

It is gratifying that there has been an awakening to the need to protect the environment from over-exploitation, pollution and contamination. The United Nations Conference on the Human Environment in 1972 was an important milestone, and much progress in awareness has been made in the years since then. It can no longer be argued that the protection of the environment is an obstacle to development. On the contrary, the care of the natural environment is an essential aspect of development.

Yet there is still much resistance. The costs of containing pollution are easier to calculate than the benefits of unpolluted air and water. There is also a temptation for a country to set lower standards than another in order to attract industry and create jobs. There is an obvious need to harmonize standards, to prevent a competitive debasement of them. Developing countries too are already experiencing industrial pollution and have an interest in establishing and enforcing standards for environmental protection. The same norms will not be appropriate for all countries, and they must make their own judgement of the trade-offs involved. But to seek to attract industry at the expense of environment might cause damage that is more costly to undo than to prevent, and it would also be likely to contribute to protectionist pressures in industrial countries.

Environmental impact assessment should be undertaken wherever investments or other development activities may have adverse environmental consequences whether within the national territory concerned, for the environment of neighbouring countries or for the global commons. There should be guidelines for such assessments, and when the impact falls on other countries there should be an obligation to consult with them. Development banks should be mindful of such factors in the development of their own projects, and be ready to assist environmental impact studies to ensure that an ecological perspective is incorporated in development planning.

Maintenance of the global commons – especially the oceans, the atmosphere and outer space – and control of the accelerating utilization of them requires the establishment of international regimes. In the absence of such authority, over-exploitation and abuse could cause irreversible damage, especially to the interests of weaker nations.

The difficulty of making progress at the global level and securing agreement in these matters between countries of vastly different resources and interests has been starkly evident in the ongoing United Nations Law of the Sea Conference. The creation of an international Sea-bed Authority will represent a breakthrough, but there is a real risk that only the least valuable and most remote portions of the seas will be under its jurisdiction, and that responsibility for research and pollution control in the 'exclusive economic zones' of 200 miles or more will not be subject to internationally agreed codes of practice. Yet halting the destruction of the oceans is of vital concern to all mankind.

It is clear to us that the growth and development of the world economy must in the future be less destructive to natural resources and the environment so that the rights of future generations are protected. Few threats to peace and the survival of the human community are greater than those posed by the prospects of cumulative and irreversible degradation of the biosphere on which human life depends.

GLOBAL 2000

1980 was also the year in which the 'Global 2000' report was published. Its history began on 23 May, 1977, when President Carter delivered an Environmental Message to the Congress. In it he announced that 'I am directing the Council on Environmental Quality and the Department of State, working in cooperation with the Environmental Protection Agency, the National Science Foundation, the National Oceanic and Atmospheric Administration, and other appropriate agencies, to make a one-year study of the probable changes in the world's population, natural resources, and environment through the end of the century. This study will serve as the foundation of our longer-term planning'. In the event, the study took three years rather than one and resulted in a three-volume report. The extract reproduced here summarizes the study's major findings and conclusions.

If present trends continue, the world in 2000 will be more crowded, more polluted, less stable ecologically, and more vulnerable to disruption than the world we live in now. Serious stresses involving population, resources, and environment are clearly visible ahead. Despite greater material output, the world's people will be poorer in many ways than they are today.

For hundreds of millions of the desperately poor, the outlook for food and other necessities of life will be no better. For many it will be worse. Barring revolutionary advances in technology, life for most people on earth will be more precarious in 2000 than it is now – unless the nations of the world act decisively to alter current trends.

This, in essence, is the picture emerging from the US Government's projections of probable changes in world population, resources, and environment by the end of the century, as presented in the Global 2000 Study. They do not predict what will occur. Rather, they depict conditions that are likely to develop if there are no changes in public policies, institutions, or rates of technological advance, and if there are no wars or other major disruptions. A keener awareness of the nature of current trends, however, may induce changes that will alter these trends and the projected outcome.

Rapid growth in world population will hardly have altered by 2000. The world's population will grow from 4 billion in 1975 to 6.35 billion in 2000, an increase of more than 50 per cent. The rate of growth will slow only marginally, from 1.8 per cent a year to 1.7 per cent. In terms of sheer numbers, population will be growing faster in 2000 than it is today, with 100 million people added each year compared with 75 million in 1975. Ninety per cent of this growth will occur in the poorest countries.

While the economies of the less developed countries (LDCs) are expected to grow at faster rates than those of the industrialized nations, the gross national product per capita in most LDCs remains low. The average gross national product per capita is projected to rise substantially in some LDCs (especially in Latin America), but in the great populous nations of South Asia it remains below $200 a year (in 1975 dollars). The large existing gap between the rich and poor nations widens.

World food production is projected to increase 90 per cent over the 30 years from 1970 to 2000. This translates into a global per capita increase of less than 15 per cent over the same period. The bulk of that increase goes to countries that already have relatively high per capita food consumption. Meanwhile per capita consumption in South Asia, the Middle East, and the LDCs of Africa will scarcely improve or will actually decline below present inadequate levels. At the same time, real prices for food are expected to double.

Arable land will increase only 4 per cent by 2000, so that most of the increased output of food will have to come from higher yields. Most of the elements that now contribute to higher yields – fertilizer, pesticides, power for irrigation, and fuel for machinery – depend heavily on oil and gas.

During the 1990s world oil production will approach geological estimates of maximum production capacity, even with rapidly increasing petroleum prices. The Study projects that the richer industrialized nations will be able to command enough oil and other commercial energy supplies to meet rising demands through 1990. With the expected price increases, many less developed countries will have increasing difficulties meeting energy needs. For the one-quarter of humankind that depends primarily on wood for fuel, the outlook is bleak. Needs for fuelwood will exceed available supplies by about 25 per cent before the end of the century.

While the world's finite fuel resources – coal, oil, gas, oil shale, tar sands, and uranium – are theoretically sufficient for centuries, they are not evenly distributed; they pose difficult economic and environmental problems; and they vary greatly in their amenability to exploitation and use.

Nonfuel mineral resources generally appear sufficient to meet projected demands through 2000, but further discoveries and investments will be needed to maintain reserves. In addition, production costs will increase with energy prices and may make some nonfuel mineral resources uneconomic. The quarter of the world's population that inhabits industrial countries will continue to absorb three-fourths of the world's mineral production.

Regional water shortages will become more severe. In the 1970-2000 period population growth alone will cause requirements for water to double in nearly half the world. Still greater increases would be needed to improve standards of living. In many LDCs, water supplies will become increasingly erratic by 2000 as a result of extensive deforestation. Development of new water supplies will become more costly virtually everywhere.

Significant losses of world forests will continue over the next 20 years as demand for forest products and fuelwood increases. Growing stocks of commercial-size timber are projected to decline 50 per cent per capita. The world's forests are now disappearing at the rate of 18-20 million hectares a year (an area half the size of California), with most of the loss occurring in the humid tropical forests of Africa, Asia, and South America. The projections indicate that by 2000 some 40 per cent of the remaining forest cover in LDCs will be gone.

Serious deterioration of agricultural soils will occur worldwide, due to erosion, loss of organic matter, desertification, salinization, alkalinization, and waterlogging. Already, an area of cropland and grassland approximately the size of Maine is becoming barren wasteland each year, and the spread of desert-like conditions is likely to accelerate.

Atmospheric concentrations of carbon dioxide and ozone-depleting chemicals are expected to increase at rates that could alter the world's climate and upper atmosphere significantly by 2050. Acid rain from increased combustion of fossil fuels (especially coal) threatens damage to lakes, soils, and crops. Radioactive and other hazardous materials present health and safety problems in increasing numbers of countries.

Extinctions of plant and animal species will increase dramatically. Hundreds of thousands of species – perhaps as many as 20 per cent of all species on earth – will be irretrievably lost as their habitats vanish, especially in tropical forests.

The future depicted by the US Government projections, briefly outlined above, may actually understate the impending problems. The methods available for carrying out the Study led to certain gaps and inconsistencies that tend to impart an optimistic bias. For example, most of the individual projections for the various sectors studied – food, minerals, energy, and so on – assume that sufficient capital, energy, water, and land will be available in each of these sectors to meet their needs, regardless of the competing needs of the other sectors. More consistent, better-integrated projections would produce a still more emphatic picture of intensifying stresses, as the world enters the twenty-first century.

At present and projected growth rates, the world's population would reach 10 billion by 2030 and would approach 30 billion by the end of the twenty-first century. These levels correspond closely to estimates by the US National Academy of Sciences of the maximum carrying capacity of the entire earth. Already the populations in sub-Saharan Africa and in the Himalayan hills of Asia have exceeded the carrying capacity of the immediate area, triggering an erosion of the land's capacity to support life. The resulting poverty and ill health have further complicated efforts to reduce fertility. Unless this circle of interlinked problems is broken soon, population growth in such areas will unfortunately be slowed for reasons other than declining birth rates. Hunger and disease will claim more babies and young children, and more of those surviving will be mentally and physically handicapped by childhood malnutrition.

Indeed, the problems of preserving the carrying capacity of the earth and sustaining the possibility of a decent life for the human beings that inhabit it are enormous and close upon us. Yet there is reason for hope. It must be emphasized that the Global 2000 Study's projections are based on the assumption that national policies regarding population stabilization, resource conservation, and environmental protection will remain essentially unchanged through the end of the century. But in fact, policies are beginning to change. In some areas, forests are being replanted after cutting. Some nations are taking steps to reduce soil losses and desertification. Interest in energy conservation is growing, and large sums are being invested in exploring alternatives to petroleum dependence. The need for family planning is slowly becoming better understood. Water supplies are being improved and waste treatment systems built. High-yield seeds are widely available and seed banks are being expanded. Some wildlands with their genetic resources are being protected. Natural predators and selective pesticides are being substituted for persistent and destructive pesticides.

Encouraging as these developments are, they are far from adequate to meet the global challenges projected in this Study. Vigorous, determined new initiatives are needed if worsening poverty and human suffering, environmental degradation, and international tension and conflicts are to be prevented. There are no quick fixes. The only solutions to the problems of population, resources, and environment are complex and long-term. These problems are inextricably linked to some of the most perplexing and persistent problems in the world – poverty, injustice, and social conflict. New and imaginative ideas – and a willingness to act on them – are essential.

The needed changes go far beyond the capability and responsibility of this or any other single nation. An era of unprecedented cooperation and commitment is essential. Yet there are opportunities – and a strong rationale – for the United States to provide leadership among nations. A high priority for this Nation must be a thorough assessment of its foreign and domestic policies relating to population, resources, and environment. The United States, possessing the world's largest economy, can expect its policies to have a significant influence on global trends. An equally important priority for the United States is to cooperate generously and justly with other nations – particularly in the areas of trade, investment, and assistance – in seeking solutions to the many problems that extend beyond our national boundaries. There are many unfulfilled opportunities to cooperate with other nations in efforts to relieve poverty and hunger, stabilize population, and enhance economic and environmental productivity. Further cooperation among nations is also needed to strengthen international mechanisms for protecting and utilizing the 'global commons' – the oceans and atmosphere.

To meet the challenges described in this Study, the United States must improve its ability to identify emerging problems and assess alternative responses. In using and evaluating the Government's present capability for long-term global analysis, the Study found serious inconsistencies in the methods and assumptions employed by the various agencies in making their projections. The Study itself made a start toward resolving these inadequacies. It represents the

Government's first attempt to produce an interrelated set of population, resource, and environmental projections, and it has brought forth the most consistent set of global projections yet achieved by US agencies. Nevertheless, the projections still contain serious gaps and contradictions that must be corrected if the Government's analytic capability is to be improved. It must be acknowledged that at present the Federal agencies are not always capable of providing projections of the quality needed for long-term policy decisions.

While limited resources may be a contributing factor in some instances, the primary problem is lack of coordination. The US Government needs a mechanism for continuous review of the assumptions and methods the Federal agencies use in their projection models and for assurance that the agencies' models are sound, consistent, and well documented. The improved analyses that could result would provide not only a clearer sense of emerging problems and opportunities, but also a better means for evaluating alternative responses, and a better basis for decisions of worldwide significance that the President, the Congress, and the Federal Government as a whole must make.

With its limitations and rough approximations, the Global 2000 Study may be seen as no more than a reconnaissance of the future; nonetheless its conclusions are reinforced by similar findings of other recent global studies that were examined in the course of the Global 2000 Study. All these studies are in general agreement on the nature of the problems and on the threats they pose to the future welfare of humankind. The available evidence leaves no doubt that the world – including this Nation – faces enormous, urgent, and complex problems in the decades immediately ahead. Prompt and vigorous changes in public policy around the world are needed to avoid or minimize these problems before they become unmanageable. Long lead times are required for effective action. If decisions are delayed until the problems become worse, options for effective action will be severely reduced.

GAIA AND MAN: THE PROBLEM OF POLLUTION

BY JAMES E. LOVELOCK

James Lovelock invented the electron capture detector, an instrument so sensitive it allowed scientists to discover the presence of vanishingly small amounts of pesticides in the atmosphere. This discovery provided the evidence Rachel Carson used in *Silent Spring*. Lovelock was also the first to discover the presence of chlorofluorocarbon (CFC) compounds in the atmosphere. He is more widely known, however, for his formulation, in collaboration with Lynn Margulis and others, of the 'Gaia hypothesis', which states that on any planet where life is found the living organisms themselves maintain the conditions they require for their survival, so the entire planet may be regarded as a single living organism. The journal *Icarus* published the first paper on 'Gaia', in 1972, the year of 'A Blueprint for Survival' and *The Limits to Growth*. Lovelock's popular book *Gaia: A new look at life on Earth* appeared in 1979. The first extract is taken from that book, and shows how environmental concerns appear when seen from a 'Gaian' perspective. The second is taken from a more recent contribution to a United Nations University conference, in which the Gaia concept is presented as the basis for a new scientific discipline, 'geophysiology'.

Nearly all of us have been told more than once by our tribal elders that things were better in the good old days. So ingrained is this habit of thought – which we pass on in our turn as we grow old – that it is almost automatic to assume that early man was in total harmony with the rest of Gaia. Perhaps we were indeed expelled from the Garden of Eden and perhaps the ritual is symbolically repeated in the mind of each generation.

Biblical teaching that the Fall was from a state of blissful innocence into the sorrowful world of the flesh and the devil, through the sin of disobedience, is hard to accept in our contemporary culture. Nowadays it is more fashionable to attribute our fall from grace to man's insatiable curiosity and his irresistible urge to experiment and interfere with the natural order of things. Significantly, both the biblical story and, to a lesser extent, its modern interpretation seem aimed at inculcating and sustaining a sense of guilt – a powerful but arbitrary negative feedback in human society.

Perhaps the first thing that comes to mind about modern man which might justify the belief that he is still hell-bent is the increasing pollution of the atmosphere and the natural waters of our planet since the Industrial Revolution, which began in Britain in the late eighteenth century and spread like a stain throughout most of the Northern Hemisphere. It is now generally accepted that man's industrial activities are fouling the nest and pose a threat to the total life of the planet which grows more ominous every year. Here, however, I part company with conventional thought. It may be that the white-hot rash of our technology will in the end prove destructive and painful for our own species, but the evidence for accepting that industrial activities either at their present level or in the immediate future may endanger the life of Gaia as a whole, is very weak indeed.

It is all too easily overlooked that Nature, apart from being red in tooth and claw, does not hesitate to use chemical warfare if more conventional weapons prove inadequate. How many of us recognise that the insecticide which is sprayed in the home to kill flies and wasps is a product of chrysanthemums? Natural pyrethrum is still one of the most effective substances for killing insects.

By far the most poisonous substances known are natural products. The *Botulinus* toxin produced by bacteria, or the deadly product of the algal dinoflagellates which cause the red tide at sea, or the polypeptide manufactured by the death-cap fungus: all three are entirely organic products and but for their toxicity would be suitable candidates for the shelves of the health food store. . . .

Could it be that pollution is natural? If by pollution we mean the dumping of waste matter there is indeed ample evidence that pollution is as natural to Gaia as is breathing to ourselves and most other animals. I have already referred to the greatest pollution disaster ever to affect our planet, which took place one and a half aeons ago with the emergence of free oxygen gas in the atmosphere. When this happened, all the Earth's surface in contact with the air and with the tidal seas became lethal for a large range of micro-organisms. These . . . were in consequence driven to an underground existence in the muds at the bottom of rivers, lakes, and sea beds. Many millions of years later, their banishment from life at the top was to some extent revoked. They are now back again on the surface in the most comfortable and secure of environments, enjoying a truly pampered existence and optimum status, while continuously supplied with food. These minute organisms now inhabit the gut of all animals from insects to elephants. . . .

The natural disaster of oxygen pollution occurred slowly enough to allow the ecosystems of that time to adapt, although it must have been at the expense of numerous species until a new ecosystem made up of those resistant to oxygen inherited the surface of the Earth.

The relatively minor environmental upheaval occasioned by the Industrial Revolution illustrates how such adaptations can take place. There is the well-known example of the Peppered Moth which in a few decades changed its wing colour from pale grey to nearly black so as to preserve its wing camouflage against predators as it rested on the soot-covered trees of England's industrial areas. It is now fast changing back to grey again as the impact of the Clear Air Act eliminates the soot. But roses still bloom better in London than in remote country areas, a consequence of the destruction by the pollutant sulphur dioxide of the fungi which attack them.

The very concept of pollution is anthropocentric and it may even be irrelevant in the Gaian context. Many so-called pollutants are naturally present and it becomes exceedingly difficult to know at what level the appellation 'pollutant' may be justified. Carbon monoxide, for example, which is poisonous to us and to most large mammals, is a product of incomplete combustion, a toxic agent from exhaust gases of cars, coke or coal-burning stoves, and cigarettes; a pollutant put into otherwise clean fresh air by man, you might think. However, if the air is analysed we find that carbon monoxide gas is to be found everywhere. It comes from the oxidation of methane gas in the atmosphere itself and as much as 1,000 million tons of it are so produced each year. It is thus an indirect but natural vegetable product and is also found in the swim-bladders of many sea creatures. The syphonophores, for example, are loaded with this gas in concentrations which would speedily kill us off if present in our own atmosphere at similar levels....

Let us now examine contemporary pollution from a Gaian rather than a human angle. So far as industrial pollution is concerned, by far the most heavily affected places are the densely populated urban areas of the north temperate zones: Japan, parts of the USA, of Western Europe and of Soviet Russia. Many of us have had a chance to view these regions from the window of an aeroplane in flight. Provided that there is enough wind to disperse the smog so that the surface is visible, the usual sight is of a green carpet lightly speckled with grey. Industrial complexes stand out, together with the close-packed houses of the workers, yet the general impression is that everywhere the natural vegetation is biding its time and waiting for some unguarded moment that will give it a chance to return and take over everything again. Some of us remember the rapid colonisation by wild flowers of city areas cleared by bombing in the Second World War. Industrial regions seldom appear from above to be the denatured deserts which the professional doomsters have led us to expect. If this is true of the most polluted and populous areas of our planet, it may seem that there is no urgent cause for concern about man's activities. Unfortunately this is not necessarily so; it is merely that we have been led to look for trouble in the wrong places. . . .

The parts of the Earth responsible for planetary control may still be those which carry the vast hordes of micro-organisms. The algae of the sea and of the soil surface use sunlight to perform the prime task of living chemistry, photosynthesis. They still turn over half of the Earth's supply of carbon, in co-operation with the aerobic decomposers of the soil and the sea-bed, together with the anaerobic microflora in the great mud zones of the continental shelves, sea bottom, marshes, and wet lands. The large animals, plants, and seaweeds may have important specialist functions, but the greater part of Gaia's self-regulating activity could still be conducted by micro-organisms. . . .

We are now well aware of the possible dangers of global pollution both of the atmosphere and of the oceans. National and international agencies are in the course of establishing monitoring stations equipped with sensors which will keep a record of the health of our planet. Satellites circling the Earth carry instruments to monitor the atmosphere, the oceans, and the land surface. So long as we can maintain a fairly high level of technology, this sensing programme is likely to continue and may even be extended. If the technology fails, then presumably other sectors of industry will also have failed and the potentially injurious effects of industrial pollution will diminish accordingly. In the end we may achieve a sensible and economic technology and be more in harmony with the rest of Gaia. I think that we are more likely to achieve this goal by retaining but modifying technology than by a reactionary 'back to nature' campaign.

GEOPHYSIOLOGY

BY JAMES E. LOVELOCK

Few of us have avoided the experience of imagining that we were the victims of some fatal but romantic disease. It usually happens after reading a medical textbook and identifying our minor symptoms with those described.

In the affluent parts of the world, society may be undergoing collectively the same experience. The difference is that the apparent hypochondria is about the world itself rather than about their individual selves. The equivalent of the medical textbooks is the ubiquitous doom scenarios. There is no shortage of planetary ailments to identify with, from the psychosociological drama of Orwell's nightmare vision to the dismal prospect of nuclear winters and acid rain.

As in hypochondria, the real problem is not that these global maladies are unreal, but the uncertainty over whether the present symptoms are prodromal of disaster or whether they are no more than the growing pains of the world.

Intelligent hypochondriacs do not consult a biochemist or a molecular biologist about their worries; they go instead to a physician. A good physician knows that hypochondria often masks a real ailment quite different from the one imagined by the patient. Could it be that our very deep concern about the state of the world is a form of global hypochrondria? If it is, then we might ask whether it is wise in such an event to seek only the advice of expert scientists like climatologists or biogeochemists. It could be that the real planetary malaise is beyond the understanding of their expertise. It might seem that we have no other options; the practice of planetary medicine does not yet exist.

Let us assume that there is some truth in the foregoing speculation and consider what might be the next step to take. It might involve the establishment of this new profession of planetary medicine. What would be the qualifications for a planetary physician? If the history of medicine is a guide, they will grow from guesses and empiricism. But early in the history of medicine, physiology, the systems science of individual humans, strongly influenced its further progress. The recognition by Paracelsus that 'the poison is the dose' was a physiological enlightenment still to be discovered by those environmentalists who seek the unattainable and pointless goal of zero for pollutants.

The discovery, by Harvey, of the circulation of the blood added further to the wisdom of medicine, as did meteorology to our understanding of the earth. The expert sciences of biochemistry and microbiology came much later; it took a long time before their new vision enhanced the practice of medicine. . . .

Geophysiology [is] a systems approach to the earth sciences. It is the essential theoretical basis for the putative profession of planetary medicine. In no way would geophysiology replace or lessen the importance of the established sciences; it is complementary to them.

MAN'S IMPACT

BY NORMAN MYERS

As people were made aware of the great disparity of income between countries of the rich north and the poor south, so, too, they learned of the extent to which natural environments in low latitudes were being altered. In particular, they came to hear of the rate at which tropical forests were being cleared. This issue is now of major international importance and is clearly part of the political agenda. That we and our governments are compelled to take note of it is due mainly to those conservationists and environmentalists who have worked to bring the fate of the tropical forests to our attention. Norman Myers, a professional ecologist, is foremost among these publicists, and as this extract demonstrates, he comes armed with a formidable array of facts, figures and examples to support his conservationist plea. The extract is taken from his book *The Sinking Ark*, published in 1979.

M an has exerted profound impact on tropical moist forests for millenia. This is apparent from the fact that suitable climatic conditions are available in roughly 12 per cent of the earth's land surface, yet only 58 per cent of this zone supports forests (true, part of the discrepancy lies in soil factors). Much of the deforestation was caused by primitive man, who burned back the forest-edges century after century. This was the case especially in Africa, where prior to modern times the forest may have been reduced by as much as one million square kilometres, or an area four times the size of Great Britain or as large as Texas and New Mexico. Through this lengthy destructive process, many thousands of species have almost certainly been eliminated by the forebears of modern man.

In recent times, forests in all three main tropical regions have been steadily reduced. The predominant factor has been peasant agriculture, coupled with the use of wood for fuel. In addition, the last 20 years have seen two major further factors. First, and especially in Central and South America, large tracts of forest have been burned to make way for modern agriculture, notably stock-raising pasturelands. Second, forests have been increasingly exploited for their highly valued hardwoods. This has been particularly significant in South-east Asia and in the West African sector of Africa's forests, and it is becoming important in Amazonia. The accelerated rate of timber exploitation has been fostered by expanding technology. Instead of the man-powered saw and axe of the 1950s, a modern chainsaw can slice through a tree in a matter of minutes. Caterpillar tractors with cable-winch and blade handle outsize logs with ease. A tree-crusher can topple and pulp several forest giants in one hour, while a complex of modern machinery can clear a whole hectare of forest in just a couple of hours.

The overall impact of this expanding exploitation of forests and forestlands is that we could be losing as much as 245,000 square kilometres of tropical forests each year, or almost 50 hectares per minute. While these are very rough-and-ready figures, they give an idea of the scale of present destruction. When the figures are extrapolated, they suggest that all tropical moist forests could be destroyed within less than 40 years.

This is a crude reckoning, since advanced technology could encourage more intensive and efficient use of forests and forestlands, thus relieving pressure on virgin areas. Conversely, as human populations increase, the urge to clear forests will grow progressively. Population growth in most of the countries in question is exceptionally high. Whereas the United Nations estimates a growth rate for the world of 1.6 per cent per year, and for developing countries as a whole of a little over 2 per cent, West and Central Africa's is put at 2.6 per cent, South-east Asia's at 2.7 per cent, and tropical America's at around 3 per cent. By the end of the century, Nigeria's populace is projected to grow from its present 76 million to 135 million, Indonesia's from 142 million to 235 million, and Brazil's from 114 million to 212 million. Still more critical than the upsurge in human numbers could be the upsurge in human aspirations. Per capita GNP in these three countries amounts respectively to only US $140, 120 and 580 per year. Crudely expressed, almost twice as many people by the end of the century are likely to generate at least twice as much pressure, and far more than that in view of their growing aspirations. It is not unrealistic, then, to surmise with IUCN and many other authorities, that the end of the century could see the elimination of large areas of tropical moist forests.

At the same time, of course, it is important to recognize that the devastation will not be evenly spread throughout the biome. At the one extreme, most lowland forests of the Philippines and Peninsular Malaysia are likely to have been logged over by 1985; much the same applies to West Africa. Little could remain of Central America's forests within another 10 years. Virtually all of Indonesia's lowland forests seem certain to have been exploited for timber by the year 2000; something similar could well hold good for Colombia and Peru, where, together with extensive areas of eastern Amazonia in Brazil, cattle ranching could claim large tracts of virgin forest. In Central Africa, however, where low human densities and an abundance of mineral resources induce far less incentive to convert the forests into quick cash, there could well be large expanses of little disturbed forest by the end of the century; and because of its remoteness, the same could apply to western Amazonia in Brazil. The overall outcome, then, is likely to be 'patchy', and a figure for average rates of forest conversion throughout the biome should be considered from the standpoint of individual countries.

Certain it is, however, that if present patterns of exploitation persist, the foreseeable future will witness the elimination of vast tracts of tropical moist forests. This would not be the first time that extensive sectors of earth's forest cover have been removed. Europe used to be forested for 90 per cent of its area until around AD 900 when steady conversion of forestlands to agriculture gained momentum. Now Europe's forests account for only 20 per cent of the continent. At the time of Columbus' arrival in North America, the moist eastern portion of what is now the United States was covered with dense forests, covering 1.6 million square kilometres to the edge of the great plains; now less than 5 per cent remain in virgin form. Some of this forest clearing did not have adverse repercussions for the agricultural communities that thereby developed; and so far as is known, very few species were eliminated, since many non-tropical creatures prove adaptable to the intrusions of man. By contrast, broad-scale elimination of forests in the tropics will have a far-reaching impact, through soil erosion, etc., on agricultural communities; it will disrupt various other forms of development, e.g. generation of energy through hydropower facilities (dams will silt up as a consequence of deforestation); and the fallout of species could well reach hundreds of thousands if not millions.

The elimination of species in such numbers would represent a distinct loss to society. Already tropical-forest species have made a major contribution to human welfare. They have supplied the origins of many staple foods, rice, millet, cassava, pigeon pea, mung bean, yam, taro, banana, pineapple and sugarcane, to name but the better known. A huge cornucopia of further foods waits to be investigated. In Indonesia alone, around 4,000 plant species are thought to have proved useful to native peoples as food of one sort or another, yet less than one-tenth have come into wide use. At least 1,650 plants of tropical forests offer highly nutritious leaves. In New Guinea, 251 tree species bear edible fruit, though only 43 have been brought into cultivation; a hitherto uncultivated fruit of South-east Asia, the mangosteen, has been described as 'perhaps the world's best tasting fruit'. A vine from tropical forests of southern China, known as the Chinese gooseberry, bears fruit with juice 15-18 times richer in vitamin C than orange juice. Nor are all these foods limited to local consumption; high-protein beans from Nigeria have found favour with Wisconsin farmers.

Moreover, tropical moist forests contain many wild relatives of modern food crops. These crops, the refined products of genetic engineering, require constant 'topping up' with fresh germ plasm in order to resist new types of diseases and pests, environmental stresses and the like, as well as to increase productivity and nutritive content. During this century, genetic resources from the wild have saved a number of important crops, including bananas, sugarcane, cocoa and coffee. To give an idea of economic values involved, groundnuts worldwide have suffered from leaf-spot diseases – a problem that proved surmountable through resistant varieties from wild forms in the rain forests of Amazonia among other areas. The annual value of eliminating the disease is estimated, by the International Crop Research Institute for the Semi-Arid Tropics, at $500 million. Similar large-scale benefits could be documented for rubber, coconut and palm oil.

Forest animals too can assist modern agriculture. Within the forests of the Thailand/Kampuchea (Cambodia) border lives a secretive cow-like creature, the kouprey. This animal is believed to have been one of the wild ancestors of the humped zebu cattle of southern Asia. So fresh cross-breeding between the two bovids could boost cattle raising throughout an entire region. Regrettably, the kouprey's survival is doubtful, due to military activities within its habitats during the past 15 years. Other wild bovids of South-east Asia's forests, such as the selatang, the tamarau and the anoa, could possibly help cattle raising. Like the kouprey, their numbers have all been severely reduced through man's disruption of their life-support systems.

Not only can tropical forests serve as sources of new and

improved foods, but they can help to keep down the numerous pests that reduce the amount of food already grown throughout the world. Despite an annual pesticide bill of several billion dollars, at least 40 per cent of our crops are lost each year to insects and similar pests, both in the fields and in storage. A sound way to control pests is to utilize chemicals from plants that have developed mechanisms to repel insects. The main source for these plants is the tropical moist forests, with their extraordinary variety of plant forms that have co-evolved in balance with their insect associates. Pest control can also be advanced through selective breeding of adapted species of insects - a method that could prove more effective and economic in the long run and result in less environmental disruption than broad-scale application of persistent toxic chemicals. For instance, the little-documented ichneumonid wasps, comprising many thousands of species in tropical moist forests, could offer much potential as predators and parasites of insect pests. According to a recent study by the US Department of Agriculture, biological control programmes that entail importation of counter-pests from abroad into the United States are believed to return $30 for every $1 invested. For example, citrus growers in Florida have been able to save their industry $25-35 million a year through a one-time outlay of $35,000 for the importation of three types of parasitic wasps.

In addition to providing a hefty boost to agriculture, tropical moist forests are earth's main repository of drug-yielding plants. The highest percentage of alkaloid-bearing plants is to be found in lowland rain forests, and the yield of these plants is the highest. At least 70 per cent of all plants that are known to possess anti-cancer properties, 3,000 species in all, exist in the tropics, and a similar proportion in tropical moist forests. The huge stock of tropical forest plants that has still to be investigated from scratch could well supply a similar proportion of anti-cancer drugs. In addition, recent research suggests that many insects, notably butterflies, offer potential for anti-cancer compounds – and tropical moist forests harbour between 1.5 and 3.5 million insect species. It is on these grounds that the US National Cancer Institute believes that the widespread elimination of tropical moist forests could represent a serious setback to the anti-cancer campaign.

To grasp what a single species can contribute to medicine, let us take a look at a small shrub of deciduous moist forests from India to South-east Asia, the Serpentine Root. This plant has been used for 4,000 years to treat snakebites, nervous disorders, dysentry, cholera and fever. In the late 1940s the plant turned out to be a fine hypotensive agent, and by 1953 it was used to relieve hypertension and schizophrenia. Shortly after that, its extract reserpine became the principal source of materials for tranquillizers. Before that time, high blood pressure strongly disposed a patient toward stroke, heart failure or kidney failure, but today this one plant helps many millions of people to lead a reasonably normal and healthy life, partially freed from a set of ailments – hypertension – that constitute the single greatest and fastest-growing source of mortality in advanced societies. As long ago as the early 1960s, this first modern tranquillizer generated sales in the United States worth $30 million per year.

In the developing world, the most widespread disease is malaria, afflicting 350 million people a year. Resistance to synthetic insecticides has been developed by fifty-seven species of mosquito (mosquitoes also spread filariasis, encephalitis, yellow fever and several other viral diseases). This means that at least one-third of all people exposed to malaria are now subject to increased risk. India, which reduced its 100 million cases in 1952 to 60,000 in 1962, recorded 6 million cases in 1976. This opens up renewed hope for the cinchona tree of Amazonia, whose bark yields quinine.

Let us also look briefly at a category of drugs that is of growing importance – those that serve as contraceptives and abortifacients. The rhizomes of a climbing vine, the Mexican yam, yield virtually the world's entire supply of diosgenin, from which a variety of sex-hormone combinations are prepared, including 'the pill'. (Apart from its exceptional role in regulating global population, diosgenin leads to manufacture of cortisone and hydrocortisone, used against rheumatoid arthritis, rheumatic fever, sciatica, certain allergies, Addison's disease and several skin diseases including contact dermatitis.) By the mid-1970s the world was using up to 180 tons of diosgenin per year; by 1985 the amount could rise to as much as 500 tons, and by 1995 to 3,000 tons, if the contraceptive needs of all women at risk are to be met. Right now, 80 million pills are used each day, and if total needs were recognized and catered for the figure would probably be 2.5 times higher. Current sales of Mexican yam materials for contraceptive pills amount to $7 million per year; when chemical compounds have been made up, the figure rises to $70 million, and when cross-counter sales for final products are totalled, the figure amounts to $700 million. In view of this end-product turnover in the commercial market-place, and in view of the fact that the yam has not been persuaded to grow anywhere but in tropical moist forests, the Mexican government decided in 1974 to seize a larger part of the action through jacking up export prices. As a result, 1 kg of diosgenin, that cost $11.75 in 1970, cost $152 in 1976.

A third category of products derives from tropical moist forests – specialist materials for industrial use. The range is wide. From South-east Asia's forests alone come latex, gums, camphor, damnor, resins, dyes and ethereal oils. In the wake of the cyclamate and saccharin controversies, there is urgent need for a non-nutritive sweetening agent, and many plant pigments, such as carotenoids in sweet-tasting fruits, serve as attractants in nature, so almost certainly are non-toxic to mammals, including man; there is prospect of several sources of sweeteners among forest plants of South-east Asia, where many fruits are exceptionally sweet tasting.

One group of industrial products is especially important, oils and lubricants. Many forest plants bear oil-rich seeds, e.g. the Babassu palm, the Seje palm, several species of the *Caryocar* genus, and a number of other trees that grow wild in Amazonia. The Babassu's fruit contain up to 72 per cent oil, which can be used to produce fibres, cattlefeed, soap, detergents, starch and general edibles, and can serve as a substitute for diesel oil. Similarly, the 'petroleum nut' of the Philippines produces a highly volatile oil, and was used by the Japanese as fuel during World War II.

Many other plants of tropical moist forests could offer utilitarian benefits to man, if their economic potential is investigated before their forest habitats are eliminated. Until fairly recently, the ramin and kuku trees of South-east Asia were considered weeds. One hundred years ago the value of the rubber tree was not remotely recognized. Who knows what new 'rubber tree' now stands in the way of some settlement project in Borneo or a ranching enterprise in Amazonia? How many tree species are there like the Monterrey Pine which existed in four local sites in California, and was undergoing steady reduction in numbers, until it was tried out as a plantation species, whereupon it became possibly the most important timber tree in the southern hemisphere? Tropical moist forests could contain many thousands of local endemic species like the Monterrey Pine, any of which could be forever lost in a single month's cutting for a forestland development project. This is not an unduly pessimistic prognosis. A tree that was once a major source of timber in Ecuador's lowland forests swiftly lost its native habitats to plantations of bananas and oil palms after its wildland home was opened up by a road in 1960; it is now reduced to twelve reproducing individuals in less than one square kilometre of forest at the Rio Palenque Biological Centre – the Centre itself being the last surviving patch of lowland wet forest along the western base of the Andes in central Ecuador, and containing almost fifty species of flowering plants no longer known anywhere else.

Not only wild species quickly disappear in their hundreds of thousands as tropical moist forests are cut and burned, but also another valuable 'resource' is likewise headed for oblivion, and that is the large number of forest-dwelling tribes who still pursue their traditional way of life. The number used to be much larger. In 1900 there were 230 tribal groups living in Brazil's sector of Amazonia, totalling one million people, but now there are only 143 groups numbering 50,000 people. On humanitarian grounds alone, forest tribes should be permitted to adapt to the outside world at their own pace. These considerations apart, the demise of forest peoples is all the more regrettable in that they represent a fund of experience whose value can hardly be estimated. Amerindians of Amazonia know of 750 plant species with medicinal properties. It was from Amazonian tribesmen who use curare, a muscle relaxant, on their arrow tips as a hunting poison, that Western-world surgeons learned of the substance's potential for human operations. A single village of forest dwellers in northern Thailand uses 119 plant varieties for medicine and 295 for food. Forest tribes of South-east Asia also supplied knowledge about the winged bean, a protein-rich plant that is now upgrading diets in over fifty countries. Many tribal peoples are aware of plant products that serve as contraceptives and abortifacients. Indonesia's National Biological Institute tells of a tribe that utilizes a forest tree as a spermicide, while certain South Pacific islands feature a number of forest plants that are used as first-month abortifacients. The World Health Organization is searching for safer and more effective materials from which to manufacture an improved 'pill', and believes the most likely source lies with tribal peoples who have used 3,000 plant species for their anti-fertility properties.

As this book has already pointed out, destruction of species and tropical forsts reflects the way both developing and developed nations go about their affairs. All are implicated; all will lose. It is appropriate therefore to end this chapter with a further dimension to the prospect of disappearing tropical forests. Due to climatic effects, there could be broad-ranging consequences for lands far outside the tropics, on a scale that would generate significant changes in lifestyle for many developed nations.

Although no conclusive scientific evidence has been presented as yet, a number of scientists believe that widespread clearing of tropical moist forests might affect climatic patterns in temperate zones. For one thing, cleared forestlands could start to reflect greater solar heat than before (the 'albedo' effect) and in turn, this could lead to changes in global patterns of air circulation, wind currents and convection processes. So far as climatologists can tell, a not unlikely outcome would be a decrease in rainfall in the equatorial zone, an increase of rainfall for lands between 5 and 25 degrees North and South, and a decrease for lands between 40 and 85 degrees in the North (not so much change in the southern hemisphere because of the greater extent of oceans). These climatic changes could prove critical for forest-growing territories of the northern temperate zones, notably the US/Canada grainlands.

Secondly, widespread elimination of tropical moist forests could contribute to a build-up of carbon dioxide in the earth's atmosphere (though it would make little or no difference to oxygen stocks). Carbon dioxide now amounts to about 0.03 per cent of the atmosphere, as compared with 78 per cent for nitrogen and 20 per cent for oxygen. The concentration of carbon dioxide has recently been increasing. Until 1860, when the Industrial Revolution stepped up the burning of fossil fuels, the concentration amounted, at most, to 290 parts per million. During the next 100 years it expanded by 20 parts or so, and the past 20 years have seen an increase of a further 20 parts. At the current rate of increase, which is itself increasing, the pre-1860 'natural' amount could well double by the year 2050 or soon afterwards.

Until recently it was thought that the increase was being absorbed partly by the oceans and partly by the earth's forests, especially by tropical moist forests with their huge capacity to soak up carbon dioxide through photosynthesis. Now, however, as forest burning overtakes the tropics, tropical forests probably serve no longer as a great natural 'sink'; rather they could become a net source of carbon dioxide. It has been estimated that if tropical forests were to be converted into carbon dioxide during the next 50 years, and to be replaced by no other vegetation that stores carbon dioxide on a similar scale, the process could dump carbon dioxide into the atmosphere at about the same rate for fossil fuels.

The consequences of carbon dioxide build-up could be severe. Carbon dioxide traps sunlight in the atmosphere and, through the 'greenhouse effect', causes the earth's temperature to rise. Twice as much carbon dioxide in the atmosphere seems likely to cause an average global increase of 2-3°C, a greater temperature change than has occurred during the past 10,000 years. As with the albedo effect, one result would be warmer and drier weather in the North American grain-growing region. A temperature increase of only 1°C could decrease US corn production by 11 per cent and could cut the gross income of spring wheat farmers by $268 million (at 1977 prices).

In addition, burning of huge amounts of tropical forest timber could lead to a great deal of particulate matter being released into the atmosphere. This troposphere dust could increase atmospheric subsidence, again leading to less rainfall.

In sum, then, elimination of tropical moist forests affects not only developing countries in question, but it could precipitate severe if not critical consequences for countries of the developed world as well. In other words, we either all lose together or, through sufficient conservation measures, we all gain together.

THE WARMING
OF THE EARTH

BY GÉRARD DORIN

During the 1980s fresh environmental concerns became prominent. They were hardly new, since scientists had been discussing them for many years, but previously they had attracted little attention from the press. As public concern increased, so did political pressure for action. In 1989, *The OECD Observer*, published in Paris by the Organization for Economic Co-operation and Development, published the article from which the following extract is taken. Gérard Dorin, of the OECD Environment Directorate, outlined the problem of the 'greenhouse effect', a phenomenon clearly linked to the clearance of tropical forest, as Norman Myers had pointed out ten years earlier. The extract is included here because it shows the way the problem was perceived by the intergovernmental agencies.

The scale of man's activities and the pace of their development have now reached the point where their cumulative effects on the environment are undermining the delicate natural and geophysical equilibria of the entire planet.

The thermal balance of the Earth's surface, which is governed by solar radiation, is highly sensitive to the concentrations of certain low-level gases: CO_2 (carbon dioxide), N_2O (nitrous oxide) and CH_4 (methane), referred to as 'greenhouse' gaes for this reason. These gases occur naturally in the atmosphere, but as a result of man's activities their concentrations have increased significantly. Other gases such as chlorofluorocarbons are exclusively man-made chemical products.

What do these gases do? In layman's terms, they allow heat radiating from the sun in the short wavelength spectrum (such as ultraviolet rays) to penetrate the Earth's atmosphere but prevent the heat that the Earth radiates back out to space in the long wavelength spectrum (infra-red rays) from escaping. This is the 'greenhouse' effect. In other words, they act as a kind of one-way thermal barrier by allowing heat from the sun to enter the atmosphere, but preventing it from leaving. The result is a gradual warming of the Earth's atmosphere, land masses and oceans.

To judge from the geological record, previous changes in the world's climate seem often to have been closely linked to the amount of atmospheric CO_2. Research into palaeoclimatology should help provide a clearer understanding of these phenomena and indicate the appropriate steps to be taken.

CO_2 is essential for life on earth. But any disruption in its natural cycle or level of concentration may have serious consequences. The rapid emergence of industrial civilization has led to a sharp increase in the concentration of atmospheric CO_2, chiefly as a result of burning fossil fuels but also because of massive deforestation of large areas of the planet. N_2O is produced naturally through the denitrification of soils; the present rise in N_2O levels is the result of burning fossil fuels and also of a massive increase in the use of nitrates as fertilizers. Methane (CH_4) is produced in part by fermentation, particularly in wetlands; the current increase can chiefly be blamed on oil and gas, but also, for example, on the development of rice cultivation and intensive animal-rearing.

Chlorofluorocarbons (CFCs, including freon) differ from these naturally occurring gases. They are exclusively man-made chemical products, are virtually indestructible and have the dubious distinction of not only actively contributing to the greenhouse effect but also destroying ozone in the stratosphere.

Energy consumption worldwide has now reached 10,000,000,000 tonnes of coal equivalent (tce) per year (in 1900 it amounted to 800 million tce). Over 80% of this energy is generated by burning fossil fuels (40% from oil, 24% from coal and 17% from gas), which releases some 20,000,000,000 tonnes of CO_2 into the atmosphere. The overwhelming magnitude of this figure provides some measure of the size of the problem. All other sources together account for merely 19%: 2% from hydroelectricity, 2% from nuclear power, 15% from biomass (i.e. wood, used mainly in the Third World).

Rapid deforestation, which although a worldwide phenomenon is concentrated mainly in the tropics, and the desertification of vast tracts of land have also contributed to the build-up in atmospheric CO_2.–

Deforestation and desertification are closely linked. The surface area of tropical rainforest has shrunk alarmingly over the last few decades as a result of demographic pressure for farmland, firewood and timber. After a few years deforested land often becomes unsuitable for agriculture, especially if it lies on a slope (through soil depletion, erosion, and so on). The forest is often no longer capable of regeneration and the land becomes semi-arid. Once the forest has disappeared, rainfall diminishes, the soil deteriorates and dries out, and the climate in the region gradually becomes more arid. The resulting familiar vicious circle, when combined with increased atmospheric CO_2, is likely to exacerbate climatic changes and desertification, as in the Sahel region.

The implications of this gradual warming for hundreds of millions of people may be catastrophic: rapid rises in sea level, prolonged drought, upheaval in the Earth's general climate.

The oceans are warming up. The sea level is currently rising at a rate of approximately two millimetres a year, a considerable amount. This rise in turn leads to coastal erosion, which has already reached worrying proportions in many areas of the world. It is thought that the rise in sea level will be accelerated through melting at the polar ice caps and thermal expansion of the ocean water as it becomes warmer. Scientists estimate that sea level will rise from one-half to two metres by the end of the next century (provided that the stability of the enormous coastal ice shelves in Antarctica remains unaffected). Since the world's most densely populated areas (Bangladesh, the Nile Delta, China, Indonesia, Japan, the Netherlands) and most urban conglomerations are to be found at sea level, the dramatic socio-economic and political implications of this rapid rise in sea level can easily be grasped.

In low-lying and densely populated coastal plains (such as Bangladesh), for example, sea walls could be built as a temporary measure to protect against flooding. But how can one stop the areas within these walls from being flooded when after heavy rainfall (particularly during the monsoon) it is increasingly difficult for the water to drain into the sea? These areas will tend to become marshy and saline, and their indigent inhabitants will flock into the major cities in what is now, unfortunately, a familiar pattern.

According to recent reports, the size and number of icebergs breaking off from the ice sheets in Antarctica seem to be increasing. Approximately 80% of the world's ice is to be found in Antarctica in sheets up to several thousand metres thick (Greenland has 20% and all other glaciers together account for less than 1%). The vast Ross and Weddell ice shelves in western Antarctica are poorly anchored to the basement rock (located below sea level) with the result that sea water penetrates into the gap between the rock and the ice over immense areas. With the rise in ocean temperatures, there is a danger that these glaciers might slip, perhaps even before the end of the next century, and break off into the sea (thereby raising sea level by about five to six metres).

Another cause for concern is the recent change in the pattern of ocean currents, an example being 'El Niño' in the Pacific and the successive droughts in South America which it seems to have caused. The main ocean currents have a major impact on the weather (temperature, rainfall) in the continents that they wash, and changes might have serious implications. What might happen to Europe were the Gulf Stream ever to change course doesn't bear thinking about.

In the last decade or so, major droughts have become more frequent in many areas of the world such as the Sahel, Ethiopia and Brazil; the list of such areas is impressive – and depressing. Is it merely coincidence, or is it a sign of changes that have already taken place in the world's climate? Major droughts, particularly when they last a number of years, as is now often the case, can ruin agriculture and national economies and bring about real catastrophes in human and social terms, through famine and forced exoduses; they may even have political repercussions (conflicts and destabilization). Even though developed countries are sometimes affected, such as the United States in 1988, the severest impact is likely to be felt in developing countries in tropical and subtropical latitudes where any damage will be compounded by a shortage of technical and economic resources.

In the tropics in particular, attempting to replace the shortage of rainfall through irrigation will pose enormous problems: how to find the vast quantities of water required, pay for the construction and maintenance of an irrigation system and then combat the adverse repercussions of such systems (increased soil salinity, and parasitic diseases such as bilharzia and malaria, which already afflict hundreds of millions of people in these regions)?

What can be done to try to avert these developments? The problem is overwhelming and will call for all nations to make extraordinary efforts for a long period of time. The fight will have to be led simultaneously on a number of fronts. Firstly, preventative measures will have to be taken. Emission of all greenhouse gases (CO_2, N_2O, CH_4, CFCs) will have to be reduced considerably. Large-scale reforestation is required at all latitudes to bring about a massive and permanent increase in the Earth's capacity to deal with CO_2. Corrective measures will also have to be taken (in water engineering, agricultural practices, and in economic and social activities) to try to counter the adverse effects of these phenomena. Will the world's nations be willing to pay the high price that these efforts of vital importance to the global community will demand?

THE WOOING
OF THE EARTH

BY RENÉ DUBOS

René Dubos, an emeritus professor at The Rockefeller University, New York and a distinguished microbiologist and pathologist, is also one of the leading thinkers and writers on environmental issues and one of the most profound. His appreciation of and love for the natural world runs very deep, as does his anger and dismay at its despoliation. Yet he does not fall into the trap of despair, suspecting that environmentalist fears of extinction are really fears of the loss of a particular way of life. Like James Lovelock, he is aware of the regenerative capacity of natural systems. As this extract from his book *The Wooing of Earth* published in 1980 shows, he rejects utterly the view that any human interference with the natural world is necessarily harmful.

When the Bengali poet Rabindranath Tagore (1861-1941) first travelled as a student from India to England in 1878, he realised immediately that the visual charm and agricultural productivity of the European countryside were the result, in his worlds, of 'the perfect union of man and nature, not only through love but also through active communication.' Travelling by railroad from Brindisi to Calais, he 'watched with keen delight and wonder that continent flowing with richness under the age-long attention of her chivalrous lover, western humanity.' For him, the shaping of the European continent by human labour constituted the 'heroic love-adventure of the West, the *active wooing* of the earth' (italics mine). Yet it is unlikely that Tagore fully appreciated the extent to which the countryside he saw from the train had been shaped by more than a hundred generations of peasants out of the forests and marshes that covered most of western Europe before human occupation.

When first seen by Tagore, Europe presented some of history's most successful landscapes created by the interplay between humankind and Earth. There was still some genuine wilderness, but it had been pushed back to mountain-tops and other areas not suitable for human settlements, where it could be admired in safety. Most of the land had been settled, but except in a few places, it had not yet been abused by industrial civilization and by formless urbanisation. Means of communication provided easy access to practically all parts of the land, integrating them into organic units but without destroying regional individuality. Villages and towns had been built with instinctive grace using local materials that made them appear to be an expression of nature. The quality of blessedness that emerges from long periods of intimate association between human beings and nature was an essential part of my own experience at the beginning of this century. In the Île de France region, where I was born and raised, what is called nature is profoundly different from the original wilderness. It has been progressively created since Neolithic times by the work of the peasantry – in Tagore's words, by the 'active wooing of the earth.'

The Île de France was almost entirely covered by trees in the Stone Age, and there is no doubt that it would rapidly return to a state of forested wilderness if it were abandoned. Although the region is commonly regarded as having charm and elegance, its qualities are largely the result of human management. The hills have such low profiles that their only remarkable features are the diversified farmlands and the carefully managed woodlands they now support. The streams are small and sluggish but their shores have been polished and are commonly associated with gentle pastoral scenes. The sky is rarely spectacular and indeed often cloudy, but the climate and the soft luminosity are favourable to an immense diversity of vegetation, much of which either has been introduced from other parts of the world or has been transformed by domestication. Villages with venerable churches crown the summits of the hills or nestle in the valleys, making the human presence everywhere a part of the scenery.

Since the clearing of the primeval forest that began in Neolithic times, the Île de France has acquired a humanised quality that transcends its natural endowments. It has repeatedly experienced destructive wars and social upheavals yet has constantly supported a high population density. Its land has remained fertile and has provided a home for many different forms of civilisation. Humanising the Île de France has admittedly resulted in the loss of many values associated with the wilderness. From the human point of view, however, at least according to my taste and that of many other people, the region is now visually more diversified and emotionally richer than it was in its original forested state. It provides a typical example of what I shall discuss later as the symbiosis of humankind and Earth.

I have used the case of the Île de France to introduce the theme of humanisation of the Earth only because this is the region of my birth and upbringing, but what I wrote about it applies to many other parts of the world as well. In most place where human beings have settled, they have created out of the wilderness artificial environments that have become so familiar that they are commonly assumed to be natural although they have a cultural origin. Every continent can boast of 'cultural environments' – to use an expression translated from the German and recently introduced into the ecological jargon – that have remained fertile and attractive for immense periods of time and have long been the true homes of humanity.

While the wilderness is still being destroyed in several parts of the world, the most extensive destruction occurred many centuries ago. Surprising as it may seem, a large percentage of the Earth's surface in the Old World was transformed by ancient peoples working with primitive tools and a few domestic animals. The process began during the Stone Age when the agricultural lands of the very first civilisations were created from the Mesopotamian wilderness between the Euphrates and the Tigris. The humanisation of the Earth has continued ever since; it was essentially completed in most of Europe and Asia during the eighteenth century. Depending upon the places, it involved deforestation, drainage, irrigation, or such spectacular changes in topography as the terracing of slopes in hilly regions and the reclaiming of land from the sea, as in the Netherlands.

Destruction of the wilderness was delayed in the New World as long as population density remained much lower than that of other parts of the Earth, although preagricultural Indians contributed to the process by the forest fires they repeatedly set in the western parts of the continent. The destruction of the American wilderness proceeded rapidly after the arrival of Europeans. When the United States Census Bureau reported the close of the frontier in 1890, immense areas of North America had been deforested, the 'breaking' of the prairie was essentially completed, and large irrigation projects were on the way.

The peasantry of the Old World and the settlers of North America thus created out of the wilderness the cultural environments that constitute most of what we now call Nature. As a result, the various regions of the Earth acquired their distinctive characteristics from agriculture and social institutions, as much as from geology, topography, climate, and rainfall. In other words, except in places that have remained in the primeval state of wilderness, the word *nature* implies human as well as physical geography.

In the temperate zone, a typical humanized landscape consists of pastures and arable lands in the low altitudes and on gentle slopes. Forests occupy almost exclusively the higher altitudes and other areas unsuited to agriculture, industry, or human habitation. Most of the bodies of water have been confined within well-tended banks, controlled by dams, rechannelled, or disciplined in other ways. Despite all this human ordering, we forget that these typical sceneries bear little resemblance to what they would be without human management. We have lived in intimate familiarity with them so long that we contemplate them in a mood of casual acceptance and reverie without giving thought to their origin and evolution. We even forget that most villages and cities are on sites first occupied by human settlements centuries or millenia ago and that ·roads, highways, and railroad tracks commonly follow trails first opened by hunters, pastoralists, and farmers ages ago.

Many of the animals and plants in humanized landscapes differ from those of the original wilderness, either because they belong to species introduced from other parts of the world or because local species have been genetically modified by selection or other biological manipulation. It is through human agency that wheat, corn, rice, barley, potatoes, tomatoes, oranges, grapefruit, and countless other crops are now cultivated far from their place of origin; that eucalyptus trees grow in California, Italy, Greece, or North Africa, often more vigorously than in their native Australia; that African violets adorn homes in most parts of the world, whether communist or capitalist politically. The tulip, now thought to be characteristic of Holland, was actually introduced there from Turkey. Almond trees, fig trees, and olive trees, which call to mind the Mediterranean region, in fact originated in Asia. One of the most enchanting Greek landscapes is a large olive grove in a valley near Delphi, which must be more than three thousand years old since it is mentioned in Homeric writings.

Above and beyond the agricultural production made possible by destruction of the wilderness, the clearing of the forest generated environmental values that have now become part of the human view of nature. It exposed the architectural skeleton of the various geologic strata – for example, the contrasting structures and textures of white chalky formations or of granitic boulders covered with lichens and mosses. Within a given ecological system, partial deforestation created furthermore an environmental diversity that provides nourishment for the senses and for the psyche. A very human harmony exudes from the mosaics of cultivated fields, pastures, and woodlands, as well as from the alternation of sunlit surfaces and shaded areas. The humanisation of the Earth has created, between clearing and woodland, a ruffled skirt of brush rich in brilliant fruit and bird life. My childhood in the farming country of the Île de France has left me vivid memories of moods that ranged from the joyfulness of the lark's call rising from the wheat fields to the quiet of adjacent woodlands.

Human intervention has profoundly transformed the surface of the Earth even in the most unlikely places. As mentioned earlier, the tall grass of the prairie that used to cover part of the north American continent emerged as an indirect consequence of forest fires set by preagricultural Indians. The moors of the British Isles, which have inspired so much literature, do not represent the original natural system of the region; they progressively developed after the deforestation that began during Neolithic times and was maintained by the population of sheep and rabbits.

Human intervention has also helped to create many of the most beloved and productive landscapes of the world. In Tuscany and Umbria much of the land was moulded by peasants who rounded the hills and shaped the slopes to create an architecture of terraces.

In northwestern Europe, hedgerow and bocage* types of farming country were created either by law or for a variety of other purposes: marking ownership, establishing drainage systems, protecting crops from the wind, and so on.

In southern China, the very artificial 'water and mountain' landscapes are among the most monumental sceneries of the world and also the most productive of edible animal and plant life.

In the agricultural areas of the island of Kyushu and other agricultural parts of Japan, trees and land seem to be trimmed to human specifications, measured to human scale. Visitors to the Islands of the Rising Sun in the nineteenth century were amazed to find them laid out as an all-embracing park with farms, villages, and temples beautifully interspersed and integrated.

Although the conscious transformation of the wilderness is more recent on the North American continent than in Asia or Europe, it has taken similar directions. The villages of New England, with their greens and open fields cosily nestled in the valleys, could not have come into existence without the clearing of the primeval forest. In Lincoln, Massachusetts, the low wetlands were kept free of trees by

*With small, scattered patches of woodland.

periodic controlled flooding, a practice that farmers called 'flooding the meadows.' Destruction of the wilderness in that region meant disappearance of certain game birds, such as the wild pigeon and the wild turkey, but the creation of open areas created habitats for many song birds: bobolinks and meadowlarks in the fields, orioles and bluebirds in the orchards, warblers darting among the treetops, swallows snatching insects from the air. The abundance and availability of low, tender new growth in the cutover forest allowed a spectacular multiplication of white-tailed deer – to the point of overpopulation.

The Pennsylvania Dutch country, too, was completely forested three centuries ago and has now been transformed into manicured fields. In the Lake Saint John region of Canada, consisting chiefly of sand plains and granitic outcrops, periodic burning keeps out the forest and favours the growth of blueberries, which find a profitable outlet on the Montreal and New York markets. All over the central and western plains and deserts of North America, the industrialisation of agriculture has led to the creation of humanised landscapes of gigantic dimensions that fit the enormous size of the original ecosystems. Over much of the world, farmland has become the most distinctive feature of the scenery. It constitutes the 'Nature' that has replaced the wilderness in the minds of both rural and urban people.

WORLD CONSERVATION STRATEGY

In the late 1970s, Robert Allen, formerly of *The Ecologist* but at that time working for the International Union for Conservation of Nature and Natural Resources (IUCN), coordinated the production of a document that in 1980 was circulated to every government. Distilled from the contributions of innumerable specialists and published in collaboration with the UN Environment Programme and the World Wildlife Fund, the *World Conservation Strategy* was meant to encourage governments to devise their own national programmes for sustainable development. Some did, including Britain, but there is little evidence that it influenced policy. The following extract is from the introduction.

E arth is the only place in the universe known to sustain life. Yet human activities are progressively reducing the planet's life-supporting capacity at a time when rising human numbers and consumption are making increasingly heavy demands on it. The combined destructive impacts of a poor majority struggling to stay alive and an affluent minority consuming most of the world's resources are undermining the very means by which all people can survive and flourish.

Humanity's relationship with the biosphere (the thin covering of the planet that contains and sustains life) will continue to deteriorate until a new international economic order is achieved, a new environmental ethic adopted, human populations stabilize, and sustainable modes of development become the rule rather than the exception. Among the prerequisites for sustainable development is the conservation of living resources.

Development is defined here as: the modification of the biosphere and the application of human, financial, living and non-living resources to satisfy human needs and improve the quality of human life. For development to be sustainable it must take account of social and ecological factors, as well as economic ones; of the living and non-living resource base; and of the long term as well as the short term advantages and disadvantages of alternative actions.

Conservation is defined here as: the management of human use of the biosphere so that it may yield the greatest sustainable benefit to present generations while maintaining its potential to meet the needs and aspirations of future generations. Thus conservation is positive, embracing preservation, maintenance, sustainable utilization, restoration, and enhancement of the natural environment. Living resource conservation is specifically concerned with plants, animals and micro-organisms, and with those non-living elements of the environment on which they depend. Living resources have two important properties the combination of which distinguishes them from non-living resources: they are renewable if conserved; and they are destructible if not.

Conservation, like development, is for people; while development aims to achieve human goals largely through use of the biosphere, conservation aims to achieve them by ensuring that such use can continue. Conservation's concern for maintenance and sustainability is a rational response to the nature of living resources (renewability + destructibility) and also an ethical imperative, expressed in the belief that 'we have not inherited the earth from our parents, we have borrowed it from our children'.

Conservation is a process – to be applied cross-sectorally – not an activity sector in its own right. In the case of sectors (such as agriculture, fisheries, forestry and wildlife) directly responsible for the management of living resources, conservation is that aspect of management which ensures that utilization is sustainable and which safeguards the ecological processes and genetic diversity essential for the maintenance of the resources concerned. In the case of other sectors (such as health, energy, industry), conservation is that aspect of management which ensures that the fullest sustainable advantage is derived from the living resource base and that activities are so located and conducted that the resource base is maintained.

Living resource conservation has three specific objectives:

to maintain essential ecological processes and life-support systems (such as soil regeneration and protection, the recycling of nutrients, and the cleansing of waters), on which human survival and development depend;

to preserve genetic diversity (the range of genetic material found in the world's organisms), on which depend the breeding programmes necessary for the protection and improvement of cultivated plants and domesticated animals, as well as much scientific advance, technical innovation, and the security of many industries that use living resources;

to ensure the sustainable utilization of species and ecosystems (notably fish and other wildlife, forests and grazing lands), which support millions of rural communities as well as major industries.

Living resource conservation is just one of a number of conditions necessary to assure human survival and wellbeing, and a world conservation strategy is but one of a number of strategies needed: a strategy for peace; a strategy for a new international economic order; a strategy for human rights; a strategy for overcoming poverty; a world food supply strategy; a population strategy. Several of these issues are properly the subject of the International Development Strategy for the Third United Nations Development Decade. All such strategies should be mutually reinforcing. None has much chance of success unless they are. The integration of conservation and development is particularly important, because unless patterns of development that also conserve living resources are widely adopted, it will become impossible to meet the needs of today without foreclosing the achievement of tomorrow's.

Conservation and development have so seldom been combined that they often appear – and are sometimes represented as being – incompatible. Conservationists themselves have helped – quite unwittingly – to foster this misconception. Too often they have allowed themselves to be seen as resisting all development – although often they have been forced into that posture because they have not been invited to participate in the development process early enough. The result has been not to stop development, but to persuade many development practitioners, especially in developing countries, that conservation is not merely irrelevant, it is harmful and anti-social. Consequently, development has continued unimpeded by conservationists yet with the seeds of its eventual failure lying in the ecological damage that conservation could have helped prevent.

That conservation and sustainable development are mutually dependent can be illustrated by the plight of the rural poor. The dependence of rural communities on living resources is direct and immediate. For the 500 million people who are malnourished, or the 1500 million people whose only fuel is wood, dung or crop wastes, or the almost 800 million people with incomes of $50 or less a year – for all these people conservation is the only thing between them and at best abject misery, at worst death. Unhappily, people on the margins of survival are compelled by their poverty – and their consequent vulnerability to inflation – to destroy the few resources available to them. In widening circles around their villages they strip trees and shrubs for fuel until the plants wither away and the villagers are forced to burn dung and stubble. The 400 million tonnes of dung and crop wastes that rural people burn annually are badly needed to regenerate soils already highly vulnerable to erosion now that the plants that bind them are disappearing.

It would be wrong, however, to conclude that conservation is a sufficient response to such problems. People whose very survival is precarious and whose prospects of even temporary prosperity are bleak cannot be expected to respond sympathetically to calls to subordinate their acute short term needs to the possibility of long term returns. Conservation must therefore be combined with measures to meet short term economic needs. The vicious circle by which poverty causes ecological degradation which in turn leads to more poverty can be broken only by development. But if it is not to be self-defeating, it must be development that is sustainable – and conservation helps to make it so. The development efforts of many developing countries are being slowed or compromised by lack of conservation. In Southeast Asia excessive clearing of forests has caused fluctuations in river flow that are lowering rice yields. Throughout the developing world the lifetimes of hydroelectric power stations and water-supply systems are being cut as reservoirs silt up – because siltation is accelerated by deforestation, overgrazing and other unwise land uses.

The activities of every organism modify its environment, and those of human beings are no exception. Although environmental modification is both natural and a necessary part of development, this does not mean that all modification leads to development (nor that preservation impedes it). While it is inevitable that most of the planet will be modified by people and that much of it will be transformed, it is not at all inevitable that such alterations will achieve the social and economic objectives of development. Unless it is guided by ecological as well as by other environmental, and by social, cultural and ethical considerations, much development will continue to have undesired effects, to provide reduced benefits or even to fail altogether. – There is a close relationship between failure to achieve the objectives of conservation and failure to achieve the social and economic objectives of development – or, having achieved them, to sustain that achievement. Hence the goal of the World Conservation

Strategy is the integration of conservation and development to ensure that modifications to the planet do indeed secure the survival and wellbeing of all people.

THE NEW INTEREST IN 'SUSTAINABILITY'

BY BRIAN JOHNSON

In Britain, a response to the World Conservation Strategy was prepared by a team sponsored by the World Wildlife Fund UK, Nature Conservancy Council, Countryside Commission, Countryside Commission for Scotland, Royal Society of Arts, and Council for Environmental Conservation. The result, beginning with an overview by Brian Johnson from which the extract here is taken, was published in 1983.

C learly, the present course of resource-waste and destruction throughout much of the world is not sustainable, nor is Britain's present pattern of industrial development or decline. Interestingly, it was in 1982 for the first time that the word 'sustainability' was used in Government statements to define a new target for British economic development. However, the concept referred to sustainable economic expansion rather than the sustainable use of resources. The concepts are not necessarily opposed. A sustainable economy, and especially an expanding one, must imply a reliable supply of resources on which to draw.

How, though, should we define the idea of 'sustainability' for a country such as Britain? Certainly it cannot mean a fixed order of life, or any arrest in the course of society's development. If any such stability is sought, it inevitably implies one or other pattern of political control or behaviour. History teaches us that, over time, preconceived notions of social stability can never in fact be maintained for very long. Besides, it is difficult to embrace any such rigid concept when the conditions of life of so many people are, as at present, so miserably and unacceptably deprived.

The idea of sustainability, rather than stability, must relate to the reasonable prospects for any society, regardless of its social or economic organization, in relation to its resource-base, especially the prospective availability of reasonably priced energy which is the prime economic mover in any modernizing economy.

This sustainability is not yet much considered by Government in relation to the British economy. But many of the poor nations of the Third World are already finding their patterns of resource-consumption unsustainable because they are, too often, trapped in cycles of deprivation. Their population expansion gives them scant chance to reduce the handicap of initial poverty and lack of investment, and their proximity to the margins of survival forces them into something akin to self-immolation – preying upon and consuming the living resources on which their long-term future depends.

Britain, however, has no such handicaps. It has, like its European partners, a stable and beneficent (if somewhat more sombre) climate for both human toil and food production. In the case of Britain, 'unsustainability' is not the result of resource-destruction through desperation, but of some more readily avoidable condition. In our case, it seems, the problem is faulty and short-sighted thinking about the husbandry of available resources.

With hindsight it is possible to see that, throughout the period since the Second World War, we in Britain have generally paid too little attention to the husbanding of natural resources both at home and abroad. It seems extraordinary, for example, how few – and how unheard – were the people who foresaw in the early post-war period that the supply of oil from the Middle East was remarkably insecure. But the interruption of its supply or the dramatic raising of its price through cartelization was an odds-on prospect even in the 1950s, as political analysts at Political and Economic Planning (PEP) pointed out.

It has too readily been assumed that the supply of oil, as of other vital materials could be sustained in ever-increasing volume to meet world demand. Instead, the whole attention of political parties and the machinery of Government has been focused upon increased production and demand.

It should be stressed at this point that the resource-problem, even when we refer to non-living or finite resources (basically metals and minerals, including oil, coal and natural gas, air and water) is rarely one of *absolute* scarcity for Britain or indeed for any other advanced industrial country. Only a very few metal ores traded in the international market are in danger of exhaustion without adequate prospects of effective substitution or recycling. The politics of supply could only in a few instances produce long-term deprivation, though the disruption which they can cause may prove economically costly and strategically dangerous. Moreover, in the case of oil and gas, the prospects are increasingly of major new discoveries, especially off the continental coastlines. These reserves are likely to extend, by several decades at least, the time in which to secure alternative sources of supply, whether from the sun or hydrogen or the more fully mastered atom.

Moreover, the shift towards a more efficient use of resources does not inevitably require cumbersome supervision or wholesale public intervention. The market system of adjustment in preferences and expectation is generally more effective and dynamic than it is given credit for. At the same time, – judicious planning and public investment that spawns a range of private initiatives in every neighbourhood could stimulate a variety of new industries. Such measures as improving the insulation of buildings has been shown – to be able to create many new jobs. At the same time, such conservation programmes can save hundreds of millions of pounds which might otherwise be devoted to extracting more costly oil and gas or constructing new power stations with all their implications of pollution and resource-use. Moreover, the employment created would be geographically spread, reducing our particularly intractable problem of regional and structural unemployment.

True, a chosen path of more resource-conserving development will require a considerable effort of discipline and restraint, and particularly of public education. But evidence is accumulating that the British public are beginning to become aware of the challenge and may be ready for new initiatives.

In the course of this initial phase in evolving a Conservation and Development Programme for the UK, a first attempt was made to find out, via a public opinion poll, more about British attitudes to resource-use and the environment. –

The first finding of the poll – that the immediate social and economic concerns of unemployment, inflation and law and order come well ahead of any public worries about pollution or resource-depletion – is hardly surprising. What is interesting, however, is that the proportion of people polled who put anxiety about pollution and resource-depletion at the top of their priorities almost doubled (to 25 per cent and 16 per cent respectively) when asked questions about their daily lives as opposed to problems of Britain or the world in general. While this can in no way be taken as definitive it does represent evidence that many people's level of concern with the issues is substantially raised when they are provided with the facts in ways which relate them to their daily lives.

People's responses to questions concerning the need to conserve resources so as to sustain development were of particular interest. Forty-nine per cent of the nationwide sample believed there to be a risk of using up the world's resources; 39 per cent and 37 per cent respectively were strongly in favour of recycling and other anti-waste measures. Well over half (58 per cent) said they would support an increase of a penny in the pound on income tax to pay for effective measures to reduce resource-waste.–

Britain has the capacity and – there is potentially the public will to see conservation incorporated on a more systematic basis into policies and plans for our future development. This desire and this evidence of a will to change is, however, impeded by four major obstacles.

The first of these obstacles is the absence of any clear public awareness of the fact that world resource-problems can affect our economic and social prospects as a nation. It was clear from the poll that many more people saw environmental problems as a world concern than a British one – the main exception to this being the urban (inner city) environment. By contrast, slightly more people saw inflation and unemployment as a British rather than a world problem. – It seems that the notion that problems of the economy and conservation are two sides of the same coin is not yet accepted in the public mind. At the most basic level of domestic experience, it is understood that a thrifty household or business is one that thrives. The message that the same applies to whole countries and economies when it comes to planning for resource-use is not one which has been taught widely in schools, discussed by the media or aired publicly in any other way.

The tendency of those in public life to ignore issues of natural resource-management upon which economic growth depends has produced the second obstacle to public acceptance of an integrated approach: the polarized ideological positions of the country's intellectual and political leadership.

This has had the effect of encouraging people to believe that, if only the structure of power in our society were altered, all our other problems would be readily soluble. It remains heresy to suggest that the policy mixes, offered by the right, left or centre, may be incapable of producing prosperity with full employment if the resource-dimension is ignored.–

The ideological barrier tends to divert us from framing the right questions. It is closely linked to an institutional barrier, which suggests that the new ideals and targets simply are out of our reach. The great inertia in the institutions of Government, business, commerce and organized labour interacts with the obstacle of ideology. Ideology, often bolstered by a single-minded concentration on consumption and economic growth, is used to defend the present role and nature of the institutions, whether they be great private corporations, or nationalized industries, trades unions, Government Departments or regulatory agencies, the CBI, the TUC, or, indeed, 'the Treasury view'.–

Unless this sort of resistance and inertia yields to the pressure of conservation-minded interest groups, then little is likely to change beyond a slight tightening and perhaps broadening of the many piecemeal conservation measures that Britain has adopted or installed in the past.

Do we, perhaps, then, need a conservationist ideology to confront the major ideologies and their supporting institutions? The idea seems fraught with danger. First, it implies doctrinal rigidity regarding values, approaches and, indeed, measures. Such rigidity is inappropriate to the new directions indicated in this book. Second, it would also instantly confront a horizon ringed with opponents.–

But if we should avoid ideology in approaching a national strategy for conservation and development, we must be guided by a conserving ethic.–

Finally, there is finance: the fourth barrier to change. The recent mood of economic gloom is not conducive to any change which increases costs. When the going gets tough, environmental and resource-problems tend to be seen as luxuries to be dispensed with as we trim every possible ounce of fat from economic activity. Such desirable goals as environmental improvement must, it is claimed, be shelved until easier times yield a sufficient surplus to pay for the more costly procedures and investments which conservation-based development will involve in the short term. – It is a basic thesis underlying the whole of this programme, that resource-conservation will, in the longer term, be the only route to economic stability.

The question of costs – and of what is a cost and what is a benefit – raises another ethical issue. A change towards non-monetary values – also implies a shift in the prices that are placed upon different goods and services by common consent. This is the point or 'no-man's-land' where intrinsic values and economic value interrelate. In fact, under market pressures, more conserving patterns of development are already producing changes in personal values. Ask anyone trying to sell a large uninsulated house. This is the positive aspect of the price mechanism: promoting changes of lifestyle. The uninsulated house, the thirsty car, etc., simply become less desirable. Thus, the notion of desirability is not just economic. It shades into social and moral considerations as well.

The price mechanism also operates eventually to embrace goods which were 'free' or unpriced before. When fresh air becomes scarce, people become prepared to pay for it through clean air technology. In a similar way, conservationists are challenging the use of a pricing system which puts into the national accounts on the credit side all the goods and services sold and leaves out the 'bads' and 'dis-services' produced.

Such radical reassessments of our pricing and accounting systems cannot expect to gain public assent in the immediate future. Today, there is an understandable reluctance to abandon any measures which encourage economic expansion. This is not just the result of materialism or greed.

Now, as Britain strives to recover from the depths of a world slump, it is inevitable that measures that are seen to add to industrial or agricultural production costs, or increase the Public Sector Borrowing Requirement, or otherwise prejudice expansion, will be looked upon askance.

We must remember, too, as we examine opportunities for resource-conserving in our economy, that it is only by the production of a surplus within the national economy that Britain can afford to pay for and restore our dangerously dilapidated and depleted social welfare system, National Health Service, the State school system and other run-down areas of our public services. Besides, environmental costs, when added to the existing prices of manufactured goods, will, in many instances, raise those prices, and such rising costs could cut consumption.–

These are familiar arguments – A properly planned strategy could become a major feature of public investment that is undertaken to stimulate demand.

Such investment, by creating employment, could actually improve the social and economic equity in our society. The example already cited is that of energy conservation where, as a recent report by the consultants Environmental Resources Ltd. demonstrates, over 150,000 new jobs could be generated if Britain were to adopt a major energy conservation-investment programme which would pay for itself within five years of completion and would save £2,800m worth of fuel per year.

The urban and rural sector reports make a similar case for other investments in our national infrastructure – for example, reconstructing our decaying Victorian sewage systems or maintaining our priceless rural heritage while creating new landscapes for tomorrow. In most of the examples – shifts in benefits (income) between groups in our society, and between this and future generations, would clearly be redistributive.–

Through our membership of the Commonwealth, our various overseas associations and memberships, our treaty obligations and signatures on Conventions, Britain has, willy nilly, developed elements of an overseas environmental policy. In general it must be said that our international steps so far have been cautious and somewhat lacking conviction. True, on several major issues of international environmental concern, Britain has taken a positive line – especially in recognizing the linkage between poverty and environmental destruction in the poorest countries. However on other policy questions such as over the Law of the Sea, the international impact of acid rain, or European proposals to require some form of environmental assessment for major development schemes, Britain has been among the more resistant to an open examination of the issues.–

Only by identifying and assessing the environmental and resource-demands that we as a nation make on our overseas trading partners and those countries who receive our aid, can we begin to examine how far we must go to eliminate those practices which undermine the sustainable development of others.–

This exercise will reveal large opportunities for British expertise, services and products abroad, especially if Britain adopts a positive view of the need for a more conserving pattern of development both in the poorer countries and at home.–

These opportunities, if tested and found to be solid and real, will demonstrate that, for a relatively modest outlay, the return to be expected from more conserving patterns of development can in many instances rapidly become good business for the individual firm or entrepreneur and for the country as a whole; in others, controls and similar mechanisms will add costs, but even here as with clean air, technology can rapidly produce new economic opportunities.

At a less mundane level, the wider vista also suggests a role for British leadership. Perhaps because of their early embarkation into industrialization and thus early laying waste of so many of their own natural resources, some countries, and Britain in particular, have had a longer time to consider, and attempt to rectify, the results of this despoliation. As a result, they have played a leading role in the international conservation movement and in establishing principles for sound resource-management.

Through the world-wide knowledge of our culture and of our language, and through the reach of our communications systems, Britain has the means to play a role far beyond that implied by our present economic standing in shaping the world culture of ideas. It is a role not unworthy of a mature, increasingly post-industrial, nation seeking new avenues for its skills and for its remarkable resources of ingenuity.

WORLD COMMISSION ON ENVIRONMENT AND DEVELOPMENT

'Sustainability' was also a major theme in the latest of what has become a series of international reports. In 1983 the World Commission on Environment and Development was established at the request of the UN Secretary-General in response to a call from the UN General Assembly, its brief to produce 'a global agenda for change'. The Commission was headed by Norwegian Prime Minister Gro Harlem Brundtland and consisted of a vice-chairman (Sudanese) and twenty members (one of them ex officio), from nineteen countries. The report was published in 1987, as *Our Common Future*. This extract outlines the global situation as it appeared to the Commission and it also says a little about the way the Commission worked.

The Earth is one but the world is not. We all depend on one biosphere for sustaining our lives. Yet each community, each country, strives for survival and prosperity with little regard for its impact on others. Some consume the Earth's resources at a rate that would leave little for future generations. Others, many more in number, consume far too little and live with the prospect of hunger, squalor, disease, and early death.

Yet progress has been made. Throughout much of the world, children born today can expect to live longer and be better educated than their parents. In many parts, the new-born can also expect to attain a higher standard of living in a wider sense. Such progress provides hope as we contemplate the improvements still needed, and also as we face our failures to make this Earth a safer and sounder home for us and for those who are to come.

The failures that we need to correct arise both from poverty and from the short-sighted way in which we have often pursued prosperity. Many parts of the world are caught in a vicious downwards spiral: Poor people are forced to overuse environmental resources to survive from day to day, and their impoverishment of their environment further impoverishes them, making their survival ever more difficult and uncertain. The prosperity attained in some parts of the world is often precarious, as it has been secured through farming, forestry, and industrial practices that bring profit and progress only over the short term.

Societies have faced such pressures in the past and, as many desolate ruins remind us, sometimes succumbed to them. But generally these pressures were local. Today the scale of our interventions in nature is increasing and the physical effects of our decisions spill across national frontiers. The growth in economic interaction between nations amplifies the wider consequences of national decisions. Economics and ecology bind us in ever-tightening networks. Today, many regions face risks of irreversible damage to the human environment that threatens the basis for human progress.

These deepening interconnections are the central justification for the establishment of this Commission. We travelled the world for nearly three years, listening. At special public hearings organized by the Commission, we heard from government leaders, scientists, and experts, from citizens' groups concerned about a wide range of environment and development issues, and from thousands of individuals – farmers, shanty-town residents, young people, industrialists, and indigenous and tribal peoples.

We found everywhere deep public concern for the environment, concern that has led not just to protests but often to changed behaviour. The challenge is to ensure that these new values are more adequately reflected in the principles and operations of political and economic structures.

We also found grounds for hope: that people can cooperate to build a future that is more prosperous, more just, and more secure; that a new era of economic growth can be attained, one based on policies that sustain and expand the Earth's resource base; and that the progress that some have known over the last century can be experienced by all in the years ahead. But for this to happen, we must understand better the symptoms of stress that confront us, we must identify the causes, and we must design new approaches to managing environmental resources and to sustaining human development.

Environmental stress has often been seen as the result of the growing demand on scarce resources and the pollution generated by the rising living standards of the relatively affluent. But poverty itself pollutes the environment, creating environmental stress in a different way. Those who are poor and hungry will often destroy their immediate environment in order to survive: They will cut down forests; their livestock will overgraze grasslands; they will overuse marginal land; and in growing numbers they will crowd into congested cities. The cumulative effect of these changes is so far-reaching as to make poverty itself a major global scourge.

On the other hand, where economic growth has led to improvements in living standards, it has sometimes been achieved in ways that are globally damaging in the longer term. Much of the improvement in the past has been based on the use of increasing amounts of raw materials, energy, chemicals, and synthetics and on the creation of pollution that is not adequately accounted for in figuring the costs of production processes. These trends have had unforeseen effects on the environment. Thus today's environmental challenges arise both from the lack of development and from the unintended consequences of some forms of economic growth.

There are more hungry people in the world today than ever before in human history, and their numbers are growing. In 1980, there were 340 million people in 87 developing countries not getting enough calories to prevent stunted growth and serious health risks. This total was very slightly below the figure for 1970 in terms of share of the world population, but in terms of sheer numbers, it represented a 14 per cent increase. The World Bank predicts that these numbers are likely to go on growing.

The number of people living in slums and shanty towns is rising, not falling. A growing number lack access to clean water and sanitation and hence are prey to the diseases that arise from this lack. There is some progress, impressive in places. But, on balance, poverty persists and its victims multiply.

The pressure of poverty has to be seen in a broader context. At the international level there are large differences in per capita income, which ranged in 1984 from $190 in low-income countries (other than China and India) to $11,430 in the industrial market economies.

Such inequalities represent great differences not merely in the quality of life today, but also in the capacity of societies to improve their quality of life in the future. Most of the world's poorest countries depend for increasing export earnings on tropical agricultural products that are vulnerable to fluctuating or declining terms of trade. Expansion can often only be achieved at the price of ecological stress. Yet diversification in ways that will alleviate both poverty and ecological stress is hampered by disadvantageous terms of technology transfer, by protectionism, and by declining financial flows to those countries that most need international finance.

Within countries, poverty has been exacerbated by the unequal distribution of land and other assets. The rapid rise in population has compromised the ability to raise living standards. These factors, combined with growing demands for the commercial use of good land, often to grow crops for exports, have pushed many subsistence farmers on to poor land and robbed them of any hope of participating in their nations' economic lives. The same forces have meant that traditional shifting cultivators, who once cut forests, grew crops, and then gave the forest time to recover, now have neither land enough nor time to let forests re-establish. So forests are being destroyed, often only to create poor farmland that cannot support those who till it. Extending cultivation on to steep slopes is increasing soil erosion in many hilly sections of both developing and developed nations. In many river valleys, areas chronically liable to floods are now being farmed.

These pressures are reflected in the rising incidence of disasters. During the 1970s, six times as many people died from 'natural disasters' each year as in the 1960s, and twice as many suffered from such disasters. Droughts and floods, disasters among whose causes are widespread deforestation and overcultivation, increased most in terms of numbers affected. There were 18.5 million people affected by droughts annually in the 1960s, but 24.4 million in the 1970s; 5.2 million people were victims of floods yearly in the 1960s, compared with 15.4 million in the 1970s. The results are not in for the 1980s, but this disaster-prone decade seems to be carrying forward the trend, with droughts in Africa, India, and Latin America, and floods throughout Asia, parts of Africa, and the Andean region of Latin America.

Such disasters claim most of their victims among the impoverished in poor nations, where subsistence farmers must make their land more liable to droughts and floods by clearing marginal areas, and where the poor make themselves more vulnerable to all disasters by living on steep slopes and unprotected shores – the only lands left for their shanties. Lacking food and foreign exchange reserves, their economically vulnerable governments are ill equipped to cope with such catastrophes.

The links between environmental stress and developmental disaster are most evident in sub-Saharan Africa. Per capital food production, declining since the 1960s, plummeted during the drought of the 1980s, and at the height of the food emergency some 35 million people were exposed to risk. Human overuse of land and prolonged drought threaten to turn the grasslands of Africa's Sahel region into desert. No other region more tragically suffers the vicious cycle of poverty leading to environmental degradation, which leads in turn to even greater poverty.

In some parts of the world, particularly since the mid-1950s, growth and development have vastly improved living standards and the quality of life. Many of the products and technologies that have gone into this improvement are raw material- and energy-intensive and entail a substantial amount of pollution. The consequent impact on the environment is greater than ever before in human history.

Over the past century, the use of fossil fuels has grown nearly thirtyfold, and industrial production has increased more than fiftyfold. The bulk of this increase, about three-quarters in the case of fossil fuels and a little over four-fifths in the case of industrial production, has taken place *since* 1950. The annual increase in industrial production today is perhaps as large as the total production in Europe around the end of the 1930s. Into every year we now squeeze the decades of industrial growth – and environmental disruption – that formed the basis of the pre-war European economy.

Environmental stresses also arise from more traditional forms of production. More land has been cleared for settled cultivation in the past 100 years than in all the previous centuries of human existence. Interventions in the water cycles have increased greatly. Massive dams, most of them built after 1950, impound a large proportion of the river flow. In Europe and Asia, water use has reached 10 per cent of the annual run-off, a figure that is expected to rise to 20-25 per cent by the end of the century.

The impact of growth and rising income levels can be seen in the distribution of world consumption of a variety of resource-intensive products. The more affluent industrialized countries use most of the world's metals and fossil fuels. Even in the case of food products a sharp difference exists, particularly in the products that are more resource-intensive.

In recent years, industrial countries have been able to achieve economic growth using less energy and raw materials per unit of output. This, along with the efforts to reduce the emission of pollutants, will help to contain the pressure on the biosphere. But with the increase in population and the rise in incomes, per capita consumption of energy and materials will go up in the developing countries, as it has to if essential needs are to be met. Greater attention to resource efficiency can moderate the increase, but, on balance, environmental problems linked to resource use will intensify in global terms.

The scale and complexity of our requirements for natural

resources have increased greatly with the rising levels of population and production. Nature is bountiful, but it is also fragile and finely balanced. There are thresholds that cannot be crossed without endangering the basic integrity of the system. Today we are close to many of these thresholds; we must be ever mindful of the risk of endangering the survival of life on Earth. Moreover, the speed with which changes in resource use are taking place gives little time in which to anticipate and prevent unexpected effects.

The 'greenhouse effect', one such threat to life-support systems, springs directly from increased resource use. The burning of fossil fuels and the cutting and burning of forests release carbon dioxide (CO_2). The assimulation in the atmosphere of CO_2 and certain other gases traps solar radiation near the Earth's surface, causing global warming. This could cause sea level rises over the next 45 years large enough to inundate many low-lying coastal cities and river deltas. It could also drastically upset national and international agricultural production and trade systems.

Another threat arises from the depletion of the atmospheric ozone layer by gases released during the production of foam and the use of refrigerants and aerosols. A substantial loss of such ozone could have catastrophic effects on human and livestock health and on some life forms at the base of the marine food chain. The 1986 discovery of a hole in the ozone layer above the Antarctic suggests the possibility of a more rapid depletion than previously suspected.

A variety of air pollutants are killing trees and lakes and damaging buildings and cultural treasures, close to and sometimes thousands of miles from points of emission. The acidification of the environment threatens large areas of Europe and North America. Central Europe is currently receiving more than one gramme of sulphur on every square metre of ground each year. The loss of forests could bring in its wake disastrous erosion, siltation, floods, and local climatic change. Air pollution damage is also becoming evident in some newly industrialized countries.

In many cases the practices used at present to dispose of toxic wastes, such as those from the chemical industries, involve unacceptable risks. Radioactive wastes from the nuclear industry remain hazardous for centuries. Many who bear these risks do not benefit in any way from the activities that produce the wastes.

Desertification – the process whereby productive arid and semi-arid land is rendered economically unproductive – and large-scale deforestation are other examples of major threats to the integrity of regional ecosystems. Desertification involves complex interactions between humans, land, and climate. The pressures of subsistence food production, commercial crops, and meat production in arid and semi-arid areas all contribute to this process.

Each year another 6 million hectares are degraded to desert-like conditions. Over three decades, this would amount to an area roughly as large as Saudi Arabia. More than 11 million hectares of tropical forests are destroyed each year and this, over 30 years, would amount to an area about the size of India. Apart from the direct and often dramatic impacts within the immediate area, nearby regions are affected by the spreading of sands or by changes in water regimes and increased risks of soil erosion and siltation.

The loss of forests and other wild lands extinguishes species of plants and animals and drastically reduces the genetic diversity of the world's ecosystems. This process robs present and future generations of genetic material with which to improve crop varieties, to make them less vulnerable to weather stress, pest attacks, and disease. The loss of species and subspecies, many as yet unstudied by science, deprives us of important potential sources of medicines and industrial chemicals. It removes forever creatures of beauty and parts of our cultural heritage; it diminishes the biosphere.

Many of the risks stemming from our productive activity and the technologies we use cross national boundaries; many are global. Though the activities that give rise to these dangers tend to be concentrated in a few countries, the risks are shared by all, rich and poor, those who benefit from them and those who do not. Most who share in the risks have little influence on the decision processes that regulate these activities.

Little time is available for corrective action. In some cases we may already be close to transgressing critical thresholds. While scientists continue to research and debate causes and effects, in many cases we already know enough to warrant action. This is true locally and regionally in the cases of such threats as desertification, deforestation, toxic wastes, and acidification; it is true globally for such threats as climate change, ozone depletion, and species loss. The risks increase faster than do our abilities to manage them.–

Human progress has always depended on our technical ingenuity and a capacity for cooperative action. These qualities have often been used constructively to achieve development and environmental progress: in air and water pollution control, for example, and in increasing the efficiency of material and energy use. Many countries have increased food production and reduced population growth rates. Some technological advances, particularly in medicine, have been widely shared.

But this is not enough. Failure to manage the environment and to sustain development threaten to overwhelm all countries. Environment and development are not separate challenges; they are inexorably linked. Development cannot subsist upon a deteriorating environmental resource base; the environment cannot be protected when growth leaves out of account the costs of environmental destruction. These problems cannot be treated separately by fragmented institutions and policies. They are linked in a complex system of cause and effect.

First, environmental stresses are linked one to another.–

Second, environmental stresses and patterns of economic development are linked one to another.–

Third, environmental and economic problems are linked to many social and political factors.–

Finally, the systemic features operate not merely within but also between nations. National boundaries have become so porous that traditional distinctions between matters of local, national, and international significance have become blurred. Ecosystems do not respect national boundaries.–

Many environment-economy links also operate globally. For instance, the highly subsidized, incentive-driven agriculture of industrialized market economies generates surpluses that depress prices and erode the viability of the often neglected agriculture of developing countries. Soils and other environmental resources suffer in both systems.–

In the past, responsibility for environmental matters has been placed in environmental ministries and institutions that often have had little or no control over destruction caused by agricultural, industrial, urban development, forestry, and transportation policies and practices. Society has failed to give the responsibility for preventing environmental damage to the 'sectoral' ministries and agencies whose policies cause it. Thus our environmental management practices have focused largely upon after-the-fact repair of damage: *re*forestation, *re*claiming desert lands, *re*building urban environments, *re*storing natural habitats, and *re*habilitating wild lands. The ability to anticipate and prevent environmental damage will require that the ecological dimensions of policy be considered at the same time as the economic, trade, energy, agricultural, and other dimensions.

What is required is a new approach in which all nations aim at a type of development that integrates production with resource conservation and enhancement, and that links both to the provision for all of an adequate livelihood base and equitable access to resources.

The concept of sustainable development provides a framework for the integration of environment policies and development strategies – the term 'development' being used here in its broadest sense.–

Sustainable development seeks to meet the needs and aspirations of the present without compromising the ability to meet those of the future. Far from requiring the cessation of economic growth, it recognizes that the problems of poverty and underdevelopment cannot be solved unless we have a new era of growth in which developing countries play a large role and reap large benefits.

Economic growth always brings risk of environmental damage, as it puts increased pressure on environmental resources. But policy makers guided by the concept of sustainable development will necessarily work to assure that growing economies remain firmly attached to their ecological roots and that these roots are protected and nurtured so that they may support growth over the long term. Environmental protection is thus inherent in the concept of sustainable development, as is a focus on the sources of environmental problems rather than the symptoms.

No single blueprint of sustainability will be found, as economic and social systems and ecological conditions differ widely among countries. Each nation will have to work out its own concrete policy implications. Yet irrespective of these differences, sustainable development should be seen as a global objective.

No country can develop in isolation from others. Hence the pursuit of sustainable development requires a new orientation in international relations. Long-term sustainable growth will require far-reaching changes to produce trade, capital, and technology flows that are more equitable and better synchronized to environmental imperatives.

The mechanics of increased international cooperation required to assure sustainable development will vary from sector to sector and in relation to particular institutions. But it is fundamental that the transition to sustainable development be managed jointly by all nations. The unity of human needs requires a functioning multilateral system that respects the democratic principle of consent and accepts that not only the Earth but also the world is one.

BE HUMAN OR DIE

BY ROBERT WALLER

The last few extracts have been taken from reports produced by groups of people and addressed principally to governments. I feel this anthology should end on a more personal note with an individual speaking directly to each of us. Robert Waller is a philosopher, poet, and novelist who has contributed much to the environmental debate. As an agricultural talks producer for the BBC and, for several years from early in 1964, as editor of *Mother Earth*, the journal of The Soil Association, he was one of the first to recognize the deeper implications of the new expressions of concern. Published in 1973, his book *Be Human or Die*, which ends with the passage below, explores the philosophy of environmentalism.

Either we prepare for change *intentionally* taking into account both material and psychological needs or we leave it to accident. And leaving it to accident compels nature to eliminate man in order to save herself. Why not? And what does that mean in terms of philosophy and religion? Nature is God's as well as man's.

In the end we shall have to organize society without recourse to further extraction of the minerals that lie beneath the surface of the earth. For millenia mankind lived without doing this. When wood was burned it was nature's interest, not nature's capital that was used, if the trees were replaced. All nature's capital plays a part in providing the interest in the form of vegetation and nutrition. If we rob nature of these capital goods and play the prodigal son, we rob ourselves, unless we repent.

Repentance . . . originally meant changing one's views – metanoia. The change in our attitude that will be needed to survive will lead to a change in the personality of man, just as the discovery of agriculture led to a change in the personality of man as recorded in the myth of Genesis. It would seem as if this change will be a blend of the pre-agricultural and agricultural man – man the exploiter. ... Morality will once again become an essential element of the good life and no one will believe that virtue can be attained simply by overcoming scarcity. The most asinine of all myths, the myth of the virtuous rich, will fade into a dark age of materialism with a memory like that of Babylon. The greatest spiritual achievements have never been associated with nations with millions of inhabitants. Our great achievements began when we were a small nation, not the second most densely inhabited nation in the world. That is the end, not the beginning of our civilization. We have lost control and simply followed the lure of wealth and power wherever it drew us without regard for form. We are but one of many other civilizations that have followed the same rise and fall.

However, I do not consider this a cause for despair, any more than one's own inevitable death is a cause for despair. It is the condition of life on earth. There is much to be learned from it and those who learn mature their personality as a consequence. The principles of human ecology are making it clear that in the long run only the craftsmen can make the optimum use of the natural resources of the earth. To maintain full employment and combat inflation, it will be necessary to put much more emphasis on individual craftsmanship; the small workshop and the small farm will come back into their own, though they will probably have to work far more in cooperation than in the past. For a long time the projects of civilization will require large numbers and large amounts of material – but so did cathedrals.

Only craftsmanship will maintain prosperity without over-pollution and inflation. Goods will be worth what we pay for them, for they will be both beautiful (well made) and durable. The conservation of stock will be more important than the flow that now constitutes the GNP. It will be recognized that the period in which demand is essential for economic survival is coming to an end. None of this can be done while the international corporation retains its present legal powers.

Such a doctrine as this has until recently been regarded as sheer sentimentality. Ecology is now teaching us – though it is a shock that we can but slowly absorb and one which many will resist to the end – that it is realism. The technologists, the industrialists and their economic supporters who align themselves with the belief in constant growth are the dreamers.

The simpler forms of the stable society – simpler only in the material sense – will be enriched by all the cultural knowledge and achievement of man since the Garden of Eden until today. It will certainly not be a society that believes 'History is bunk' but one that sees its place in the historical tradition of man's self-discovery and self-display. This historical sense, so absent in the industrial society of progress with its reduction of history to some vague notion of evolution, will guard us against going back to previous social forms. 'We have been here before' is a bore: it is man's nature to explore the new. The idea of progress was new: the idea of ever-renewable resources and energy was new. The time is coming when at the revival of the idea of progress men will say 'Oh, we have been there before'. In this sense of the constant search for the new, we do not know what any future society will be like. It is this that will make the future a challenge. What will it be like? It will not be an intensification of present trends. Dismal though this prospect may seem to my generation brought up in the vain hopes of the industrial dreamers, it will appear to our children as a mysterious challenge, a new way of learning more about themselves. Our insatiable rape of the earth and our smug satisfaction with our immoral society of the idealized virtuous millionaire is losing authority with the young. They can see that we have not liberated ourselves from history and that religion and morality are as real as ever, even though they must be recreated with deeper insight and new forms.

The interest of the young in simpler forms of life is part of their search for themselves – for the Self. The conservation corps and do-it-yourself craftsmanship are an indirect tribute to the fact that man only discovers himself as craftsman and in touch with 'the Other'. The young who behave as if they were the sons of millionaires and entitled to do what they wish, where they wish and in any part of the world, have missed the point of youth's rebellion. Delightful as surf bathing is it cannot be a way of life: nor can drug taking which is a substitute for experience of the Other. True and satisfying experiences are found only in contemplation and real work. They depend on union of Self and Other. Drug taking is a short cut that destroys judgment. Yet the hope behind these perversities is of new discoveries of the reality of the Self. The Self which has been smothered under our material triumphs and hopes must someday resurrect itself. The Self is a positive dynamic force, the real creator of existence. If the word 'Self' seems too vague and mystical we do better to think of it as the maturing of the whole person through a relationship with the Other, both active and passive.

In pursuit of this historical aim which is in harmony with the evolution of man, the young have the chance now to create a new patriotism to take the place of the exploitive nationalism which is holding up the development of the universal society. In this way the universal and the local can be complementary. Out of the old imperial-economic patriotism should grow the real love of country that was buried under the material temptations. The new generations can love their country for itself and not for its capacity to cover the globe in red or turn £x thousand into an exponential quantity in seven years. The young should be the patriots that we pretended to be and would probably have liked to be. They must show the Conservatives what conserving one's country really means: and they must show the Socialists what fellowship really means – that it is more than banging the drum about equality and liberty and calling one's fellows comrade. Equality and liberty are destructive when the soul is empty and the head mindless. Let us be united by a love of country based on ecological humanism.

The intention to create a true patriotism and to shame the unpatriots is revolutionary: it will need courage and it may even demand martyrs. The unpatriots will not take kindly to being shown what real love of country is. ... The unpatriots 'love' their country because it provides them with power, wealth and position. The new patriots will love their country because it is beautiful, because it gives joy, because it is united in fellowship and on this basis safeguards liberty and equality as well. They will turn the old myth that was used to send the people to the Somme into a reality. The will to do it must be there because the mere pretence inspired the pathetic heroes of old. But now we must not be deceived in our aims.

These friends of their country should find out how to resist by the non-violent use of force the aesthetic destruction of their society. They should obstruct with their bodies the building of hideous blocks of offices – instead of multiplying their savings by investing in them, as they are invited to do. They should obstruct the Concorde, obstruct Heathrow, picket factory farms. They should strengthen the movement to enforce the ecological utilization of materials. Their declared aim should be a fertile, beautiful, fraternal and healthy land. A healthy land – that should be the slogan of the new patriots. ... We do have to beware of movements that simply aim to conserve the environment of a middle and upper class elite. This will undermine the patriotic and fraternal ground of the movement. No village, for example, should be conserved by means that drive out the working class, especially the farm workers, by raising the price of houses beyond their means. This may be conservation but it is at a price that destroys patriotism. We must see to it that the movement is Whole and not for the benefit of any one section of the community alone – not even the young. The property owning democracy ... is a moneylenders' society and unpatriotic.

A movement inspired by the love of country would shake the young out of their self-centred violence and sullen rebellion of 'opting out'. They should stop exploiting affluence for their own pleasure while at the same time condemning it. The cause of beauty has never before been a revolutionary aim. The Left, so far, has suffered the terrible affliction of a cultural starvation. It has damaged their society irreparably. . . .

In time of war and misfortune people often turn again to poetry and to wondering how they have gone astray and lost the true path of the Self. In times of prosperity they are often distracted from such philosophical reflection. Indeed in many ways the ideal circumstance for creative renewal and religious and philosophic depth of experience is provided by the rich civilization with an inherited culture that is falling into hard times and losing confidence in mere material power. I predict that as industry and the rational way of life cease to deliver the real goods, we shall turn inward and outward in new ways. The international business corporation with its growth dynamism that subjugates nature and man to its system will be overthrown or collapse of its own accord: men will seek a true international spirit that can be expressed in the old notion of the Fatherhood of God: the local community will once again become important as the best environment for the personal life and craftsmanship. But the sense of the universal will prevent a relapse into the narrow personality of the nationalist and the provincial.

A prayer found in Old St Paul's Church, Baltimore, written in 1692, has frequently been reprinted in recent times. People are feeling its truth and are in need of it:

'You are a child of the universe, no less than the trees and the stars: you have a right to be here. And whether or not it is clear to you, no doubt the universe is unfolding as it should. Therefore be at peace with God, whatever you conceive him to be, and whatever your labour and aspirations, in the noisy confusion of life keep peace within your soul. With all its shams, drudgery and broken dreams, it is still a beautiful world. Strive to be happy.'

The . . . prayer [is a] human being speaking:
BUT
If a man's environment is to be standardized so that he will tolerate a society largely owned and planned by development corporations dedicated with government encouragement to exponential growth and served by technology, we shall finish with a total inhumanity. We must plan on a basis of reason served by ecological humanism. It is

not enough to think; we must keep bringing our thought nearer to truth by action, otherwise we shall lose our personality. Our cause is the redemption of reason and the subordination of the rationalists who at present cheat us of our humanity.

Be human or die.

Sources and Acknowledgements

'A Fable for Tomorrow' and 'Elixirs of Death' by Rachel Carson: from *Silent Spring* (Hamish Hamilton, 1963)

'Disturbance and Dilemma' by Robert L. Rudd: reprinted by permission of Faber & Faber Ltd from *Pesticides and the Living Landscape* (1965)

'The Chlorinated Hydrocarbons' by Kenneth Mellanby: from *Pesticides and Pollution* (Collins, 1967)

'Factory Farming' by Ruth Harrison: from *Animal Machines* (Vincent Stuart, 1964)

'An Agricultural Revolution' by Marion Shoard: from *The Theft of the Countryside* (Gower Publishing, 1980)

'Where Does Responsibility Lie?' by Frank Fraser Darling: reproduced from *Wilderness and Plenty* with the permission of BBC Enterprises Ltd (1980)

'The Historical Roots of Our Ecological Crisis' by Lynn White Jr; from *Science* Vol 155, 10 March 1967, pp 1203-7, copyright © 1967 by the AAAS

'Prospect' by Lewis Mumford: from *Man's Role in Changing the Face of the Earth* edited by William L. Thomas Jr, copyright © 1956 by The University of Chicago. All rights reserved

'The Social Use and Misuse of Technology' by Barry Commoner: from *Ecology, the Shaping Enquiry* edited by Jonathan Benthall (Longman, 1972)

'The Tragedy of the Commons' by Garrett Hardin: from *Science* Vol 162, 13 December 1968, pp 1243-8, copyright © 1968 by the AAAS

'Destructiveness of Man' by George Perkins Marsh: from *Man and Nature or Physical Geography as Modified by Human Action* (1864), copyright © 1965 by the President and Fellows of Harvard College

'Too Many People' by Dr Paul R. Ehrlich: from *The Population Bomb* (revised edition). Copyright © 1968, 1971 by Paul R. Erlich. Reprinted by permission of Ballantine Books, a Division of Random House, Inc.

'The Theory of Population' by Thomas Malthus: from *An Essay on the Principle of Population as it affects the future improvement of society with remarks on the speculations of Mr Godwin, M Condorcet, and other writers* (1798)

'Population Pressure on the Environment' by Frances Moore Lappé and Joseph Collins: from *Food First: The Myth of Scarcity* (Souvenir Press, 1980)

'The True Hunger Gap and the Calorie Swindle' Georg Borgstrom: reprinted with permission of Macmillan Publishing Company from *The Hungry Planet: The Modern World at the Edge of Famine*, copyright © 1965, 1967, 1972

'Malthus and the Productivity of Farms' by Petr Alekseevich Kroptokin: from *Fields, Factories and Workshops* (1898)

'Smokeless Fuel' by John Evelyn: from his *Diary* (1656)

'Coketown' by Charles Dickens: from *Hard Times (1854)*

'A Morning Bath' and 'Questions and Answers' by William Morris: from *News from Nowhere* (1891)

'Taming Technology' by Alvin Toffler: from *Future Shock* (The Bodley Head, 1970)

'Of the Natural Condition of Mankind as Concerning Their Felicity and Misery' by Thomas Hobbes: from *Leviathan* (1651)

'A Blueprint for Survival' by Edward Goldsmith, Robert Allen, Michael Allaby, John Davoll and Sam Lawrence: from *The Ecologist*, Worthyvale Manor, Camelford, Cornwall (January 1972)

'Of the Stationary State' by John Stuart Mill: from *The Principles of Political Economy* (1848)